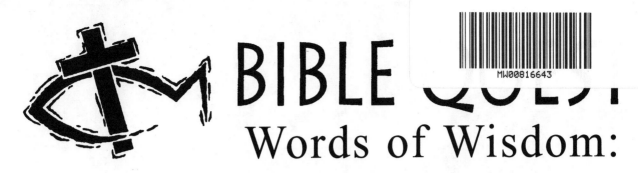

BIBLE QUEST
Words of Wisdom:
Job, Psalms & Proverbs

STUDENT WORKBOOK

AUTHOR
MARNI SHIDELER MCKENZIE

EDITORS
MRS. NELLIE E. CONSTANCE
MRS. LOIS EADES, M.A.

COVER ART & GRAPHIC DESIGN
TROY D. RUSSELL

PROJECT EDITOR
TOM M. CONSTANCE JR.

EXPLORER'S BIBLE STUDY
P.O. BOX 425
DICKSON, TN 37056-0425

*We believe the Bible is God's Word, a divine revelation, in the original language
verbally inspired in its entirety, and that it is the supreme infallible authority
in all matters of faith and conduct.*
(II Peter 1:21; II Timothy 3:16)

Printed in the United States of America

Published by Explorer's Bible Study
2652 Hwy. 46 South
P.O. Box 425
Dickson, TN 37056-0425
(800) 657-2874

Contents

About the Author

Marni Shideler McKenzie is married to William H. McKenzie, III. They live in Batesville, Mississippi, where Bill is in private law practice. They have three children, Melanie, William, and Joanna, and are active in community efforts and the ministries of their local church. Marni attended the University of Mississippi as a Carrier Scholar and received B.A. and M.A. degrees in English. While in college, Marni became serious in her efforts to nurture her relationship with Jesus Christ, and began to study the Bible carefully. She "retired" from a brief high school teaching career when their children were born and has used her spare time ever since for organizing or teaching Bible study classes to adults and children. She credits her husband for giving her the freedom to study Scripture and the opportunity to teach three Explorer's Bible Study classes continually since 1979.

Marni has written the **Bible Quest** course **God's People - God's Land**, **Promises Fulfilled - Luke & Acts**, and **Words of Wisdom: Job, Psalms and Proverbs** for Jr. and Sr. High students. In addition to Bible Quest, Marni has also written an illustrated children's book, **An Alphabet of Bible Creatures**, and a 12-part study series for adults on the Apostles Creed entitled **The Creed and the Christian**.

Bibliography

A great debt is owed the many Bible authorities whose writings have been used as a resource in writing and preparing this material.

A Note to Parents and Teachers

If you have said 'yes' to the call of God to teach, you have accepted one of the most important challenges in building the future kingdom. In James 3:1 we read *"Not many should become teachers, knowing that there will be a stricter judgment."* It takes a great commitment to put yourself in a place of responsibility in which children and young students will make life-changing decisions based on the life and teaching you put before them. But knowing the high expectations God has for those who commit to this calling should not deter you from this wonderful and powerful opportunity to serve in this way. As you see the loving response to God from a child or student, it is difficult - if not impossible - to imagine NOT teaching! It becomes a compelling urgency that God rewards in so many ways that you'll wonder why there was ever a question mark after the words, "Should I consider teaching?"

Whether you are a home schooling parent, a Sunday School teacher, or a Christian educator, God has chosen you to teach! As a teacher, you will have a great influence in the lives of your children or students. You have been given the responsibility by God to mentor these lives spiritually. It is an awesome responsibility but you don't have to do it alone! God is with you every step of the way.

Teach each child faithfully, prayerfully and consistently in His Word. . .know it, believe it, live it and then teach it. Teaching is impossible without the first three. We hope this Bible curriculum will help guide you through this process.

A guide for those who are called to teach. A teacher must have:

1. A personal commitment to Christ.

2. A love for students with a desire to see them understand the Word of God.

3. A call to the ministry through God's Word.

4. A personal commitment to daily Bible study and to complete the lesson each week.

"And these words which I command you today shall be in your heart. You shall teach them diligently to your children, and shall talk of them when you sit in your house, when you walk by the way, when you lie down, and when you rise up."
Deuteronomy 6:6-7

A Note to the Student
How to Use this Workbook

You are about to embark on a great adventure - the study of God's Word. We have called this study **Bible Quest** because you will be on a quest for knowledge, understanding and application of the many wonderful truths found in the world's most read book - the Bible.

As you begin each lesson, pause to pray for the Holy Spirit to guide you as you seek the treasures to be found in the Word. There is no need to use anything but your Bible in answering your questions. Commentaries and study notes in your Bible can be helpful, but the goal of this study is for you to discover what God wants to communicate to **YOU** through the lesson. After you have completed your lesson you may wish to go back and read a Bible commentary to further clarify what you have studied.

Daily Questions: Work the assigned questions each day. The discipline of daily Bible study will soon become part of your regular routine. You will find that the questions are challenging, interesting, and fun to do!

Lesson Notes: You will find helpful insight and ways to personally apply what you have studied in the 'notes' section of your lesson.

Bible Journal and Memory
We suggest that you get a spiral notebook or 3 ring binder and keep a Bible Journal of your study of Job, Psalms and Proverbs. You will find this elephant symbol throughout your lessons, along with reference(s) for **suggested** memory verses. The books of Job, Psalms and Proverbs are filled with wonderful verses to "hide in your heart". Some lessons have more verses included in the suggested memory than most students will be able to learn in one week. We suggest that you look through the verses listed and select the ones that you feel you would like to memorize. Even though you may be unable to memorize all of the suggested verses, we recommend that you write them all in your Bible Journal and do your best to master as many as you can each week. Writing the verses will make it easier for you to memorize. You may also want to use your Bible Journal to write down important things that you have learned as you study your lesson. . . or use a page to illustrate a story from a lesson. Be CREATIVE!

Your word I have hidden in my heart, that I might not sin against You!
Psalm 119:11

As you study. . .

1. Pray that God will give you understanding.

2. Find out what the Bible says.

3. Choose to live God's way every day.

4. Never stop learning and growing. . .there is always MORE!

How much do you know?

Before you begin your study of POETICAL BOOKS, let's take a pop quiz to test your Bible knowledge. Since this test is designed to find out what you know right now, answer the questions without using your Bible. To find out how well you did, look at the answers printed on page 4. Don't be discouraged if you miss a few. Before the end of your study of POETICAL BOOKS, you will know the answer to every one of these questions!

1. Where did Job live?
   a) Uz
   b) Oz
   c) Ur
   d) Ono

2. How many children did he have at the beginning of the book?
   a) 2
   b) 4
   c) 8
   d) 10

3. What did God think of Job?
   a) He thought he needed some discipline.
   b) He thought he was one of a kind in his goodness on earth.
   c) He had not noticed him before.
   d) He thought he was not being a good example for others.

4. Who was the unusual visitor in heaven who was allowed to discuss Job with God?
   a) Satan
   b) Elijah
   c) Adam
   d) Noah

5. Which of the following men were his friends?
   a) Abraham
   b) Noah
   c) Eliphaz
   d) Elvis
   e) Sinbad
   f) Bildad
   g) Gomer
   h) Zophar

From the list below find the words or proper names that will have something to do with the study of Job.

Bildad	blameless
comfort	confess
Creator	Elihu
Eliphaz	grief
Job	mediator
redeemer	Satan
suffering	upright
Uz	Zophar

B	Q	T	H	G	I	R	P	U	Z	R	G	R	J	E
I	L	U	N	N	G	S	Q	E	F	E	I	R	G	G
L	C	A	J	I	P	A	B	L	F	D	Z	Z	P	C
D	K	O	M	R	O	T	A	I	D	E	M	S	O	V
A	B	S	M	E	Y	A	V	P	D	E	N	N	I	C
D	I	C	Z	F	L	N	G	H	G	M	F	G	R	L
K	O	W	M	F	O	E	Z	A	C	E	C	U	R	V
H	Y	O	O	U	E	R	S	Z	S	R	Z	Z	Z	A
S	X	G	A	S	L	O	T	S	C	S	O	K	X	X
Q	O	A	W	E	I	T	U	M	A	B	D	Y	F	J
Z	P	Z	O	P	H	A	R	D	A	Y	D	O	R	X
S	R	Z	N	B	U	E	T	B	K	H	I	U	O	S
T	F	J	X	S	K	R	L	C	B	C	V	U	S	Q
C	O	M	L	X	E	C	N	C	V	L	H	I	L	A

Notes

Close Up and Personal

Job was a real person, admired by men and approved by God, and not a character in a fable or parable.

prophet - one who delivers divine messages

contemporary - occurring or living at the same time as another

patriarch - men who served as heads of their families (Abraham, Isaac, Jacob, etc.)

Who Was Job?

While you won't find an article about Job (pronounced "jobe") in an old history book, you can find out some details about him from other books in the Bible. The prophet Ezekiel quoted what God told him about Job and two other very important men who were faithful to God. In Ezekiel 14:14, God said that the situation at that time was so bad for Israel that "*though these three men, Noah, Daniel, and Job, were in it, they would deliver only themselves by their righteousness.*" In the New Testament, James included Job in the category of the old prophets who should be studied: "*My brethren, take the prophets, who spoke in the name of the Lord, as an example of suffering and of patience. Indeed, we count them blessed who endure. You have heard of the perseverance of Job, and seen the end intended by the Lord; that the Lord is very compassionate and merciful*" (James 5:10-11). From these two Bible references, we can learn that Job was a real person, admired by men and approved by God, and not a character in a fable or parable. He was also considered a **prophet** and a man whose life demonstrated that patience in suffering is possible when a person is in a real relationship with God.

Where Did Job Live?

In Job 1:1, it is stated that Job lived in the land of Uz. Jeremiah mentioned this place in Lamentations 4:21, "*Rejoice and be glad, O daughter of Edom, that dwells in the land of Uz.*" If Uz is associated with Edom then it was near to, but outside of, the land given to Abraham in Canaan. So, Uz was somewhere in what we would now consider the Middle East, outside the area of present-day Israel.

When Did Job Live?

As you read the book of Job, watch for the following things that helped scholars date it as **contemporary** with the book of Genesis or about the same time that Abraham, Isaac, and Jacob lived. For one thing, Job acted as the spiritual leader of his family and offered sacrifices to God while he worshiped. In Genesis, this was practiced by such men as Cain, Abel, Noah, Abraham, Isaac, and Jacob. For another thing, there was no mention of Moses, God's written law, a central place of worship such as the tabernacle or temple, or any organized priesthood. The absence of these puts the book of Job at an early time in Bible history. Also, Job's wealth was described in terms of the livestock he owned, as was the wealth of the **patriarchs** of Genesis, instead of in silver and gold as in the time of King Solomon or later. Furthermore, there were several references to the Great Flood by Job and his friends during their speeches. They each spoke of it as if the information they held were common knowledge. This would have been the case if Job were from the same era as Abraham's family. Job could possibly have had direct or indirect contact with Noah himself, who lived three hundred and fifty years after the Flood, or at the least, with one of Noah's three sons, who lived even longer. Surely Noah's sons and their wives were eager to share their knowledge of what had happened to the earth as a result of the worldwide flood. Since Job lived 140 years after God spoke to him in the final chapters of the book, many think that he was probably 70 when the test started, because God doubled everything he had in the beginning. Living to the age of 210 was not uncommon in the early years after the Flood, but would have been abnormal centuries later. Finally, many of the names of individuals or references to groups of people found in Job can be found listed in the Table of Nations in Genesis 10 or in the first half of the book of Genesis. These are the most common reasons for dating the book of Job at the same time as the parts of Genesis which record the lives of the patriarchs of Israel.

The book of Job is classified as poetry. However, instead of pairing sounds to make a rhyme, Hebrew poets paired thoughts to make a point.

What Kind of Book Is the Book of Job?

The book of Job is classified as poetry. However, instead of pairing sounds to make a rhyme, Hebrew poets paired thoughts to make a point. This patterning in Bible poetry is called parallelism. Like parallel lines, two thoughts were lined up side by side, separate, yet heading in the same direction. Sometimes they expressed the same thought in two different ways: *"Why did I not die at birth? Why did I not perish when I came from the womb?"* (Job 3:11). At other times two extremes were described to make a point: *"The old lion perishes for lack of prey, and the cubs of the lioness are scattered"* (Job 4:11). Actually, the first two chapters and the last one in Job are written in prose or story-form, but the rest of Job is full of these word-picture duets.

The most common reason given for studying Job is that it will help the reader to explore the meaning of suffering, but the careful Bible student will soon discover that the book of Job teaches much more than that.

Why Should the Book of Job Be Studied?

The most common reason given for studying Job is that it will help the reader to explore the meaning of suffering, but the careful Bible student will soon discover that the book of Job teaches much more than that. For example, from Job's friends who travel long distances to comfort him in his great suffering, we can learn how not to be "miserable comforters"--from their mistakes! Also, the stages of grief through which a person moves when facing any kind of loss will be identified. Further, the student will enjoy the many references to

God can be served not for what He gives but for who He is--our matchless Creator, who longs to be in relationship with His creation.

Creation, the Great Flood, and even the separating of nations at the Tower of Babel. Students of the book of Job will have a renewed appreciation for the unequalled power of God described through numerous "word pictures." The value of a godly attitude and the spiritual fruit of self-control will also be highlighted as the various debates between Job and his comforters are explored. Finally, the last chapters will record God's personal appearance to Job, not to answer all Job's questions as to why Satan was allowed to test him so severely, but to reveal what Job knew to be true: that God can be served not for what He gives but for who He is -- our matchless Creator, who longs to be in relationship with His creation. Job is far from a dull book of poetry -- it is a jam-packed record of practical wisdom for those living in the world today. Get ready for a great study!

MEMORY: JOB 1:21; JOB 2:10

Bildad	blameless
comfort	confess
Creator	Elihu
Eliphaz	grief
Job	mediator
redeemer	Satan
suffering	upright
Uz	Zophar

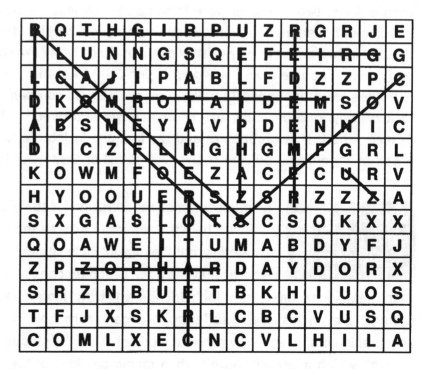

Questions

Study Procedure: Read the Scripture references before answering questions. Unless otherwise instructed, use only the Bible in answering questions. Some questions may be more difficult than others but try to answer as many as you can. Pray for God's wisdom and understanding as you study and don't be discouraged if some answers are not obvious at first. Do not read the study notes for this lesson until AFTER you have completed your questions.

Day One: Vocabulary Review.

1. Unscramble the following words to get the correct vocabulary word for the definitions:

   a) orppthe _____ one who delivers divine messages

   b) rarconymetrop _____ occurring or living at the same time as another

   c) ptrraaishc _____ men who served as heads of their families

   (Abraham, Isaac, etc.)

2. From the notes, write down at least one fact that would help answer each of the following questions about the book of Job.

   a) Who was Job? _____

   _____

   _____

   b) Where did he live? _____

   _____

   _____

   c) When did he live? _____

   _____

   _____

   d) What kind of book is it? _____

   _____

   _____

   e) Why should it be studied? _____

   _____

   _____

Day Two: Read Job 1:1-5.

1. What "real life" details about Job are given in the first verse?

   _____

   _____

   _____

2. How was his relationship to God described? _____

_____

_____

3. Job was obviously a very rich man. Fill in the blanks with correct number of each that Job had.

_____ a. daughters

_____ b. sons

_____ c. sheep

_____ d. camels

_____ e. yoke of oxen

_____ f. female donkeys

4. In your own words, describe Job's family life. _____

_____

_____

_____

MEMORY: JOB 1:21

Day Three: Read Job 1:6-22.

Note: God allowed the writer of the book of Job to reveal something to the reader that Job himself was not allowed to know-- that Job was about to become the object of a great spiritual test.

1. What unusual visitor was allowed to appear in the presence of God? _____

_____

2. How did God describe Job to him? _____

_____

_____

3. What reason was given to God for why Job was such a good servant?

a) "He's scared to death of You!"

b) "His daddy was one of Your favorites, too."

c) "You've given him everything a man could want and protected him, too!"

4. God allowed Satan to remove all Job's earthly possessions to prove that Job would still be faithful to God even without all the blessings he enjoyed. How did the test turn out? _____

_____

_____

5. Challenge Question: Match the description of Satan's activities or methods with the Scripture reference from which they come.

_____2 Corinthians 11:14   _____ John 8:44   _____1 Peter 5:8   _____Acts 5:3

   a) Be sober, be vigilant; because your adversary the devil walks about like a roaring lion, seeking whom he may devour.

   b) But Peter said, "Ananias, why has Satan filled your heart to lie to the Holy Spirit and keep back part of the price of the land for yourself?"

   c) And no wonder! For Satan himself transforms himself into an angel of light.

   d) You are aware of your father the devil, and the desires of your father you want to do. He was a murderer from the beginning, and does not stand in the truth, because there is no truth in him. When he speaks a lie, he speaks from his own resources, for he is a liar and the father of it.

MEMORY: JOB 6:14; 1 PETER 5:8-9

Day Four: Read Job 2:1-10.

1. Not willing to accept defeat, Satan proposed another test. What was it and how did Job react to it? _____

_____

_____

2. Job's wife was no doubt also overwhelmed with all their recent losses. She said to Job: *"Do you still hold fast to your integrity? Curse God and die!"* In what way was this a very dangerous reaction on her part?

   a) She was unknowingly lining up on the side of Satan.

   b) She was encouraging her husband to give up at a time when he was at his weakest and would be most tempted to agree with her.

   c) She was revealing her own lack of faith in God and His goodness.

   d) All of the above.

3. What can we learn from Job's response to this second terrible test? _____

_____

_____

4. Beside each of the following references, write down the symptoms of Job's illness.

   a. 2:12_____

   b. 3:24_____

   c. 7:5 _____

   d. 9:18_____

e. 19:17 _____

f. 19:20 _____

g. 30:30 _____

Day Five: Read Job 2:11-13.

1. Name Job's three friends and the places from which they came.

_____

_____

_____

2. Bible Research Project: Look up each of the names of Job's friends in a concordance or Bible dictionary, along with the places in which they lived. Write down anything interesting you discover.

_____

_____

_____

_____

_____

_____

_____

_____

_____

_____

_____

_____

_____

_____

3. What was their reaction upon seeing Job? _____

_____

_____

_____

4. What is your response to the tragedy in another's life? How effective is just being silently present when someone is suffering? _____

_____

_____

5. Now take a few minutes to read your study notes for this lesson.

Notes

For Your Information (Job 1-2)

Special Information

We live in the "information age." There is information about every subject imaginable available to us today, and it is all as close as the local library, television, or our home computers. But if you are searching for the truth about a subject, you better check your source. Who is putting out the information you are using? What are their *credentials*? What is their purpose in giving out this information? Did they get their facts by observing the subject themselves, or are they trusting the words of other sources? False or incomplete reports can lead people in dangerous directions. However, there is one source of information that you can always trust--the Bible. Much of the Bible is history: the Holy Spirit directed specially selected men to record specific events that they had personally witnessed or about which they had read the preserved records. Yet many portions of the Bible are prophecy: the Holy Spirit directing men to write down specific events before they happened! We call this kind of information *revelation*: God revealing things about the future--and in the area of creation, about the past-- that man could never have known, because no man was present to witness the event.

In the book of Job, we will encounter both history and revelation. Facts about Job are given in the opening chapter that anyone alive in that day could have known, but the information about what was going on in heaven with God and *Satan* (means adversary or opponent) could not have been known unless God had chosen to reveal it to the writer of the book of Job. In fact, it appears that Job himself was never let in on the real cause of his suffering; only future Bible students would be allowed to have that important missing piece of information. The information about the activities of Satan can be helpful to us so that we can be aware of how he wants to turn our trust away from God. Before we look at the revelation part, let's take a look at the earthly facts.

Earthly Situation

Job was a man who was well-known in the Eastern portion of the world--what we would today call the Middle East. He evidently was a successful farmer and rancher and took seriously his responsibilities as a father to his ten

credentials -proof of ability or position

. . . there is one source of information that you can always trust-- the Bible.

revelation - something revealed

Satan - the devil

The information about the activities of Satan can be helpful to us so that we can be aware of how he wants to turn our trust away from God.

blameless - without fault; whole, complete, morally and physically healthy

upright - honest; morally correct; straight in the sense of following God's will

shunned - avoided

feared -felt a deep reverence for

Job was wise enough to know that his children were capable of "looking good" on the outside while having secret sins on the inside. So, regularly he sent for them or sent word to them regarding their spiritual situation and offered sacrifices to God on their behalf.

children. Job 1:1 described him as *blameless* and *upright*. He *feared* God while, at the same time, he *shunned* evil. From the list of the livestock he owned, we can see he was a wealthy man. His children evidently had good relationships with one another since they took turns going from brother to brother's home on their "day." This could mean on their different birthdays, as when Job later talks of his "day" as the day of his birth (Job 3:3), or perhaps just when it was their turn to host a feast on a special day of the year. Job was wise enough to know that his children were capable of "looking good" on the outside while having secret sins on the inside. So, regularly he sent for them or sent word to them regarding their spiritual situation (sort of like a "spiritual check-up") and offered sacrifices to God on their behalf.

How did Job know to do this? God evidently let His will be known about the right way to worship Him, because as early as Genesis 4, in the incident involving Cain and Abel, the first family knew what was expected of them in regard to using sacrifices in worship. Whether there were written documents at this time or just information passed from one to another about God's will, we do not know.

Situation in Heaven
Job 1:6-2:6

God pulled back the curtain here and revealed what we could never have known if He had not wanted to tell us. A scene in heaven was described in which the sons of God, a term used for angels in some places in the Bible, came before God. An evil angel, Satan, was allowed to come, too (Job 38:7). We are not told why God would allow Satan to have any access to Himself, especially when he came to criticize God's human followers, so we must just accept it as a fact. Satan's normal territory was earth, and the Lord asked him if he had noticed His servant Job, with whom God was so pleased. Satan had noticed but suggested to God that Job was not really as good as he seemed. *"Does Job fear God for nothing?"* Satan asked. He requested that God let him take away all the blessings God had given Job, for he was sure that Job would quickly change from trusting God to cursing Him. Surprisingly, God allowed this test to see if Job would serve God even without any outward sign that God was present and powerful in his life. God believed that Job would stay faithful.

Job's Response
(Job 1:13-22)

Without a moment to catch his breath, Job was told of tragedy after tragedy involving the loss of all his livestock, most of his servants, and all of his children. Remarkably to us, but just as God predicted, Job did not curse God for his problems. He tore his clothes and shaved his head in the traditional signs of grief and *"fell to the ground and worshiped."* Job recognized correctly that everything he had was a gift of God, and that he would have to leave it all behind at his own death. He was just losing it all a bit early. He did not blame God but, instead, blessed His name. What a man!

Job recognized correctly that everything he had was a gift of God, and that he would have to leave it all behind at his own death. He was just losing it all a bit early.

Satan Goes to Plan "B"
(Job 2:1-7)

Down, but not out, Satan returned to God where he had to hear God's approval of Job's reaction to Satan's recent actions against him. Satan said that, if only God would let him hurt his own physical body, then Job would certainly curse God in his pain. God allowed Satan to test Job in this way with a provision that Job's life would not be taken. Satan struck Job with a horrible illness involving painful boils or sores over his entire body.

Job's Response
(Job 2:9-10)

So miserable that he had to use a pottery fragment to scrape between the sores, Job still did not blame God. His wife, no doubt as grieved as he about all their losses, saw his illness as the last straw. She could not see God's help anywhere and she urged him to give up, too. How sad when we try to pull others down to our level of bitterness and hopelessness! She was allowing herself to be used to do the devil's own work, to tempt Job to curse God. Job, however, was strong enough in faith for both of them and refused to take her advice. *"In all this Job did not sin with his lips."*

How sad when we try to pull others down to our level of bitterness and hopelessness! She was allowing herself to be used to do the devil's own work, to tempt Job to curse God.

God Was Right; Satan Lost Again!

The record of Job might have ended right here and we would have had many good lessons. However, just like regular life and the suffering that comes with it, not everything that gets interrupted with tragedy gets "fixed" instantly. We will have many more things to learn from Job and from the three friends who traveled long distances to be with him. Job has more to endure yet in this long-term illness and his deep grief.

Job's Friends

Eliphaz, the Temanite, was probably a relative of Esau's (Genesis 36:4) and, like the other two friends, Bildad and Zophar, had had to travel a great distance to comfort Job. It is thought that Job's physical illness lasted for many months (Job 7:3). The friends certainly are to be admired for just quietly joining him in his grief for the first seven days they were there.

The friends certainly are to be admired for just quietly joining him in his grief for the first seven days they were there.

Time-Out for Bible Background: Just Who Is Satan?

There are two Old Testament passages that traditionally have been studied for information about Satan. As you read them, notice the information about his creation and original purpose, then try to find the reasons for his fall from favor with God. Check what you find with the summary that will follow these passages.

Ezekiel 28:12-19:

> 12 "Son of man, take up a lamentation for the king of Tyre, and say to him, 'Thus says the Lord GOD: "You were the seal of perfection, full of wisdom and perfect in beauty.
>
> 13 You were in Eden, the garden of God; every precious stone was your covering: the sardius, topaz, and diamond, beryl, onyx, and jasper, sapphire, turquoise, and emerald with gold. The workmanship of your timbrels and pipes was prepared for you on the day you were created.
>
> 14 "You were the anointed cherub who covers; I established you; you were on the holy mountain of God; you walked back and forth in the midst of fiery stones.
>
> 15 You were perfect in your ways from the day you were created, till iniquity was found in you.
>
> 16 "By the abundance of your trading you became filled with violence within, and you sinned; therefore I cast you as a profane thing out of the mountain of God; and I destroyed you, O covering cherub, from the midst of the fiery stones.
>
> 17 "Your heart was lifted up because of your beauty; you corrupted your wisdom for the sake of your splendor; I cast you to the ground, I laid you before kings, that they might gaze at you.
>
> 18 "You defiled your sanctuaries by the multitude of your iniquities, by the iniquity of your trading; therefore I brought fire from your midst; it devoured you, and I turned you to ashes upon the earth In the sight of all who saw you.
>
> 19 All who knew you among the peoples are astonished at you; you have become a horror, and shall be no more forever.'"

According to this passage, Satan is a fallen angel, a creation of God.

Therefore, he is in no way equal to God. He is limited in power and position. He was created to be an angel of highest rank, a cherub, anointed to cover God's throne with praise. He was full of wisdom until iniquity or sin was discovered in him. He was guilty of pride and God cast him out of heaven. He had been allowed even in Eden, and we have more information about that in Genesis 3. Satan would continue to do evil things on earth, but God promised that one day he would be stopped, burned with fire, and then, all who used to fear him, would be surprised at how powerless God had made him in the end.

Isaiah 14:12-14:

> 12 "How you are fallen from heaven, O Lucifer, son of the morning! How you are cut down to the ground, you who weakened the nations!
> 13 For you have said in your heart: 'I will ascend into heaven, I will exalt my throne above the stars of God; I will also sit on the mount of the congregation on the farthest sides of the north;
> 14 I will ascend above the heights of the clouds, I will be like the Most High...'

Here in this passage, Satan is called Lucifer, meaning "light-bearer." He tried to make himself equal to God, to take over God's position. But God took him down from his high place and promised a future judgment on his actions.

He was created to be an angel of highest rank, a cherub, anointed to cover God's throne with praise. He was full of wisdom until iniquity or sin was discovered in him.

Bible Research

I. Satan has many names:

A. the adversary	1 Pet. 5:8,9
B. the god of this age	2 Cor. 4:4
C. the prince of the power of the air	Eph. 2:1-3
D. accuser of the brethren	Rev. 12:10; Job 1:6-12
E. the enemy	Matt. 13:39
F. the tempter	Matt. 4:3
G. a roaring lion	1 Pet. 5:8-10
H. the father of lies	Jn. 8:44
I. a deceiver	Rev. 12:9
J. a murderer	Jn. 8:44

However, contrary to what we usually think, Satan is not the master of hell. Hell is a place prepared for him and the fallen angels in the final judgment (Matthew 25:41).

However, the Christian has hope for the future, help and purpose in the present, and forgiveness for past sins.

II. Satan has four main methods of operation:
- A. Satan deceives people by transforming himself into an angel of light (2 Cor. 11:14).
- B. Satan tempts people to sin (Matt. 4 and Lk. 4, Satan's temptation of Jesus).
- C. Satan blinds the minds of the unbelieving so that they may not come to the light (2 Cor. 4:4).
- D. Satan emphasizes a person's past--accusing and bringing condemnation to them.

However, the Christian has hope for the future, help and purpose in the present, and forgiveness for past sins. Satan is real and is not to be taken lightly. Ephesians 6:12 warns that we wrestle not against flesh and blood. But Satan is defeated--Christ has already won the victory over him, and when we trust in God, Satan cannot defeat us. As in the life of Job, Satan has limited access to us now, but we can always call on God for help and power to withstand him (Hebrews 2:14).

BIBLE QUEST
LESSON 3

Questions

Study Procedure: Read the Scripture references before answering questions. Unless otherwise instructed, use only the Bible in answering questions. Some questions may be more difficult than others but try to answer as many as you can. Pray for God's wisdom and understanding as you study and don't be discouraged if some answers are not obvious at first. Do not read the study notes for this lesson until AFTER you have completed your questions.

Day One: Vocabulary Review - Match the word with its definition.

_____1. blameless a) avoided

_____2. credentials b) something revealed

_____3. feared c) honest

_____4. revelation d) proof of ability or position

_____5. Satan e) without fault

_____6. shunned f) the devil

_____7. upright g) felt a deep reverence for

8. Review from Lesson 2: What is the definition and purpose of "revelation" in the Bible? _____
   _____
   _____
   _____

9. Write down what Job said after each of Satan's attacks in chapter one and chapter two:
   a) _____
   _____
   b) _____
   _____

10. Bible Research: Using the list given, fill in the blank with the correct Bible reference for the following descriptions of Satan (some references may be used more than once).
    a) adversary_____
    b) god of this world_____
    c) prince of the power of the air _____
    d) accuser of the brethren_____
    e) the enemy _____
    f) the tempter _____
    g) like a roaring lion_____
    h) father of lies _____
    i) deceiver _____
    j) murderer _____

1 Peter 5:8-10   John 8:44   Revelation 12:9   2 Corinthians 4:4   Ephesians 2:1-3   Revelation 12:10
Matthew 13:39   Matthew 4:3

11. List any other people in the Bible you can find who were tempted by Satan to turn away from God and His will.

_____

_____

_____

Day Two: Read Job 3.

1. Job did not curse God, but he did curse something. What was it? _____

_____

2. Why did he curse it? _____

_____

3. In your own words, list a few of the things that Job wished had happened on the day of his birth that would have kept him from surviving. (Use 3:11-19.) _____

_____

_____

4. In 3:20-23, what question was Job really asking?

    a. Hey, who turned on the lights?

    b. Why is life wasted on someone who would rather be dead?

    c. Where is God hiding?

    d. Who asked you?

MEMORY: JOB 4:17; 5:7, 17-18

Day Three: Read Job 4 and 5.

1. Name the good things and the bad things Eliphaz had to say about Job in the early verses of Chapter 4. _____

_____

_____

2. Read Job 4:7-11. What did Eliphaz really think about the cause of Job's suffering? _____

_____

3. What incident was Eliphaz describing in Job 4:12-21? _____

_____

4. In Job 5, Eliphaz continued to show that he thought he had Job's situation all figured out. In his experience he had seen the "foolish taking root" (v. 3), meaning that some people do get blessed for a little while before they lose everything. Why did this not apply to Job's situation?

_____

_____

_____

5. Read Job 5:8-27. What did Eliphaz want Job to do and why? _____
_____

Day Four: Read Job 6.

1. Read Job 6:1-13. Quote phrases from this passage - or use your own words - to describe just how bad Job felt. _____
_____
_____

2. What did Job expect from his friend Eliphaz instead of accusations and criticism? Give verse.
_____
_____

3. Give the verses from Job 6:15-30 that match these feelings of Job's:

   a. _____ "When I first saw that you had come, I had such high hopes of getting some relief from my great pain. But you failed to bring me what I so desperately needed. To my shock, instead of an oasis in my desert of trouble, you have been a disappointing mirage."

   b. _____ "Have I ever asked a favor of you before?"

   c. _____ "If you insist on talking so much, even when you see how much pain I am in, at least tell me something that I don't know. I would know if I had sinned against God and brought all this on myself. If it were true, which it isn't, I would be the first to admit it and would not need you to point it out to me! I can still tell right from wrong."

Day Five: Read Job 7.

1. Job was so miserable that his days and nights seemed to either drag on endlessly or hurry by without change or meaning. Write down some of the word-pictures he used to express these feelings. _____
_____
_____

2. In 7:11-21, Job cried out in complaint to God with a series of questions. Fill in the blanks with the missing words and make note of the verse that was quoted.

   a. Am I a sea _____ or a _____ that You set a guard over me? (v. _____)

   b. What is man, that You should exalt him . . . That you should visit him every morning, and _____ him every moment? (vs. _____)

   c. Will You not look away from me, and let me alone till I _____?
   (v. _____)

     d. Have I _____? What have I done to You, O _____?

       (v. _____)

     e. Why have you set me as Your _____? (v. _____)

     f. Why then do you not _____ my transgression and take away my _____?

       (v. _____)

3. Do you have any comments on what you have just studied in these passages? Please write them below. _____

   _____

   _____

   _____

   _____

4. Now take a few moments and read the notes for this lesson.

Notes

Comforting Words (Job 3-7)

Job Breaks the Silence (Job 3)

After a week of silent suffering in the presence of his friends, Job broke the quiet with a series of curses for the day he was born. With dramatic language he expressed his wish that darkness would cover that day or that it would be completely struck from the calendar. He continued his complaint with a wish that no one would have been around to take care of him when he was born or that he had been born dead and immediately put in the grave. There, at least, he reasoned, he would not have had to suffer as he was in the present. Job even wondered aloud why light was given to him when he only wanted the darkness of death. His worst fears had come true, and he knew no ease, quiet, or rest - only trouble. Job was in great emotional, spiritual, mental, and physical pain. His words powerfully revealed the depth of his grief.

His worst fears had come true, and he knew no ease, quiet, or rest -- only trouble.

Comforting Mission

Job's three friends had agreed to come and try to *comfort* Job (2:11). The Hebrew word for comfort was *nacham* (naw-kham'), to sigh or to breathe strongly. In New Testament Greek it was *paraclete* which meant to come along side of, to soothe, or to console. Yet, the speeches of these friends, were about as soothing as alcohol on a wound or rocks in a shoe! Comforting they were not—at least not when they broke their seven days of silence and tried to respond to Job's expressed grief.

comfort- to console in time of grief or fear

18

Timing Is Critical

Eliphaz was probably the oldest of the three friends who were named and so was expected to speak first. He should have known that Job was speaking out of indescribable pain and have allowed him some freedom to grieve without criticism. However, Eliphaz evidently felt he could not let Job's complaints about still being alive go unanswered. This brought up the first factor in effective comforting: timing.

Just because it appears that someone has spoken foolishly or wickedly, no immediate comment is necessary.

Just because it appears that someone has spoken foolishly or wickedly, no immediate comment is necessary. There are several things that should be considered: Can a person in severe pain really hear what we are trying to say? Even if he can, how will he be affected by our words? Will what we are about to say help him or hurt him even more? Why do we want to say this at this time anyway? Is it for our benefit or the sufferer's? Could it not wait until he is in a better frame of mind to receive it? It is important to realize that in the business of comforting, timing is critical.

deteriorated - became worse in appearance or usefulness

Eliphaz Responds (Job 4)

Eliphaz made a brief attempt to start with a positive comment about how much Job had done for others. But this quickly *deteriorated* into a criticism of how poorly Job was acting now that he was in trouble. To make matters worse, Eliphaz then declared that no innocent or upright person would be in Job's shape, because God punished only those who deserved it. To add to his authority, Eliphaz described a scary vision he had had. He thought it would serve as a warning to Job to quit denying his guilt. God would certainly judge such sin. With friends like Eliphaz, Job needed no enemies!

It is important to realize that in the business of comforting, timing is critical.

Criticism Continued (Job 5)

Eliphaz challenged Job to bring out some witnesses for himself, but before Job had a chance to do so, Eliphaz quickly started *elaborating* on his own experience. The problem with Eliphaz was that he thought he had "seen it all." He believed that there could be no exceptions--that Job must be a sinner who had been allowed "to take root" (5:3) briefly and enjoy the good things of life only until judgment could catch up with him. Such a man, he believed, was suddenly cursed, *"his sons far from safety . . . crushed in the gate"* and robbed of his harvest by the hungry. These things had happened to Job, but the truth was that Eliphaz was limited in his experience, was

elaborating - giving attention to great detail

prematurely - occurring before the natural or appropriate time

Seeds of love and obedience do not always produce health and happiness on earth for the person who planted them, but they will result in future heavenly rewards.

mirages - optical illusions in which non-existent bodies of water reflecting objects are seen

He needed tenderness and truthfulness at a time like this -- not blunt personal opinions.

monotonously - without any variety

ignorant of the complete situation, and, so, was wrong about Job. There was truth in Eliphaz's belief that "we reap what we sow," but he had insisted that all rewards were always given during a person's earthly life. He judged Job **prematurely**. Seeds of love and obedience do not always produce health and happiness on earth for the person who planted them, but they will result in future heavenly rewards.

Job's Turn (Job 6)

Job answered Eliphaz by admitting his words sounded "*rash*" (3) but explained that that was only because his suffering was so terrible. Job felt as if God Himself were attacking him and saw death as the only way to stop the overwhelming suffering. Job reminded Eliphaz that he was not made of stone or bronze but of normal human flesh and that he felt the pain intensely. He needed tenderness and truthfulness at a time like this -- not blunt personal opinions. To anyone in such a situation, Job remarked, "*kindness should be shown by his friend*" (14). However, Job's friends had been as disappointing as dried-up streams or desert **mirages**. Eliphaz's remarks had only increased Job's pain. What Job needed was some tenderness, some truthful compassion, and for his friends to watch for better timing in speaking to him. Let's check our own comments to others by this standard.

Talking to God (Job 7)

Job described the misery of his present life with several "word pictures": a servant longing for shade or pay day; a man unable to sleep and wishing for morning; day after day passing swiftly but **monotonously** like a weaver's shuttle; and finally a cloud vanishing from sight. Job then cried out to God asking for an explanation of what was happening to him: Was God playing with him like a fisherman after a sea serpent or trying to scare him by interrupting his sleep with dreams or visions? Why did God even take time to notice a man? In frustration, Job finally prayed for God to show him any of the sins he might have missed, and then he would ask for forgiveness. It looked as if Eliphaz's words had begun to affect Job negatively. He had begun to doubt himself and what he knew to be true of his relationship with God.

Questions

Study Procedure: Read the Scripture references before answering questions. Unless otherwise instructed, use only the Bible in answering questions. Some questions may be more difficult than others but try to answer as many as you can. Pray for God's wisdom and understanding as you study and don't be discouraged if some answers are not obvious at first. Do not read the study notes for this lesson until AFTER you have completed your questions.

Day One: Review of Job 3 through 7. Vocabulary: Choose the best definition for each word.

_____ 1. comfort
   a) to warm
   b) to console in time of grief or fear
   c) to silence

_____ 2. deteriorated
   a) joined in the discussion
   b) remained behind the rest
   c) became worse in appearance or usefulness

_____ 3. elaborating
   a) giving attention to great detail
   b) delivering a baby
   c) causing great boredom or fidgeting

_____ 4. mirages
   a) mirror images
   b) helpers for the elderly
   c) optical illusions in which non-existent bodies of water reflecting objects are seen

_____ 5. monotonously
   a) without any variety
   b) quietly
   c) with only one person present

_____ 6. prematurely
   a) without regard to age or ability
   b) occurring before the natural or appropriate time
   c) without parental permission

7. Find some of the "word pictures" that Job used to describe how he felt. (Use Job 3, 6, and 7.)

_____

_____

8. What was wrong with Eliphaz's response to Job in chapter 4 and 5? _____

_____

_____

9. What do you think would have been a better way to comfort Job? _____

_____

_____

Day Two: Read Eliphaz's second speech in Job 15.

1. From verses 1-3, Eliphaz implies that Job is a (a) stupid soul, (b) wind bag, or (c) devil.

2. In verses 4-6, Eliphaz accused Job of some spiritual failures. Name them. _____

   _____

   _____

3. Match the section of verses with the appropriate summary:
   a) Just who do you think you are? _____
   b) Basically, man is a sorry sort of creature, full of sin. _____
   c) Let me tell you what I know! _____
   d) The wicked person always has many troubles. _____

   verses 20-35   verses 14-16   verses 7-13   verses 17-19

   MEMORY: JOB 12:10; 13:15

Day Three: Read Job's response to Eliphaz's second speech in Job 16 and 17.

1. What did Job think about his friends' help so far? _____

   _____

   _____

2. What did Job say he would have done if he had been in their position? _____

   _____

   _____

3. Pick out several phrases that describe how Job was feeling at this point. Write them down

   below and include the verse where they are found. _____

   _____

   _____

   _____

4. Read Job 16:18-22. For what did Job wish? _____

   _____

   _____

5. Read Chapter 17. Name a few of the things that had been hard for Job to bear. _____

   _____

   _____

   _____

Day Four: Read Eliphaz's last speech in Job 22.

1. Eliphaz came right out and accused Job of great wickedness. What specific things did he say Job had done?_____

_____

_____

2. Do you think Eliphaz was right? Explain. _____

_____

_____

3. From 22:21-30, what did Eliphaz want Job to do? _____

_____

4. What was wrong with Eliphaz's advice?

   a) nothing

   b) It sounded good, but Job's sin had not brought on his suffering. Eliphaz did not know the whole situation.

   c) When people are hurting, they don't need others to make them feel guilty. They just need to know someone cares.

   d) Eliphaz was acting like he knew Job's heart. No person can fully know what's going on inside another person. That's the business of the Holy Spirit.

 MEMORY: JOB 22:21-22

Day Five: Read Job's response to the last speech of Eliphaz in Job 23 and 24.

1. From 23:1-7, what did Job think God would do if he could find Him? _____

_____

_____

2. Even though Job expressed his pain and confusion, he was sure about a few things. What were they? _____

_____

_____

3. Read Job 24. Eliphaz had declared in his speeches that the wicked always get caught. However, in this chapter Job gave many examples of the wicked getting away with their sinful actions, at least in their present life. Describe a few of these situations. (Use 24:2-17.)

_____

_____

4. From verses 18-21, write down what Job thought should have happened to the evil doers.

_____

_____

5. What do you think Job was trying to get across in this chapter? _____

_____

_____

_____

_____

6. Now take a few minutes to read your study notes for this lesson.

Notes

Good Grief

Such things as moving, changing jobs, switching schools, failing a class, losing an election, divorce, marriage, graduation, having more or less money or free time, retirement, sickness, family tensions, relationship changes, or even holidays could cause people to grieve.

---

shock - an unexpected or sudden upset of mental, emotional, or physical balance

---

Examining Grief

A nurse named Elizabeth Kubler-Ross, a pioneer in the field of grief-counseling, devoted herself to helping dying patients work through their grief and wrote of her discoveries in a book entitled *On Death and Dying*. While helping her patients come to terms with death, she observed five stages through which these people commonly passed: *denial, anger, bargaining, depression, and acceptance*. Others, following her lead, discovered that the process of grief with its various stages could also be seen in the people who loved a dying person, even though they themselves were healthy. In fact, later it was discovered, that any person going through any change—good or bad—might display symptoms of grief over a particular loss they felt. Such things as moving, changing jobs, switching schools, failing a class, losing an election, divorce, marriage, graduation, having more or less money or free time, retirement, sickness, family tensions, relationship changes, or even holidays could cause people to grieve. Not everyone passes straight through all five stages named by Kubler-Ross; someone in grief might get stuck in one stage or return to another they had already experienced. A simpler outline of grief adopted by current researchers include these: *shock*, suffering, and recovery.

Using this outline, a griever like Job, at the beginning of a loss or change, would experience a sense of shock. He sat silently for a week just absorbing the terrible news of the death of his children, servants,

24

and loss of all income. When his friends began to speak, as Eliphaz did in these recent lessons, Job was just starting to really suffer—he was just beginning to come out of the shock and face the long-term effects of what had occurred. He was unable at such a time to benefit from Eliphaz's advice, even if it had been correct, which it was not.

Walking with the Grieved (Job 15)

Instead of understanding that Job had been speaking out of great suffering, Eliphaz criticized him in his two remaining speeches. He called Job's earlier words *"unprofitable talk"* which could *"do no good"* (3). Eliphaz reminded Job that the friends present with him were *"older than your father"* and certainly knew more than Job did about life. Job, Eliphaz thought, should be quiet and just listen to their words (10). He showed his insensitivity to Job and ignorance about the grieving process when he remarked, *"Why does your heart carry you away…that you turn your spirit against God, and let such words go out of your mouth?"* (12, 13). Eliphaz declared that all men are sinners—none were pure (14-16), a fact Job would have agreed with—but Eliphaz did not stop there. He began a long discussion of how every wicked man has troubles, implying that since Job had such sorrow, he must be among the wicked (20-35). Eliphaz's words did not help Job through his suffering stage—they made things worse!

A very important part of moving from shock to suffering, and closer to the recovery period, is to admit that there has been a loss.

Working through Grief (Job 16)

A very important part of moving from shock to suffering, and closer to the recovery period, is to admit that there has been a loss. This might seem obvious, but many people move from shock to denial instead of allowing themselves to admit and then feel the effects of a loss or change. When getting over the shock period, a person needs to talk about what has happened, and they need to do so freely, without anyone's criticism or judgment. No one can help what they feel, but they can choose what to do with those feelings. They can admit them to God, to themselves, and to others, and then choose to release them to God for His help and healing. That will bring them closer to recovery. However, if they choose to deny their feelings or simply to hide them from others, they cannot fully recover.

Job chose the "healthy" way of grief: he openly expressed his sadness as well as his disappointment in the actions of his friends: *"Miserable comforters are you all!"* He continued in verse 4, *"I also could speak as you do, if your soul were in my soul's place....But I would strengthen you with my mouth, and the comfort of my lips would relieve your grief."* However, Job admitted, *"My grief is not relieved."* That was an honest statement and was necessary for Job to admit if he were to face his pain and move beyond it. Just how bad did Job feel? He felt as if God had been fighting him and had turned him over to the wicked (7-14). He wanted so much to find a way to talk to God (21), but he knew of no one to help him.

Offering comfort to a long-term sufferer could certainly challenge the best of friends, and Job's friends did not measure up.

Still Suffering (Job 17)

"My spirit is broken, my days are extinguished, the grave is ready for me... (1). The suffering period of grief can last a long time. Some Bible scholars believe that Job endured about nine months of this overwhelming physical sickness in addition to the initial losses of children, servants, and livestock. Offering comfort to a long-term sufferer could certainly challenge the best of friends, and Job's friends did not measure up. He called out to them anyway in verse 10, *"But, please, come back again, all of you, for I shall not find one wise man among you."* Job felt so alone—he wanted someone to give him some hope of recovery: *"Where then is my hope?"* (15).

Holding on to Hope

The Hebrew word for *hope* is *tiqvah* which means cord or rope. Hope is what separates the Christian from the non-Christian in the grieving process. The Christian has a cord of hope that connects him to God who can bring about recovery. There are over 120 uses of the word hope in the Old and New Testaments, most of which refer to God or Christ as our hope. Although not everything that happens to a Christian is good, Christians still have the hope in God's promise to bring good out of every situation to the ones *"who love God and are the called according to His purpose"* (Romans 8:28).

Eliphaz's Last Try (Job 22)

profitable - rewarding

In his third and final speech Eliphaz asked Job a series of questions: *"Can a man be **profitable** to God, though he who is wise may be profitable to himself? Is it any gain to the Almighty that you are righteous? Or is it gain to Him that you make your ways blameless?"* As usual, he did not pause for a response, but if he had, and if Job had not been so deep in grief, perhaps Job could have explained some things. First, it is true that God does not need anything from any man, but a man's righteous living certainly does please God. It is sort of like saying thank-you to Him for the gift of life and relationship with Him that he has been given. Job's kindness and goodness certainly pleased God.

Next, Eliphaz jumped right into a very serious and **vicious** attack on Job's reputation. He named, as if he had proof, a list of Job's sinful past actions (1-11). However, the reader knows from the first chapter of Job that, according to God's evaluation, Job was a *"blameless and upright man...one who feared God and shunned evil"* (1:8). After such mean and unfounded remarks by Eliphaz, it was difficult to enjoy the words of praise for God which followed in verses 12-14, even if they were true. Eliphaz followed his praise of God with a warning to Job about not *"keeping the old way which wicked men have trod ...whose foundations were swept away by a flood"* (16). He urged Job to seek God, to listen to Him, to pray to Him, and receive His help. However, nice advice from a mean mouth is generally not effective. Job, in the end, will be the one to help Eliphaz get right with God.

vicious - dangerously aggressive

Still Suffering (Job 23)

The suffering part of the grieving process continued as Job answered Eliphaz with this statement, *"Even today my complaint is bitter; My hand is listless because of my groaning. Oh, that I knew where I might find Him, that I might come to His seat!"* (2,3). Job knew his only source of help was God, and He believed that God would understand and help him. Job could not find a way to God, but he knew God still had an eye on him. He was for a moment lifted from the valley of grief to a mountain of hope: *"When He has tested me, I shall come forth as gold"* (10). However, as is common in one suffering so deeply, the high moment dissolved into a period of despair and even an anguished blaming of God: *"Therefore I am terrified at His presence; when I consider this, I am afraid of Him...because I was not cut off from the presence of darkness, and He did not hide deep darkness from my face."*

However, nice advice from a mean mouth is generally not effective. Job, in the end, will be the one to help Eliphaz get right with God.

Exceptions to Eliphaz's Experience (Job 24)

Job finished his defense against Eliphaz's claims with some things he had learned in his own lifetime. Frequently, Job illustrated, wicked men did not get punished in their lifetime. However, Job believed and stated that God certainly was aware of their actions and would one day bring them low. His point? If there were exceptions to Eliphaz's experiences and Job could list several, then it followed that Job could be an exception to Eliphaz's claim that all who suffer terribly must be guilty of some terrible sin.

We cannot know everything involved in another's suffering, and so we should be humble in our approach and cautious in giving counsel.

Closing Comfort If you have experienced loss or change recently or even in the past, allow yourself to admit the feelings associated with each situation. Tell God everything in prayer and ask Him for a few good comforters to help you sort through feelings and work toward recovery or needed adjustment. Learn from this study that good comforters will not always be who you thought they would be, but God can be trusted. Hold on to the hope He has offered; He will not fail you.

On the other hand, if you have been like Eliphaz, quick to speak and slow to lovingly listen, then you need to repent, apologize, and start again. We cannot know everything involved in another's suffering, and so we should be humble in our approach and cautious in giving counsel. Listening, praying, and showing loving action are the best tools to use in helping people work through their grief.

BIBLE QUEST

LESSON 5

Questions

Study Procedure: Read the Scripture references before answering questions. Unless otherwise instructed, use only the Bible in answering questions. Some questions may be more difficult than others but try to answer as many as you can. Pray for God's wisdom and understanding as you study and don't be discouraged if some answers are not obvious at first. Do not read the study notes for this lesson until AFTER you have completed your questions.

Day One

1. Write a short definition for the following words.

   a) profitable: _____

   b) shock: _____

   c) vicious: _____

2. What are the stages of grief? _____
   _____
   _____

3. What are some things that could cause a person to grieve? _____
   _____
   _____

4. What did Job need from Eliphaz and what did he get? _____
   _____

5. Read Job 8. Give the verse(s) that match(es) the thought expressed below:

   a) God doesn't make mistakes. _____

   b) Your sons were probably punished for their sins. _____

   c) If you would stop now and pray to God, and stay pure and upright, He would give you everything back and then some. _____

   d) Just look at the past for the truth. _____

   MEMORY: JOB 8:20

Day Two: Read Job 8, 9, and 10.

1. In Job 8, Bildad compared those who forget God to some fragile things he had observed in nature. List them. _____
   _____
   _____

2. Read Job 9. Job admitted in verses 2-4 that no man could stand before God and debate with Him. So, how can we come near a holy God? Read 1 Timothy 2:5. _____

_____

3. Job looked further into the past than Bildad suggested. He looked all the way back to creation. List some of the creative activities of God. _____

_____

_____

_____

4. Job knew that God was in charge of everything but was confused about the change he thought had taken place in their relationship. What verses showed his misunderstanding of God's actions toward him? _____

_____

_____

5. Read 10:1-7 and then choose the best summary.

     a) Just go ahead and kill me know!

     b) Why is this happening? Have you changed your methods and started acting as a human being would? You know I am not a wicked person.

     c) What have I done to deserve this?

6. For what does Job give God the credit in verses 8-13?_____

_____

_____

MEMORY: JOB 19:25-26

Day Three: Read Job 18 and 19.

1. What emotion did Bildad criticize Job for showing in Job 18? Comment on this. _____

_____

_____

_____

2. In verses 5-21, Bildad described what happened to the wicked. Had any of these things happened to Job? Give verses. _____

_____

3. Read Job 19. Who did Job really blame for what was happening to him?_____

_____

4. What personal relationships had Job lost during this time of suffering? _____

_____

_____

5. What one relationship was he sure of, even in his terrible suffering? _____

_____

Day Four: Read Job 25, 26, and 27.

MEMORY: JOB 28:28

1. Job had not claimed to be without any sin, but he had claimed innocence from any particular sin that would have brought on his terrible suffering as punishment from God. Did Bildad believe him? Explain. _____

_____

_____

2. Read Job 26:1-3. Job asked Bildad four "how" questions. Choose the answer below that you think would have been the most truthful response to all four.

   a) A whole lot.

   b) Not a bit.

   c) You did a little bit of good.

   d) No comment.

3. Read Job 26:5-14. Job returned to the theme of God as Creator, the power above all powers. Choose a few of the things God can do and list them below. _____

_____

_____

_____

4. Read Job 27. What verses show Job's determination to stand firm in his belief that he had lived his life in a way that pleased God? _____

5. Read Job 28.

   a) Which verses describe God's power? _____

   b) Which verses describe God's wisdom? _____

Day Five: Read Job 29, 30, and 31.

1. Pick the best title for chapter 29 from the choices below:

   a) "Nobody Knows the Troubles I've Seen"

   b) "If They Could See Me Now"

   c) "Those Were the Good Old Days"

   d) "I Must Have Lost My Touch"

2. Read Job 30:1-8 and write down what you discover about men who chose to be "outcasts."

_____

_____

_____

3. Which verses in Job 30:9-31 describe:

    a) the abuse Job received from onlookers _____

    b) the physical symptoms of his illness _____

4. Read Job 31, Job's final speech. After having heard all the false allegations of his friends, Job must have felt forced to defend himself. What verses describe his past good deeds?

_____

_____

5. Job's final words (vs. 35-40) revealed a bit of a "demanding" spirit toward God. What phrases seem to be a bit arrogant, even in such terrible circumstances? _____

_____

_____

6. Now take a few minutes to read your study notes for this lesson.

Notes

God as Creator

Bildad's Turn

Bildad, like Eliphaz, never considered an opinion other than his own.

The second friend of Job's who had traveled a distance to comfort him was named Bildad the Shuhite. There is a mention of Shuah in the family line of Abraham (Gen.25:2). Perhaps Bildad had come from Canaan to see Job. Eliphaz, the eldest friend, had spoken first and had emphasized his own experience. Bildad called on Job to look back to history, and in agreement with Eliphaz, he hoped to convince Job to "come clean" of whatever sins had brought on such terrible suffering. Although bold, Bildad remained blind to the unique situation in which Job was found. Bildad, like Eliphaz, never considered an opinion other than his own. His words could not bring comfort to Job but they can provide a background for some interesting spiritual teaching for us.

Look Back (Job 8)

Bildad criticized Job's last words, and then he cruelly implied that perhaps Job's sons deserved to be killed (4). Further, he added, if Job would just seek God and straighten up, God would restore everything as it had been. He urged Job to review history. There he would see that no one who forgot God prospered for long. Such a person lived a fragile life, just waiting for destruction, like a spider-web or a vine. Bildad was saying what he believed to be true about Job, that Job had not been living right with God, and so needed to repent. What was true in some situations was not true in Job's, but Bildad could not see that.

Job Looks Way Back -- to Creation (Job 9)

Job did not jump into a defense of himself here. He took Bildad's advice and looked back—way back—to the power of God in Creation. Job had a correct knowledge of just who God was. Job knew God to be the greatest of all greats—the power above all powers. He agreed with Eliphaz and Bildad that no mere man could stand before God and answer Him even one time out of a thousand (3). Man's goodness or righteousness was nothing when laid alongside that of God's. Job mentioned a few of the creative activities of God. These references are quite interesting when we consider that they reveal that Job and his **contemporaries** had an advanced understanding of the universe around them. Some of the statements found in Job have only in recent years been "verified" by scientific observation.

contemporaries - people living at the same time as each other

"He alone spreads out the heavens" (8). The idea that our universe is spread out and expanding has just been verified by astronomers who have observed and measured galaxies moving away from ours. It appears that the universe is "unwinding" from an earlier more **compact** position. Job mentioned the constellations called the Bear, Orion, and the Pleiades that were made by God. These were known in Job's day and used as reference points for navigation and travel. Why? Because their positions could be calculated due to the "built in" mathematical precision and order placed in the universe by a thoughtful Creator. Job added, *"He does great things past finding out, yes, wonders without number"* (10).

compact - packed together or solidly united

Like his friends, Job did not know that Satan had been allowed to test him in order to prove that Job would serve God even without personal gain. However, Job knew that, ultimately, God was responsible for absolutely everything. As a result, he cried out to God for help and mercy, deeply aware of the big difference between Creator God and created man. Job spoke in detail about his misery and grief at feeling a separation from God (14-31). His knowledge of God as Creator and ultimate Judge led Job to wish out loud for a mediator, a go-between, to reach God for him. This is what should happen to all of us (32-35). God put within each of us the ability to observe His creative acts and to realize His greatness. From that knowledge should be birthed a desire to know Him, right along with the realization that we cannot reach Him alone. We all need a mediator. How wonderful that the Bible has revealed that such a **mediator** exists in Jesus Christ. Job and friends looked forward to the coming of such a One, while we look back at His coming. From whatever side of the cross we seek, the answer is the same—God became our Mediator when He put on human form and allowed Himself to enter our world to be our Savior.

> **mediator** -a person who helps settle or reconcile opposing sides in a dispute

> **intricate** - complicated, extremely complex

> *Job and his friends looked forward to the coming of such a One, while we look back at His coming. From whatever side of the cross we seek, the answer is the same--God became our Mediator when He put on human form and allowed Himself to enter our world to be our Savior.*

Job's Pain Continued (Job 10)

Job gave *"free course"* to his *"complaint"* (1). He did not know why the God he loved and served seemed to be abandoning him. He knew that God knew that he was not guilty of anything that would have brought on such judgment. His complaint here included a beautiful description of how intimately involved God as Creator is in the formation of every human life: *"Your hands have made me and fashioned me, an intricate unity; ...did You not pour me out like milk, and curdle me like cheese, clothe me with skin and flesh, and knit me together with bones and sinews? You have granted me life and favor, and Your care has preserved my spirit. And these things You have hidden in Your heart; I know that this was with You"* (8-13). After such a wonderful beginning, Job wondered out loud why lately his life had been so tortured. Again, in his deep pain and depression, he wished for death.

Bildad and Job: Round 2 (Job 18)

Bildad obviously did not appreciate the insights Job had as much as we do. *"How long till you put an end to words?"* was his response to Job's speeches. Then, from verses 5 through 21 Bildad described what happened to people like Job who presumably opposed God. What was particularly cruel in these remarks was that some of these things had already happened to Job: *"nor will his wealth continue, nor will his possessions overspread the earth . . . for futility will be his reward. It will be accomplished before his time."*

Job's Turn Again (Job 19)

"How long will you torment my soul, and break me in pieces with words?" Job was certainly honest in his evaluation of Bildad's counsel; Bildad was no comforter. Job knew that only God could help him with whatever was causing his suffering. He described his sense of isolation by listing the relationships that he had lost during this terrible time of physical and emotional anguish: *"My relatives have failed, and my close friends have forgotten me....I call my servant, but he gives no answer;...my breath is offensive to my wife...even young children despise me...my bone clings to my skin and to my flesh, and I have escaped by the skin of my teeth"* (13-20).

What Job Did Know

Deep down inside himself, Job knew one thing for sure, that the God of Creation had made a way to reach him, and that Way was a personal Redeemer. Speaking as a prophet, Job declared the promise of a future resurrection in the presence of his Redeemer: *"I know that my Redeemer lives, and He shall stand at last on the earth; and after my skin is destroyed, this I know, that in my flesh I shall see God, Whom I shall see for myself, and my eyes shall behold, and not another"* (25-27).

Deep down inside himself, Job knew one thing for sure, that the God of Creation had made a way to reach him, and that Way was a personal Redeemer.

Redeemer Explained

In the Old Testament, the word for *redeemer* was the Hebrew word *goel*. God introduced the concept through a law He made protecting defenseless people. For example, if a woman were widowed or without a father or brother to include her in his inheritance and care, the law allowed for her to seek a near relative to take her into his household and "redeem" any property that had been lost due to a lack of a male heir [See Leviticus 25:25, 47-55]. The near relative could refuse to help her, but it was considered a shameful thing not to be the *goel* for a person in need. Not just anyone could be a redeemer, however; a *goel* had to have three qualifications: (1) rich or powerful enough to buy or win back what was lost; (2) willing to take on the responsibility of another person's welfare; and (3) nearest in kinship to the person asking for help. The book of Ruth illustrated the practice of this custom with Ruth's approach to Boaz to be her **kinsman** redeemer [See Ruth 3]. However, the ultimate Redeemer to whom Job looked was Jesus. As God, He is certainly rich and powerful enough to pay off our debt of sin—and He paid dearly with His own life; as fully human, He is related

kinsman - a relative

to us by birth; and, in keeping with His godly nature, He is willing to take us in as His own.

Bildad's Last Blow (Job 25)

There was nothing new in this speech. Mercifully, for Job, it was short, blasting home the same two points: God is great; man is not. Job knew that already, so Bildad was of no more help to him than Eliphaz had been. In fact, that's what Job said to him in 26:1 and 2: *"How have you helped him who is without power…How have you counseled one who has no wisdom?…."* The answer? Not very well.

There was nothing new in this speech. Mercifully, for Job, it was short, blasting home the same two points: God is great; man is not.

Job Praises His Creator God (Job 26:5-14)

If Bible historians are correct and Job was contemporary with Abraham and his family, then only about 350 years had passed since the worldwide flood that had destroyed all but those on Noah's ark. If you view the time line below, you'll see that Noah lived about 350 years after the flood, and so firsthand knowledge of the drastic changes in the earth would have been available to the world through him or his sons.

Time line of Job

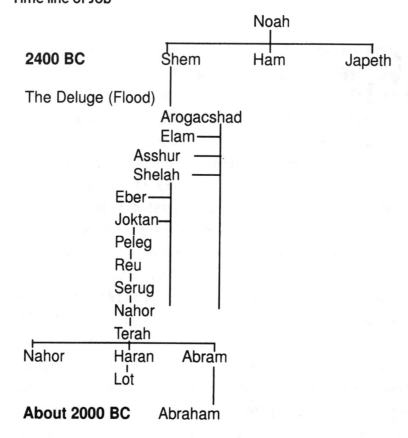

Noah

2400 BC   Shem   Ham   Japeth

The Deluge (Flood)

Arogacshad
Elam
Asshur
Shelah
Eber
Joktan
Peleg
Reu
Serug
Nahor
Terah

Nahor   Haran   Abram
Lot

About 2000 BC   Abraham

It seemed from what we had of the speeches of Job and his friends, that the common man knew a lot about the power of God as Creator and Lord of the universe. This concept of God as Creator—and there is no greater power than the One Who made it all—is a primary truth of the Bible. In fact, the very first sentence in the Bible stated it: *"In the beginning, God created the heavens and the earth"*(Genesis 1:1). This truth fits perfectly with what the writer of Hebrews said about what was required in coming to God: *"But without faith it is impossible to please Him, for he who comes to God must believe that He is, and that He is a rewarder of those who diligently seek Him"*(Hebrews 11:6). God gave us the overwhelming evidence of Himself in Creation so that everyone everywhere could believe that He exists! *"For since the creation of the world His invisible attributes are clearly seen, being understood by the things that are made, even His eternal power and Godhead, so that they are without excuse . . ."* (Romans 1:20). God wanted man to know that He exists and that He is the ultimate Creator God. The Bible repeated this theme from Genesis to Revelation so that not even the casual reader could miss it. Take a few moments and look up some of these other references: Deut. 4:32; Ps. 148:1-5; Is. 42:5; John 1:1-3; Acts 14:15; Acts 17:22-25; Rom. 1:24-25; Rev. 14:6-7.

God revealed Himself clearly to all as Creator God.

Back to Job 26

God revealed Himself clearly to all as Creator God. Job knew this and so had laid the correct foundation for his faith. God takes all those who want to know Him a step farther—letting them know that the Creator wants to have a relationship with His creatures. Since the Scriptures, at least not in the form that Moses would put them, did not exist at the time of Job, God had evidently let people know directly through revelation what He expected them to do in the matter of approaching Him. Adam and Eve, Noah, and the patriarchs all had had personal revelation of God's will and plan about blood sacrifice and the coming Redeemer, and, evidently, had passed on to others what they were told.

God takes all those who want to know Him a step farther—letting them know that the Creator wants to have a relationship with His creatures.

In Job 26:5-14, Job spoke boldly about God's creative acts. As noted earlier, some of the things mentioned by Job have been seriously explored and confirmed by modern scientists. In his book, The Remarkable Record of Job, Dr. Henry Morris, a noted creation scientist, gives fuller explanation to such work. A few examples are given below.

v. 7 *"stretches out the north over empty space and hangs the earth on nothing."* We have a north pointing axis on our earth which itself is held in place by the invisible force of gravity, thus suspended by "nothing" seen.

v. 8 *"He binds up the water in His thick clouds."* This is one of many references Job makes to God's power to put water in clouds and hold it till needed, *"yet the clouds are not broken under it."* In other places Job speaks of the weight of the clouds—a fact modern man would later uncover--that water vapor and air have differing weights that factor into rainmaking along with the electrical charges released by lightning. (See Job 28:24-27; 37:11,16.)

v. 10 *"He drew a circular horizon on the face of the waters."* The circular horizon correctly refers to the spherical shape of earth. Job could have told later inquirers that the earth was not flat.

No matter how hard they pushed him, Job did not back down from his view that he was not hiding any secret sin that would make him fall into the category of the wicked.

Job Maintained His Integrity (Job 27)

No matter how hard they pushed him, Job did not back down from his view that he was not hiding any secret sin that would make him fall into the category of the wicked. *"My righteousness I hold fast, and will not let it go,"* he cried (27:6). Then he detailed what he knew to be true of those who opposed God—to them came a terrible end with no hope for recovery.

Job's Source Was God (Job 28)

Job returned to his theme of praise for God's unequalled abilities to do what no other could do: God *"overturns the mountains at the roots . . . and His eye sees every precious thing"* (9 and 10). Job's friends had attempted to show their wisdom, but Job pointed to the only source of true wisdom, God Himself: *"For He looks to the ends of the earth, and sees under the whole heavens"* (24). If a man wants godly wisdom, he must begin by fearing the Lord and departing from evil (28).

From his low point in suffering, Job recalled the high moments of his past.

Those Were the Days! (Job 29)

From his low point in suffering, Job recalled the high moments of his past. He was healthy then, with loving family and attentive friends, free to serve others generously with time, money, and love. He remembered that *"I chose the way for them, and sat as chief; so I dwelt as a king in the army, as one who comforts mourners"* (25). Now he was without comfort.

Look at Me Now
(Job 30)

Job began this mournful chapter with these words, *"But now they mock at me . . ."* In describing how low he had fallen, however, Job gave an interesting insight into a situation that would later cause many an archaeologist to let his imagination run wild. Job described the low-class **ruffians** who were mocking him in his misery. He said they were hungry and struggled to live off what they could rummage from their environment. They were regularly chased off from normal society and shouted at like thieves. They were forced to live in caves or "clefts of valleys," and they made noises like animals. They were of questionable intellect and "sons of vile men." Centuries later the remains of men who had lived in caves would launch all sorts of speculation as to who they were and when they lived. Job's comments showed that "cave men" were social misfits who lived apart from but contemporary with regular society. Job would have laughed at the notion that these "sons of fools" were ancestors of his or any other civilized citizen.

ruffians - lawless, rowdy persons

A Bit of "I" Trouble
(Job 31)

With this chapter, *"the words of Job are ended"* (40). Repeatedly accused of actions he had not taken or attitudes he had not held, Job seemed almost forced to defend himself with particular facts about his past righteous acts. In statement after statement he denied giving in to lust, lies, laziness or loose living. He invited investigation and promised to endure appropriate punishment if found guilty. However, all his self-defense seemed to stir him to overstep his place as God's servant. With a definitely demanding tone he spoke of wanting to face the Almighty and hear Him answer: *"I would declare to Him the number of my steps; like a prince I would approach Him."* In a later lesson we'll see how God spoke to Job soon after this statement was made, and how quickly Job regretted his wrongfully demanding attitude.

Repeatedly accused of actions he had not taken or attitudes he had not held, Job seemed almost forced to defend himself with particular facts about his righteous past acts.

Questions

Study Procedure: Read the Scripture references before answering questions. Unless otherwise instructed, use only the Bible in answering questions. Some questions may be more difficult than others but try to answer as many as you can. Pray for God's wisdom and understanding as you study and don't be discouraged if some answers are not obvious at first. Do not read the study notes for this lesson until AFTER you have completed your questions.

Day One: Review

1. Vocabulary Review. Fill in the vocabulary word that matches the definitions below.

ACROSS

1. complicated, extremely complex
3. a person who helps settle or reconcile opposing sides in a dispute
4. packed together or solidly united
5. a relative
6. a lawless, rowdy person

DOWN

2. people living at the same time as each other

2. What is a *goel*?

   a) a Hebrew girl

   b) a relative who acts as a "redeemer" for a needy person

   c) a creation scientist who defends the Bible

3. What was Job's explanation for "cave men"? _____

   _____

4. Pick out something you found interesting from the notes that had to do with God's role as Creator and tell your group about it. _____

   _____

   _____

Day Two:　Read Zophar's speech in Job 11.

　1.　Summarize the different things for which Zophar criticizes Job in the following verses:

　　　a)　11:1-3 _____

　　　b)　11:4-5 _____

　　　c)　11:6 _____

　　　d)　11:7-9 _____

　2.　In verses 13-20, Zophar said something helpful for Christians, although it did not apply to Job at that time. Under the following headings, **summarize** what Zophar suggested should be done if a sinner wanted relief from suffering.

　　　a) If . . . _____

　　　_____

　　　_____

　　　b) Then . . . _____

　　　_____

　　　_____

　　　c) Because . . . _____

　　　_____

　　　_____

　　　d) And . . . _____

　　　_____

　　　_____

　　　e) But . . . _____

　　　_____

　　　_____

 MEMORY: JOB 23:10

Day Three:　Read Job's Response to Zophar in Job 12-14.

　1.　What emotions did Job show in verses 1-3 of Job 12? _____

　_____

2. From 12:7-25, what belief did Job have in common with his three friends about God?

    a) He gives everyone what he deserves.

    b) He cannot be reached by men.

    c) He's got the whole world in His hands.

3. From Job 13:1-12, write down some of the things Job said about his friends. _____

_____

_____

_____

4. From Job 13:20-23, what did Job want from God? (Read Job 9:34 for help in understanding this.)

_____

_____

_____

MEMORY: 1 CORINTHIANS 15:51-53

Day Four: Read Job's response to Zophar (continued).

1. From Job 14:1-12, how did Job view life?

    a) It's short.

    b) It's full of pain.

    c) It's boring.

2. What verse in Job 14 referred to a physical resurrection? _____

3. Find some New Testament references that describe or explain resurrection. _____

_____

_____

_____

_____

Day Five: Read Zophar's last speech in Job 20 and Job's response in Job 21.

1. In Job 20, Zophar said that a hypocrite will perish like:

    a) _____(v. 7)

    b) _____(v. 8) or

    c) _____(v. 8)

2. From Job 20:12-29, how long will the wicked man enjoy his sinning and why? _____

_____

_____

_____

_____

_____

3. In Job 21:1-21, Job told Zophar that he had noticed something about the wicked that Zophar had missed. What was it? _____

_____

_____

_____

_____

4. According to Job, when will the wicked face judgment? _____

_____

_____

5. Now take a few moments and read the notes for this lesson.

Notes

Victim or Victor: Dealing with Long-Term Suffering

Relationships

Do you know what makes life worth living but can also make life miserable? Relationships with other people! In the last lesson much of the emphasis was on God as the Creator of all. However, if that were all that we knew of God, then we might just be afraid of Him—overwhelmed by such enormous power, dwarfed by His magnificence. But the second big *doctrine* introduced in Scripture was that God desired to be in relationship with His creation, particularly with man. Instead of recording statistics or other scientific or historical data, God chose to document relationships for us in the one book that revealed His true nature. Think about it: Adam and Eve, Cain and Abel, Abraham and Sarah, Joseph and his brothers, Moses and Israel, Elijah and Jezebel, Mary and Elizabeth, Jesus and His disciples, and Paul with the early churches—God wanted us to see that relationships are very important. Sometimes they are helpful and happy while other times they are destructive and bring great grief.

doctrine - something taught as a body of truth or principles

deprived - denied use of or access to something

Back to Job. The reason he was suffering so much was because of all his relationships. He had suddenly been *deprived* of employees and children and

43

estranged - removed from someone or something once familiar or loved

later ***estranged*** from his wife and now the three friends who came to comfort him. Why? Because he cared for them all. He was in relationship with them. Even his spiritual and mental pain were caused by his feeling that he was out of his normal relationship with God.

Zophar the Gopher

The featured friend of this lesson was Zophar which rhymes with "gopher." A gopher is a burrowing rodent found in the plains area of the United States. Its name is from the French *gaufre* which means "honeycomb," referring to its underground burrows. Like a gopher, Zophar undermined Job's fragile physical, spiritual, and emotional foundation with the digging remarks of his two speeches. The name *Zophar* meant "hairy" or "rough" –an appropriate description of the ***abrasive*** manner in which he spoke to Job.

abrasive - rough; rubbing or wearing off

Zophar's First Speech (Job 11)

Without even a polite "hello," Zophar took his turn to speak to Job. He accused him of being wordy ("full of talk"), not factual ("empty talk"), irreverent ("when you mock"), and hypocritical ("you have said, 'My doctrine is pure, and I am clean in your eyes'"). Zophar was criticizing Job without factual evidence. He assumed Job deserved what was happening because of some hidden sin. Zophar would not back down from the idea he held in common with his friends Eliphaz and Bildad: suffering is caused when God punishes wickedness. In the New Testament, Jesus corrected this thinking in John 9:2-3 when asked to give the cause for the original blindness of a man He had just healed: "'Rabbi, who sinned, this man or his parents, that he was born blind?' Jesus answered, 'Neither this man nor his parents sinned, but that the works of God should be revealed in him.'" Jesus was saying that some suffering was allowed simply as a vehicle to display the glory of God in its relief or dependence on God in its endurance.

Jesus was saying that some suffering was allowed simply as a vehicle to display the glory of God in its relief or dependence on God in its endurance.

Zophar pointed, helpfully he must have thought, to the creative greatness of God (7-11) and then made a sarcastic comment about the impossibility of finding wisdom in an empty-headed man like Job (12). Finally, Zophar urged Job to reach out to God in honest repentance and to receive God's certain help (13-19). That was a good suggestion, but it did not apply to Job. The final insulting comment about the fate of the wicked (Zophar meant someone like Job) made things even worse (20).

Job's Mood Shows (Job 12)

Angry and defensive, Job responded to Zophar (1-4). Job knew that people in good health and happy situations did not need to vent their grief with words to friends or questions to God. As a lamp was despised in the mind of one who was seated comfortably in the light (5), Job's words had seemed inappropriate and unnecessary to his three friends. He agreed with Zophar and the others that God was the Creator of all and was in charge of everything that happened to everyone everywhere (7-25). However, in his current pain, he did not need more information like this from his friends; he needed their compassion while he struggled with his confusing feelings about why God-- who could do anything--had allowed all this to happen to him.

What Job Really Needed (Job 13)

"Worthless physicians" was what Job called his friends (4). *"Your platitudes are proverbs of ashes, Your defenses are defenses of clay"* (12). How could his friends have been better helpers?   First of all, they needed to recognize some of the harder aspects of long-term suffering:

> **platitudes** - trite or overused remarks or statements

1. **Repetition or monotony** wears away even what is solid. A chronic sufferer needs a buffer or a cushion from the constant grinding away of pain. Emotions become raw and the body becomes fragile in such circumstances. Spiritually, the person needs some time apart with God in praise, prayer, and study. A friend could help provide that. Emotionally a long-term sufferer needs scheduled change. This could be a change of position, view, menu, activity, or location. Physically, a person in constant pain needs to be clean, fed, loved, and allowed adequate medical care. Job's friends could have taken him somewhere and tended his wounds, made him more comfortable, helped him plan for the future, or even prayed with him. Criticizing him had not helped at all.

2. **Isolation** occurs when a person is shouldering great sorrow or illness. Such a person needs a few compassionate people to help him or her bear the load. Sometimes the sufferer "wears out" the people closest to him and will need others to step in and take turns listening to and assisting with the daily needs. These three friends had a relationship with Job or they would not have bothered to come see him, yet they did not use their connection with him in a helpful way. We must examine ourselves to see if we have been the friends we need to be to those in long-term trouble.

However, in his current pain, he did not need more information like this from his friends; he needed their compassion while he struggled with his confusing feelings about why God-- who could do anything--had allowed all this to happen to him.

Job Turned to God (Job 13, cont.)

"Though He slay me, yet will I trust Him. Even so, I will defend my own ways before Him" (15). The first part of this verse has been quoted often as an example of Job's extreme faith in God, similar to Abraham's in being willing to sacrifice Isaac (Genesis 22). Job was not sure that he would live through his present suffering and he wanted his friends to know that though they thought God was against Job, Job himself would still trust God. Satan's plan had failed. Further, Job, in the second part of that verse, held on to his own conviction that he was innocent of his friends' charges.

Job turned to God (13:20-22) and repeated what he had requested in Job 9:34: *"Withdraw Your hand [of judgment] far from me, And let not the dread of You make me afraid."* Job wanted to talk to God directly, but he needed some relief and courage before he could do that. If there were any sin in his life, although Job knew of none at that time, he wanted God to reveal it. The accusations of his friends had begun to make him doubt himself, at least for the moment.

Life Is Short (Job 14)

True to the characteristics of a long-term sufferer, Job questioned the purpose and meaning of his life. It was short and full of trouble. He longed for more: *"If a man dies, shall he live again?"* How many people have wondered about the possibility of life after earthly death? No doubt inspired by the Holy Spirit, Job answered his own question: *"All the days of my hard service I will wait, till my change comes. You shall call, and I will answer You; You shall desire the work of Your hands"* (14-15). In the New Testament Paul wrote of the change in the earthly bodies of believers that was promised: *"Behold, I tell you a mystery. We shall not all sleep [die], but we shall all be changed—in a moment, in the twinkling of an eye, at the last trumpet. For the trumpet will sound, and the dead will be raised incorruptible, and we shall be changed. For this corruptible must put on incorruption, and this mortal must put on immortality"* (1 Corinthians 15:51-53).

However, whether believer or unbeliever, ready or not, each person faces God in a life after death (Acts 24:15). There are no Scriptures that indicate a second chance for unbelievers.

However, whether believer or unbeliever, ready or not, each person faces God in a life after death (Acts 24:15). There are no Scriptures that indicate a second chance for unbelievers. Where and how a person spends eternity is determined in this present life by the personal response made to the offer of salvation through Jesus Christ.

Zophar's Second Speech (Job 20)

Zophar's whole message here was summed up in its introduction in verses 4 and 5: *"Do you not know this of old, since man was placed on earth, that the triumphing of the wicked is short, and the joy of the hypocrite is but for a moment?"* Zophar was admitting that although Job had once enjoyed blessing and pleasure in his early life, now what always happened to the wicked had finally caught up with him: loss of reputation (7), great suffering (22), fear (25), public exposure (27), and loss of wealth (28).

Job's Observation of the Wicked (Job 21)

Instead of helping Job, the friends had hurt him by refusing to let go of their own understanding of God's workings. In self-defense, Job shared his own observations of the lives of many wicked people he had seen, and his testimony offered an exception to his friends' earlier claims that the wicked are always punished in this life. In verses 7-26, Job gave example after example of godless people living rich, healthy, and long earthly lives. Job was not trying to say that God was not just, but instead that God's justice was not limited to this life. *"For the wicked are reserved for the day of doom; they shall be brought out on the day of wrath"* (30). What Job was trying to get Zophar and the others to see was that if the wicked often do not suffer on this earth for their rebellion against God, while facing sure judgment later, then would it not also follow that the righteous could be allowed to suffer in this life, receiving the full blessing of God's approval in the life after death?

| They Did Not Understand | Most of Job's relationships had been shattered, and yet, sadly, the ones remaining had not helped him during this |

long-term period of suffering and grief. However, even this proved God correct in His assessment of Job: stripped of everything and everyone, he still held on to his faith in God. Satan was wrong—the relationship of a man with God can outlast everything else: *"Though He slay me, yet will I trust Him."*

Most of Job's relationships had been shattered, and yet, sadly, the ones remaining had not helped him during this long-term period of suffering and grief.

Questions

Study Procedure: Read the Scripture references before answering questions. Unless otherwise instructed, use only the Bible in answering questions. Some questions may be more difficult than others but try to answer as many as you can. Pray for God's wisdom and understanding as you study and don't be discouraged if some answers are not obvious at first. Do not read the study notes for this lesson until AFTER you have completed your questions.

Day One: Review.

Vocabulary Review -- Matching

    a) estranged   b) abrasive   c) doctrine   d) platitudes   e) deprive

1. _____   removed from someone or something once familiar or loved

2. _____   rough; rubs or wears off

3. _____   denied use of or access to something

4. _____   something taught as a body of truth or principles

5. _____   trite or overused remarks or statements

6. In a past lesson, we learned that the first great truth of Scripture is that God is Creator of all. What is the second great truth? _____

_____

7. What are some of the special problems of those with long-term illnesses or on-going difficult situations? _____

_____

_____

8. What practical actions can concerned persons take to help in these situations? _____

_____

_____

_____

_____

9. What were the basic differences in Zophar and Job's understanding of suffering? _____

_____

_____

_____

_____

Day Two: Read Job 32.

1. Who is the new man on the scene here?

   a) Dr. Who

   b) Yuhu

   c) Elihu

   d) Buhu

 MEMORY: JOB 28:23-25

2. Do you think he had a good reason to be angry at Job and at the three friends? _____

   _____

   _____

   _____

   _____

3. What personal details are given about him in this chapter? _____

   _____

   _____

   _____

4. Read Job 33. In what way did Elihu say Job had been wrong or unrighteous?_____

   _____

   _____

   _____

5. List some of the ways in which God speaks to man to keep him out of trouble (15-30). _____

   _____

   _____

   _____

Day Three: Read Job 34.

1. In what verses does Elihu claim to quote Job? _____

2. Do you agree with Elihu that Job "drinks scorn like water" or "goes in company with the workers
   of iniquity"? _____

   _____

   _____

3. Draw a line for each important fact about God to the group of verses from which they come.

   a) He sees all. He doesn't need anyone to tell Him anything.   (10-12)

   b) God cannot sin.   (13-15)

   c) There is no higher authority than His. He holds everything together.   (16-20)

   d) God is impartial. He always judges correctly.   (21-28)

4. Read Job 35. Elihu was disturbed that Job had said in effect, "What's the use of living a good life before God if this is what happens?" (35:1-3) How would you have answered such a question? _____

_____

_____

_____

Day Four: Read Job 36.

1. From verses 1-4, how would you describe Elihu's attitude? _____

_____

_____

2. From 5-12, explain what Elihu thought Job should have done. _____

_____

_____

_____

3. Reread verses 13-23. What did Elihu think Job had done? _____

_____

_____

4. In verses 24-33, Elihu returned to the recurring theme of God as C __ __ __ __ __ R

Day Five: Read Job 37.

MEMORY: JOB 37:14, 23-24

1. In verse 14, Elihu said, "Stand still and consider the wondrous works of God." How would this have helped Job? _____

_____

_____

_____

2. Match the following "wondrous works" with the verses from which they come (fill-in the blank).

   a) _____ He spread out the skies.   v. 10

   b) _____ He makes glaciers.   v. 18

   c) _____ He is in charge of the thunder and lightning.   v. 6

   d) _____ He causes the wind to swirl in ways that affect the weather.   v. 12-13

   e) _____ He directs the precipitation that falls.   v. 2-5

3. Bible students and commentators have many differing opinions about Elihu. When God spoke in the next chapters, He did not comment about him by name. What is your opinion of Elihu and the helpfulness of his words to Job? _____

_____

_____

_____

_____

4. Now take a few moments and read the notes for this lesson.

Notes

Elihu, An Angry Young Man

Where'd He Come From?
(Job 32)

A fourth friend was introduced in this lesson who had not been mentioned at the beginning with Eliphaz, Bildad, and Zophar. Evidently, Elihu, a much younger man, had been patiently and politely listening to the speeches of the older men and Job. However, after they all had finished, he was not satisfied with how the friends had spoken with Job nor with how Job had claimed innocence while suggesting that God had been unfair. So, Elihu, possibly a relative of Abraham (see Genesis 22:21), spent six chapters trying to set them all straight.

Elihu Corrects Job
(Job 33)

Elihu certainly had high self-esteem! *"My words come from my upright heart; my lips utter pure knowledge . . . Truly I am as your spokesman before God"* (3, 6). He had heard Job claiming innocence and then saying God had still counted him as an enemy (8-11). Elihu understood this to mean that Job thought God had been unfair. Remember, no one involved knew about the opening chapter of Job in which God revealed Satan's challenge. So, all Job knew was that his conscience was clear and yet God had allowed all this suffering to occur. His friends thought he was hiding something. Elihu was willing to consider another idea about suffering--that God allowed it to purify His saints. But first, in this chapter, Elihu reminded Job of an important truth: *". . . God is greater than man . . . He does not give an accounting of any of His words"* (12, 13). This was really an important point--no matter what a person might think is happening, one thing is certain--God's ways are higher than man's ways, and He does not have to explain everything to him. It is important that we guard our attitude toward God. We may not understand what is happening to us, but we can still believe that God will only act in a way that is consistent with His holiness and goodness.

It is important that we guard our attitude toward God. We may not understand what is happening to us, but we can still believe that God will only act in a way that is consistent with His holiness and goodness.

proclaim - to announce publicly

perverted - used in an improper way

contradicts - expresses the opposite idea

God will give no direction to His children that contradicts what He has already said in His Word.

Hearing from God

Elihu told Job that God spoke to a person in several ways to keep him from *"the Pit"* (18, 22, 24, 28, 30). Evidently that was where Elihu thought Job was headed if he did not repent of his wrong thinking about God's character. Elihu said God could speak in a dream or vision (15), through an illness (19), or through a messenger or mediator (23). Eliphaz had already shared a vision in chapter 4; Job had been experiencing a terrible illness throughout the book; and now Elihu was the *"one among a thousand"* acting as a messenger. Elihu was to **proclaim** the uprightness of God (23) and Job was to admit that he had *"sinned and **perverted** what was right"* (27) and then receive forgiveness and healing. The only problem was that Job could not admit to sins he had not committed and was unable yet to see that his attitude toward God had become a bit demanding. God Himself would correct Job about this.

One important point needs to be made about hearing from God. Whatever the mode of delivery--whether in a dream or vision, a situation like an illness, or through a person claiming to speak for God--each message should be carefully compared with what the Bible already has recorded. God will give no direction to His children that **contradicts** what He has already said in His Word.

Elihu Continued
(Job 34)

Elihu made two criticisms of Job. First, Elihu thought Job claimed God had been unfair or unjust. Secondly, Elihu believed that Job claimed to suffer without a good reason. If all Job's speeches were reviewed, one could find verses here and there that revealed anger and confusion about God's part in all Job's suffering as well as many verses claiming his innocence. However, Job admitted that his great grief and suffering caused him to talk out of sheer pain and frustration. It was easy for Elihu to stand by and criticize while healthy and untouched by any of Job's problems. Elihu could have used a few lessons in compassion along with Job's first three friends. Elihu continued his speech by defending God's justice with many examples, but Job would not have disagreed with any of those claims.

What Good Is Being Good?
(Job 35)

Elihu believed Job to have asked something like this, "What's the use of being good if this is what I get?" Elihu answered that while Job's badness or goodness would not actually hurt or help God, who was so above him, bad or good actions would certainly have an effect on Job himself (2-8). This is something to think about. Many "good" actions may seem to go unnoticed by others, and we might occasionally think, "Does what I do really matter?" The answer is that it does. In the here and now, society benefits when people act with justice and kindness; in eternity, no action done in the character of Christ will go unrewarded. So, whether you think it matters or not, keep doing right. We still reap what we sow.

Elihu, like the others, lacked the full story about what was happening to Job, and he believed that God had not answered Job yet because of Job's *"pride"* and *"empty talk"* (12-16). Poor Job. No earthly comforter could be found.

Returning to one of the biggest themes in Job, Elihu called for Job to focus on the greatness of God who created everything.

Was Elihu Saying Something New? (Job 36)

Many students of Scripture differ on what to think about Elihu. He said of himself in this chapter, *"For truly my words are not false; One who is perfect in knowledge is with you"* (4). He is seen as arrogant and out-of-line by some, while others think he is closer to the truth than Job's other friends. When God spoke in the final chapters of Job, He did not refer to Elihu by name as He did when He reprimanded the other three. Also, Job himself did not respond to Elihu with a speech as he had to the others. Either Elihu's comments were not worth mentioning because they added nothing new, or they were closer to what Job needed to hear and therefore did not require correction. God seems to have left it up to the reader's personal **discernment** to evaluate Elihu's speeches.

discernment - the ability to detect something that is not obvious; the ability to comprehend something mentally

Elihu continued in chapter 36 through verse 23 to repeat many of the book's earlier themes. He, too, believed Job was hiding some sin and had brought on the suffering himself.

Look Up! (Job 36:24-33; 37)

Returning to one of the main themes in Job, Elihu called for Job to focus on the greatness of God who created everything. He paused in 37:14 to say: *"Listen to this, O Job; stand still and consider the wondrous works of God."* Certainly such a consideration would put most of our **puny** problems in perspective and pep up our **faltering** faith. However, the physical pain of the body and the emotional loss of friends and family that Job had experienced still needed to be expressed and treated. Elihu was not wrong in pointing out Job's need for an attitude adjustment, but he certainly could have shown some compassion for Job's suffering while he was at it. There are many situations in which we are unable to know "why?" Job's friends seemed to miss that truth. However, all of them knew and longed for their suffering friend to see, in every situation we can look to the divine "Who"--He will never fail us and will always act ultimately for the good of those who love Him.

puny - small, undersized

faltering - being unsure or unsteady in action or voice

Questions

Study Procedure: Read the Scripture references before answering questions. Unless otherwise instructed, use only the Bible in answering questions. Some questions may be more difficult than others but try to answer as many as you can. Pray for God's wisdom and understanding as you study and don't be discouraged if some answers are not obvious at first. Do not read the study notes for this lesson until AFTER you have completed your questions.

Day One: Review.

MEMORY: JOB 37:5-7

Vocabulary Review -- Matching

a) contradicted   b) discernment   c) faltering   d) perverted   e) proclaim   f) puny

1. _____   being unsure or unsteady in action or voice
2. _____   used in an improper way
3. _____   the ability to detect something that is not obvious
4. _____   small or undersized
5. _____   to make a public announcement
6. _____   expressed the opposite idea

7. In Job 33, Elihu described three ways that God speaks to man. List them along with any other ways in which He speaks to people. _____

_____

_____

_____

8. What should a Christian use to evaluate what he thinks he has heard from God?_____

_____

_____

9. Describe what you found helpful and unhelpful in Elihu's speeches to Job._____

_____

_____

_____

_____

Day Two: Read Job 38.

1. The Lord used this time to speak to Job. In what way did He appear? Write down any explanation you have for this. (Read John 1:18.) _____

_____

_____

2. Job had been wanting a chance to question God about all his sufferings. However, in verses 1-3, what happened instead? _____

_____

_____

3. God questioned Job about ten different parts of the physical world He had created. Read the verses included in each part, give the subject described, and make at least one comment about something that catches your interest in each. A few are done for you.

Verses	Subject	Comments
a) 4-7	The Beginning of Creation	It is interesting to think that the angels "shouted for joy" at the creation of the world. They celebrated the occasion with God.
b) 8-11	_____	_____
c) 12-15	_____	_____
d) 16-18	Oceans	It was only in the last century or so that man discovered "springs in the sea" and rivers. God had recorded it first here.
e) 19-21	_____	_____
f) 22-24	_____	_____
g) 25-28	_____	_____
h) 29-30	Ice	Glaciers could be described this way. They move slowly and freeze the land and waters beneath them as they move.

i) 31-33　　_____　　_____
　　　　　　　　　　　　　　　　　　　　_____
　　　　　　　　　　　　　　　　　　　　_____
　　　　　　　　　　　　　　　　　　　　_____

j) 34-38　　_____　　_____
　　　　　　　　　　　　　　　　　　　　_____
　　　　　　　　　　　　　　　　　　　　_____
　　　　　　　　　　　　　　　　　　　　_____

Day Three:　Read Job 39.

God asked Job questions about the creation of animal life at the end of chapter 38 and throughout chapter 39. Match the animals listed below with the phrase from the description of their living habits or characteristics.

1. _____　　hunt prey and crouch in dens
2. _____　　scorns the tumult of the city, doesn't obey a driver
3. _____　　spreads its wings toward the south
4. _____　　young ones are healthy, grow strong with grain
5. _____　　its young cry to God for food
6. _____　　mounts up and nests on high
7. _____　　leaves her eggs on the ground and runs faster than a horse
8. _____　　snorts majestically and paws the valley; smells the battle from afar
9. _____　　live wild in the mountains
10. _____　　won't plow or sleep by your manger

a) ostrich　　g) goats
b) hawk　　　h) deer
c) horse　　　i) raven
d) eagle　　　j) lions
e) wild ox
f) donkey

11. Read Job 40. Of what attitude in Job did God not approve? (vs. 1-2) _____

_____

_____

12. Summarize Job's response in verses 3-5. _____

_____

_____

13. God had not finished making His point with Job. Read verses 6-14 and select the summary statement(s) below that you think best fits the passage.

a) You certainly have a short memory!

b) Did you think attacking My character would make you look better?

c) When you can do what I do, then I'll answer all your questions.

d) Excuse Me! I didn't know I had to answer to you!

Day Four: Continue in Job 40 and Read Job 41.

1. God gave the first of two final illustrations of His power in creation. The land animal He described for Job in verses 15-24 was called _____.

2. Although many Bibles have footnotes that explain this creature as being a hippopotamus, reread the passage and note below any descriptive phrases that seem to point to a much larger and stronger creature than even that. _____

   _____

   _____

   _____

3. Read Job 41. God used this whole chapter to describe a huge sea creature called Leviathan. Again, go through the chapter noting the unusual physical characteristics of this creature and match them with the corresponding verses.

a) _____	breathes out fire and smoke	(1,2)
b) _____	air-tight rows of scales	(3-5)
c) _____	terrible teeth all around	(6-7)
d) _____	treats brass like wood and iron like straw	(9)
e) _____	makes ocean boil and foam	(14)
f) _____	can't be captured	(15-17)
g) _____	can't be eaten or sold	(18-21)
h) _____	underbelly sharp and acts like a plow	(27)
i) _____	can't be tamed	(30)
j) _____	frightening appearance	(31)

4. What kind of animals do you think leviathan and behemoth are? _____

   _____

   _____

5. The key to understanding why the Lord would give most of two chapters to a description of these creatures is Job 41:10, *"No one is so fierce that he would dare stir him up. Who then is able to stand against Me?"* Try to put this in your own words. _____

   _____

   _____

Day Five: Read Job 42.

MEMORY: JOB 42:2

1. What verses recorded Job's confession to God? (a) _____ What verses showed Job's sincere repentance? (b) _____

2. What did God say about Eliphaz, Bildad, and Zophar? _____

   _____

   _____

3. What did God do for Job in verses 10-17 and when did He do it? _____

_____

_____

_____

4. Take a few minutes and think about the whole book of Job. Write down two or three major lessons you learned from your study. _____

_____

_____

_____

_____

_____

_____

_____

_____

_____

_____

_____

_____

_____

_____

_____

5. Now take a few moments and read the notes for this lesson.

Notes

God Speaks Out (Job 38-42)

Job had been so pressured to defend himself before the accusations of his three friends that he had allowed that defensive attitude to carry over to his relationship with God.

Job Questioned (Job 38)

The opportunity for which Job had been longing suddenly and dramatically arrived—a meeting with God Himself. In Job 37, Elihu had tried to get Job ready for the whirlwind of God's presence: *"Hear attentively the thunder of His voice, and the rumbling that comes from His mouth . . . Stand still and consider the wondrous works of God"* (2, 14). Beginning with chapter 38, God unfolded before Job the wonders of His creation. Throughout his suffering, Job had not denied his Creator, but he had wondered whether or not God had been unfair in allowing such suffering to come to one like himself who had faithfully obeyed God. Job had been so pressured to defend himself before the accusations of his three friends that he had allowed that defensive attitude to carry over to his relationship with God. He focused so much on his own innocence that he became confused in his thinking about the eternally perfect ways of God. God appeared to Job here to correct Job's thinking, and He began the correction by asking Job questions.

Stand like a Man
(Job 38)

In past chapters, Job expressed his desire to meet with God and correct Him by pointing out how he had not deserved such suffering. But the first point God made with Job was that, if Job wanted to correct God about anything, Job would have to know more than God. God's opening remarks showed that this was definitely not the case: *"Who is this who darkens counsel by words without knowledge? Now prepare yourself like a man; and I will question you, and you shall answer Me. Where were you when I laid the foundations of the earth?"* (2-4). The main point of the next chapters was that if Job could not understand and explain the activities of creation or even control all of God's creatures, then he certainly was not in any position to question the actions of the One who made everything.

But the first point God made with Job was that, if Job wanted to correct God about anything, Job would have to know more than God.

Interrogation: How Much Do You Know?
(Job 38:1-38)

God questioned Job about ten aspects of creation, and Job had not yet gained full understanding of any of them. Exploration and understanding of these ten areas are still challenging the scientific world today:

1. Original creation (4-7)
2. The great flood (8-11)
3. The cycle of night and day (12-15)
4. Oceans (16-18)
5. Light (19-21)
6. Snow and Hail (22-24)
7. Rain (25-28)
8. Ice (perhaps referring to glaciers or polar ice caps) (29-30)
9. Constellations (31-33)
10. Clouds and weather systems (34-38)

What about the Animals?
(Job 38:39-39:30)

Next, God used questions relating to ten representatives of the animal kingdom to test Job's knowledge of creation.

1. Lions (38:39-40)
2. Ravens (38:41)
3. Mountain goats (39:1a)
4. Deer (39:1b-4)
5. Wild Donkeys (39:5-8)

6. Wild ox (39:9-12)

7. Ostrich (39:13-18)

8. Horse (39:19-25)

9. Hawk (39:26)

10. Eagle (39:27-30)

Your Turn, Job!
(Job 40:1-5)

God paused from His creation count-down to allow Job to go ahead with his planned correction of God. However, God's examples of the wonders of creation had corrected Job instead. Job was so humbled by the awesome creative power of God that he declared meekly, *"Behold, I am vile; what shall I answer You? I lay my hand over my mouth. Once I have spoken, but I will not answer; yes, twice, but I will proceed no further."* Job was waking up to the truth about God that the accusations of his friends had made him doubt. However, God was not through with him yet. Challenge of God's actions or judgment was not to be taken lightly. Two more creatures were to be introduced to further *accentuate* the difference in the power of the Creator God and the strength of a created man.

vile -morally repulsive; extremely unpleasant

accentuate -emphasize

Behold Behemoth!
(Job 40:15-24)

The word "behemoth" seems to have meant gigantic beast. Many Bible commentators compare it to a hippopotamus, but the description of its characteristics seem to point to an even larger animal than that: *"He is the first of the ways of God; only He who made him can bring near His sword"* (19). The behemoth had strength in its hips or hindquarters, powerful stomach muscles, a tail that moved like a cedar; muscular thighs, bones like brass beams, and ribs like iron bars. It could lie around as it wished, unafraid of other beasts, the flooding Jordan river, or even of hunters. Man could not control him, but God could.

Job was waking up to the truth about God that the accusations of his friends had made him doubt.

Look at Leviathan!
(Job 41)

In this chapter a huge sea creature was introduced. Leviathan described here had been mentioned in other places in the Bible as well. In Isaiah 27:1 it was explained as being a great dragon, but one that God could capture and destroy. Other references emphasizing its size and God's control over it were found in Psalm 74:13,14 and Psalm 104:25,26. As they did with the behemoth, commentators tried to compare leviathan to a common animal— this time they chose the crocodile. However, you should read the following descriptive phrases of this creature and then decide whether or not you can agree with such an identification of it. The leviathan …

1. could not be caught with hook or line (1,2)
2. could not be tamed or trusted (3,4,5)
3. could not be eaten or sold to merchants (6)
4. could not be harpooned, speared, or otherwise overcome (7,8,9)
5. had limbs of graceful proportions and mighty power (12)
6. had an *impenetrable* outer coat; could not be bridled (13)
7. had a mouth which could not be opened by man; terrible teeth all around (14)
8. had scales on its body in airtight rows that could not be separated (15-17)
9. when it sneezed, it flashed light; its eyes glowed and out of its mouth and nostrils went light, heat, smoke, and fire. (18-21)
10. its flesh was folded and thick and its heart hard as stone
11. when it pulled itself to full height, the bravest feared because of its appearance and crashing movements (25)
12. like the behemoth, it could not be killed with sword, spear, dart, or javelin (26)
13. it treated brass like rotten wood and iron as straw (27)
14. the sharp scales on its underbelly ploughed up the dirt as it moved along (30)
15. its rapid movements in the sea caused foaming and bubbling (31)
16. it had no equal among any other creature on earth (33)

impenetrable -cannot be pierced

A pioneer in the creation science field, Henry Morris, made the connection of the dragons of those medieval reports with what we call dinosaurs in our present-day studies.

While characteristics 2, 8, 10, and 15 could describe a crocodile, what about the others—especially those listed in #9 which included the breathing out of fire and smoke? What was being described here that you have heard about? How about a dragon? As recently as the fifteenth century dragons were described in cultural writings and art in many parts of the world. Some of those countries specifically listed in the *Encyclopedia Americana* under the heading of dragons were Egypt, Babylon, Canaan, Greece, Italy, Libya, Nordic areas [Wagner's opera *Siegfried* was about a dragon], China, the Aztecs of Mexico, as well as Peru's Nazca culture. A pioneer in the creation science field, Henry Morris, made the connection of the dragons of those *medieval* reports with what we call dinosaurs in our present-day studies. After all, the word *dinosaur* from the Latin for "terrible lizard" was only coined about two hundred years ago and was not used in earlier times like Job's. Job must have

medieval -having to do with the Middle Ages

had first-hand knowledge of such creatures in his day, or God would not have used them as examples of His creative power. On page 118 of the *Remarkable Record of Job*, Morris wrote: "Dragons of various kinds were capable of breathing out fire—at least according to traditions from all parts of the world . . . Perhaps more to the point, dinosaur fossils have been ***excavated*** that show a strange protuberance, with internal cavity, on the top of the head. It is conceivable that this could have served as sort of a mixing chamber for combustible gases that would ignite when exhaled into the outside oxygen."

excavated -uncovered by digging

If Morris were correct, and behemoth and leviathan were examples of the largest land and water dinosaurs, then the summary of creation in Genesis 1 and 2 that placed the creation of all animals on the same day as man was given further proof in the book of Job. God had described behemoth and leviathan as living at the same time man lived, not millions of years before.

We belong to Him, both by creation and by redemption, and He has the right to do with us whatever He will. We can trust Him, no matter what comes our way in this life, knowing that in the balances of eternity, the Judge of all the earth will do right".

Morris summarized what he saw to be the main thrust of Job: "Therefore, God's central message to Job, and to us, is not an explanation of why the righteous suffer, but rather a call to sound belief in creation and an emphasis on our stewardship over that creation, under God. Afflictions that come our way can then be placed in proper context. We belong to Him, both by creation and by redemption, and He has the right to do with us whatever He will. We can trust Him, no matter what comes our way in this life, knowing that in the balances of eternity, the Judge of all the earth will do right" (*The Remarkable Record of Job*, pp. 108-109).

The Last Word
(Job 42)

Job broke his silence here and confessed his sin at speaking without really knowing what he was talking about. He turned away—repented—from such thought and behavior and God forgave him. God immediately ***reprimanded*** the first three friends for not speaking of Him what was right—in insisting that Job must have sinned against God and brought on the suffering. God told them to go to Job—the one they had thought to be a vile sinner--and have him pray and make sacrifices for them that they might be forgiven, too. While Job prayed for his friends, God began to generously restore all that Job had lost. Soon friends and relatives who had kept their distance during his suffering, returned to him with gifts of silver and gold. The

reprimanded -corrected; rebuked

number of his livestock doubled but not the number of his children—after all, through the promise of resurrection, he would see the first ten again. The final blessing listed for Job was an extended life—he lived to see four generations of his family, dying *"old and full of days."*

Don't You Love a Happy Ending?

God wants a happy ending for your life, too. Your life may be full of suffering and overflowing with problems, but from the book of Job you should have learned that God can be trusted to do the right thing for you and all who love Him. He Who made everything can surely keep your life going until He can restore all the blessings you have lost or missed through the promise of His Resurrection because of your faith in Jesus Christ. Job longed for a Redeemer to come. You do not have to wait—your Redeemer has come and He wants to help you now and forever. Humble yourself, turn to God, and receive His help. Not even Job—and there was *"none like him on the earth"*—could make it without God's forgiveness, help, and love.

Job longed for a Redeemer to come. You do not have to wait--your Redeemer has come and He wants to help you now and forever.

Questions

Study Procedure: Read the Scripture references before answering questions. Unless otherwise instructed, use only the Bible in answering questions. Some questions may be more difficult than others but try to answer as many as you can. Pray for God's wisdom and understanding as you study and don't be discouraged if some answers are not obvious at first. Do not read the study notes for this lesson until AFTER you have completed your questions.

Day One

1. Vocabulary: Circle the closest synonym for each word below.

     a) accentuate: (1) season for flavor   (2) raise to a higher level   (3) emphasize

     b) excavated: (1) uncovered by digging   (2) pulled out   (3) left off

     c) impenetrable: (1) painful   (2) fearless   (3) cannot be pierced

     d) medieval: having to do with (1) medicine   (2) the Middle Ages   (3) Satan

     e) reprimanded: (1) corrected   (2) reminded   (3) praised

     f) vile: (1) alive   (2) repulsive   (3) contained

2. Write some of the things you can remember about these subjects from the study of the book of Job?

     a) Satan: _____

     _____

     b) grief: _____

     _____

     c) comforting others: _____

     _____

     d) God as Creator: _____

     _____

     e) attitude: _____

     _____

Day Two: Introduction to the Psalms.

1. How many psalms are included in the book of Psalms? _____

2. There are five groups or books of psalms within the whole collection. Match the final words of each psalm in the group with its book number.

     a) "Blessed be the Lord forevermore! Amen and Amen."

     b) "Blessed be Lord God of Israel from everlasting to everlasting! And let all the people say, 'Amen!'"

     c) "Blessed be the Lord God of Israel from everlasting to everlasting! Amen and Amen."

     d) "Let everything that has breath praise the Lord. Praise the Lord!"

e) "And blessed be His glorious name forever! And let the whole earth be filled with His glory. Amen and Amen. The prayers of David the son of Jesse are ended."

Book I: Psalm 1-41 _____   Book II: Psalms 42-72 _____   Book III: Psalms 73-89 _____

Book IV: Psalms 90-106 _____   Book V: Psalms 107-150 _____

3. Most people associate this person with the writing of the Psalms (a) _____. However, from the introductory information before each of the following psalms, fill in the blank with some other authors who were identified.

b) _____ Psalm 42

c) _____ Psalm 50

d) _____ Psalm 72

e) _____ Psalm 89

f) _____ Psalm 90

Day Three: Read Psalms 1-3.

MEMORY: PSALM 1:1-6

1. Use the verb phrases in Psalm 1 to complete the following summary of its message:

Blessed is the person who doesn't . . .

a) _____

b) _____

c) _____

But instead does . . .

d) _____

e) _____

2. Who are represented by the tree and the chaff in this psalm and what are their differences?

_____

_____

_____

_____

3. Psalm 2 is a psalm which described the coming of Christ or Messiah. What phrases seem to refer to Him here? (Make sure you write down the verse numbers you used.)_____

_____

_____

_____

_____

_____

4. Read Psalm 3. Which of the following problems did David personally face according to this psalm? Be prepared to defend your answers with verses from the psalm.

   a) insomnia (inability to sleep)

   b) being surrounded by thousands of enemies

   c) discouraging comments

   d) lack of faith

Day Four: Read Psalms 4-7.

1. List the things that God had done or would do for the psalmist in Psalm 4. _____

   _____

   _____

   _____

   _____

2. What did the ungodly people need to change about their lives according to the following verses of Psalm 4?

   a) v. 2 _____

   _____

   b) v. 4 _____

   _____

   c) v. 5 _____

   _____

3. Read Psalm 5. Contrast what the godly and the ungodly can expect from God.

   Godly: _____

   _____

   Ungodly: _____

   _____

4. Read Psalm 6. List the physical problems David had in this psalm for which he needed God's help. _____

   _____

   _____

5. Read Psalm 7. The heading of this psalm mentions Cush, a Benjamite, who evidently caused David trouble. Read 2 Samuel 16:5-13 and summarize what had happened to David in this situation. (Note: in this passage "Cush" is called "Shimei.") _____

   _____

   _____

   _____

6. Write down some phrases from Psalm 7 that explain what David thought God would do to defend those who love Him from their enemies. _____

_____

_____

_____

_____

Day Five: Read Psalms 8-10.   MEMORY: PSALM 8:1

1. Psalm 8 praises the God of Creation. What examples of His handiwork are given here? _____

_____

_____

2. After thinking about the greatness of God's creation, what was the psalmist most amazed about?
    a) that God wasn't tired
    b) that God paid so much attention to humans
    c) that God had not outlawed pollution

3. Psalms 9 and 10 were originally one psalm written as an *alphabetic acrostic*.
    a) Look in a dictionary and find out what *alphabetic acrostic* means and explain it below.

    _____

    _____

    b) Write your own acrostic psalm of sentences of praise to God using your first name. Use some "parallelism" if you can, too.

    Example: **M** agnify the Lord with me!

                A pplaud the Creator of all!

                R eceive His forgiveness and grace.

                N ever refuse His wisdom and correction.

                I n all things, everywhere, thank Him for His unending love!

    Your turn: _____

    _____

    _____

    _____

    _____

    _____

    _____

    _____

    _____

    _____

    _____

    _____

4. Read Psalms 9 and 10. Which described God's punishment of enemy *groups* and which described God's punishment of wicked *individuals*? _____

_____

5. Write down any thoughts you have about the problems caused when any nation makes laws or takes actions which are not in line with God's clearly stated will in the Bible._____

_____

_____

_____

_____

6. Now take a few minutes and read the notes for this lesson.

Notes

Surveying the Psalms

What Is a Psalm?

By definition, a psalm is a song sung to the musical accompaniment of a plucked instrument. The Book of Psalms was called a *psalter* in the early church from the Latin word for "harp songs." In Hebrew, the Psalms were entitled *Tehillim,* meaning "praises." However, these poems set to music were not all praise; some were full of problems, too! The careful reader will find them expressing grand worship along with great worry, just like the prayers and hymns of God's people today!

However, these poems set to music were not all praise; some were full of problems, too! The careful reader will find them expressing grand worship along with great worry, just like the prayers and hymns of God's people today!

How about Some Statistics?

There are one hundred and fifty psalms by at least seven different authors covering over one thousand years of Israel's history—from Israel's exit from Egypt to the return of Israel from her captivity in Babylon. The main author was King David who wrote to express his own love for God as well as to provide patterns of worship and praise for his whole nation. According to the New Testament, the early church continued to use these psalms in her worship services. See 1 Cor. 14:26; Eph.5:19; and Col. 3:16 for references.

Why Don't They Rhyme?

As in the Book of Job, the writers of the Psalms used the Hebrew poetical method called parallelism which paired thoughts instead of pairing sounds. By using *parallelism* instead of rhyme, the beauty of the psalms' imagery was more "translatable" to different languages and cultures.

The Psalms Have Sections

The 150 psalms were collected in five books or sections: Book I: 1-41; Book II: 42-72; Book III: 73-89; Book IV: 90-106; and Book V: 107-50. David is credited with writing the majority of the psalms, and his psalms can be read like a diary of his faith, his failings, and his favor with God. However, the psalms were inspired by the Holy Spirit as surely as the rest of the Bible and so are bigger than any one person's faith story. As you read them, stop often to ask yourself, "Do these words express the desire of my heart, the questions I have been asking, or the needs in my life?" Pray them, sing them, or cry them out to the God who still hears and answers.

As you read them, stop often to ask yourself, "Do these words express the desire of my heart, the questions I have been asking, or the needs in my life?" Pray them, sing them, or cry them out to the God who still hears and answers.

Three Themes

Throughout this study of Psalms, three major themes will be emphasized.

CREATOR

First, God as Creator was a major focus of the psalmists' praises. Psalm 8 of the lesson just completed is a well-known psalm with this focus: man made in God's image—*"a little lower than the angels."* Charles Spurgeon once commented on David's use of the creation theme: "In his youth, the psalmist, while keeping his father's flocks, had devoted himself to two of God's great books: nature and Scripture; and he had so thoroughly entered into the spirit of these two volumes that he was able to compare and contrast them, magnifying the excellency of the Author of both."

CHRIST

The coming Christ or Messiah of Israel was another major theme repeated in Psalms. Jesus had said in John 5:39: *"You search the Scriptures, for in them you think you have eternal life; and these are they which testify of Me."* So, in this study of Psalms expect many, many references to the first and second comings of Christ. Some examples follow:

The King: Ps. 2 (Acts 4:25-26); Ps. 118:26 (Mt.21:9)

The Son of Man: Ps.8 (Heb.2:6-11)

The Resurrection: Ps.16 (Acts 2:25-31); Ps.22:1-21(Matt.27:35-46)

The Crucifixion: Ps. 22:1-21(Matt. 27:35-46)

The Shepherd: Ps. 23 (John 10)

The Sacrifice for Sin: Ps. 40:6-8 (Heb. 10:1-10)

The Betrayal: Ps.41:9 (John 13:18-19)

The Royal Bridegroom: Ps.45 (Heb.1:8-9)

The Ascension: Ps. 68:18 (Eph.4:7-16)

The Rejection: Ps. 69:4 (John 15:25); 69:8 (John 7:3-5); 69:9 (with John 2:17 & Rom.15:3)

The Eternal Son: Ps. 102:25-27 (Heb.1:10-12)

The Divine King-Priest: Ps.110 (Matt.22:41-45; Acts 2:34-35; Heb.1:13; 7:17-21; 10:12-13)

The Stone: Ps. 118:22-23 (Matt.21:42)

COVENANT

The third major theme of the Psalms is the covenant relationship of God with man. In the lessons that follow, incidents in the life of David will be used to illustrate and explain the beautiful binding power of God's covenant with His people. A covenant, according to the teachings of the Bible as well as the history of the world, is a solemn bond or binding contract between partners, sealed with blood. The blood seal, taken either from the agreeing partners or a substitute animal or representative, emphasizes the seriousness of the bond being formed. The covenant language still common to the modern marriage ceremony "till death do us part" points to the very real consequences of trying to "break" covenant. It was well understood in ancient days that nothing but the death of a covenant partner could stop the fulfillment of the covenant promises. In a covenant, the terms were made clear about what was required of the partners. In the case of God's covenant with us, He made the terms, spelling out what He expected from us in the Scriptures or as they are sometimes called, the Old and New Testaments or Covenants. However, God knew we would be unable to keep our part without His keeping power, and so He showed His willingness to accept us even when we had nothing to bring to the bond, by sealing it with His own blood—not ours. When a person was in covenant with God—through faith that Messiah would come (for Old Testament believers) or through faith that Messiah had come (for New Testament believers), he was promised protection, provision, and a purpose for his life from God. In return, he was expected to willingly offer himself for God's use.

The covenant language still common to the modern marriage ceremony "till death do us part" points to the very real consequences of trying to "break" covenant. It was well understood in ancient days that nothing but the death of a covenant partner could stop the fulfillment of the covenant promises.

Covenant Symbolism

The entering of a covenant with God or with another person was often accompanied by one or more of the following activities: an explanation of the requirements of the covenant, a sealing of the transaction with blood, eating a special meal together, exchanging gifts, taking on a sign (like a ring in marriage or circumcision for the Jewish male), building a memorial, allowing others to witness the transaction, making a written record for each party to keep, and/or exchanging clothing or weapons to show mutual protection and identification.

***Hesed*, A Many Splendored Thing!**

David's life-story gave many rich examples of his covenant with God and his understanding of covenant principles. David especially used covenant-related words in his psalm writing. The Hebrew word *hesed* was used to describe the covenant benefits that can be enjoyed by God's grace. It was so rich a word, however, that the translators had a difficult time putting it into English. So, it was translated by more than twenty different words. Some of them follow: love, kindness, lovingkindness, mercy, steadfast love, and faithfulness. People outside of the covenant were referred to as "ungodly" or "wicked" and were often contrasted with the "godly" or "righteous" ones or "saints." Words like "remember" were used to relate to covenant, as well, drawing attention to the promises and requirements of covenant relationship. Covenant truths will be pointed out and explained throughout the entire study of Psalms.

Psalm 1

The first psalm introduced the overall theme for the Book of Psalms: covenant blessings were for covenant keepers. Those belonging to God were first to separate themselves from the sinful ways of the wicked, those outside of covenant. Sin was recognized as being *progressive*, something that increased with time and opportunity. In Psalm 1, the godly person was first warned not to walk near the ungodly since that would only put him in the situation to be tempted to stop for a closer view. Such stopping or standing most often would have lead to taking a seat to participate more fully in sinful activities. However, separation from sin was not enough to guarantee God's blessing. A godly person must also be *situated* in the right place and *saturated* with the Word of God. Like a tree planted near a good water source, God's children needed to be placed where they could drink deeply from His Word. Deep drinking would produce strong roots, and only strong roots produced good fruits! The psalmist compared the righteous to planted trees, not wild ones, because they had lives directed by God. They did not develop through a series of accidents, but had a definite place and purpose. The godly bloomed and bore fruit where they were planted—they certainly could not do so where they were not! In contrast, the ungodly would not stand up and flourish, especially under the future judgment of God. They were rootless, fruitless, and as useless as *chaff*. Of course, only one man, Jesus Christ, ever lived completely separated from sin and saturated by the Word of God, but when we enter His covenant, we can have His help and strength to live our lives in such a way that we can be called "blessed."

progressive -continually increasing in extent or severity

situated -located, placed, fixed

saturated -soaked completely

chaff -the husks of grain separated from the seed; worthless matter

In Psalm 1, the godly person was first warned not to walk near the ungodly since that would only put him in the situation to be tempted to stop for a closer view.

Psalm 2

To understand this psalm, the reader must realize that the speakers being quoted change a few times. First, the writer of the psalm asked why nations or national leaders would dare get together and plot to overthrow God's plans for His hand-picked leader. He quoted their plans against God and His Anointed saying, *"Let us break Their bonds in pieces and cast away Their cords from us."* How foolish to oppose God! The psalmist pointed out that God was laughing *derisively* at such opposition and would soon speak in wrath or deep displeasure announcing what no world power could ever stop, *"Yet I have set My King on My holy hill of Zion."* Then, the identity of God's Anointed was revealed as God announced, *"You are My Son, today I have begotten You."* God had promised the kingdoms of the world to this Son.

derisively -characterized by mocking or ridiculing

So, when you read the word Messiah, Christ, or Anointed be aware that they are synonymous titles used to describe God's own Son.

Those who did not accept Him would be broken in judgment with a *"rod of iron"* or dashed to *"pieces like a potter's vessel."* The truly wise rulers of the world should not oppose God's Anointed but instead *"serve the Lord with fear."* Blessings were promised to *"all those who put their trust in Him."*

NOTES ON GOD'S ANOINTED

Mashiach (mah-shee-ahch) was the Hebrew word for *anointed one* and the source of our word *messiah*. Found 39 times in the Old Testament, it came from a verb meaning to anoint or to consecrate by applying the holy anointing oil to an individual. Mashiach or messiah was often used to describe anointed kings or the high priest. In Psalms and in Daniel it was used to refer to David's anointed heir, the king of Israel and ruler of all nations (Ps. 2:2; 28:8; Daniel 9:25,26). When Jesus' followers spoke of Him they called Him in Hebrew *Yeshua ha Mashiach* , Jesus the Messiah. The Greek translation of the same word was Christos, or in English, Christ. So, when you read the word Messiah, Christ, or Anointed be aware that they are **synonymous** titles used to describe God's own Son.

WHICH ANOINTED ONE?

But, how can we be sure that the Anointed of this psalm is not just a king like David or Solomon since the word can mean that sometimes? In Acts 4:25 and 26, the persecuted followers of Jesus quoted this psalm as proof that Jesus was the real Messiah and that persecution or opposition to the gospel was to be expected. However, as the psalm declared, all opposition to the Christ would finally be silenced and judged. Whose side are you on?

synonymous - expressing or implying the **same idea**

| Psalm 3 and Psalm 4 |

The heading information for Psalm 3 described it as being written when David was fleeing Absalom. Many Bible scholars believe that Psalm 3 and Psalm 4 were both written at this time with Psalm 3 being David's morning prayer and Psalm 4 being his evening one. David was the true king of Israel but had left Jerusalem to live in exile after his son Absalom opposed him. David was in great grief. First, he was shocked that his own son would rise up to overthrow him, and next, he felt betrayed by a close counselor named Ahithophel who had stayed with Absalom to help overthrow him. 2 Sam. 13-16 should be read for the full background details of this psalm. Absalom had made himself popular with a large group of followers, and David knew the seriousness of the situation. However, David was confident in the One who had never failed him. He made his needs known in prayer to God, while offering praise for the comfort and peace he was even then receiving. He still had **skeptics** to deal with: *"Many are they who say of me, 'There is no help for him in God,'"* but he stated what he knew: *"But You, O Lord, are a shield for me, My glory and the One who lifts up my head."* David was well aware of the

skeptics -those who maintain a doubting attitude

covenant protection God provided him and sang of those benefits in these two psalms. In Psalm 4 David warned those outside the covenant that they needed to repent of their ways because God would not bless them otherwise: *"Meditate within your heart on your bed, and be still. Offer the sacrifices of righteousness, and put your trust in the Lord"* (4:4,5). A practical proof of David's trust in God, even when outnumbered by earthly enemies, was that in both psalms he mentioned being able to lie down and sleep in peace. If a person is trying to fix problems by himself, he will not usually rest comfortably. Only when he realizes that his covenant God will not fail to protect and provide for His own, can he rest and sleep in peace. How are you sleeping these days?

David had an order or pattern or purpose for his prayertime with God. Do you? Do you meet Him every morning on purpose, being careful not to let the day fill up with other demands before you have your planned time in God's presence?

The Pause

A word that appears frequently in the psalms between stanzas is the Hebrew word *selah*. Its meaning is debated but many believe it to be a musical notation that indicated a pause or change in the musical accompaniment for the effect of meditation or consideration of what had just been sung. So when you come to a *selah* in a psalm, do not read or sing it, just pause and consider the stanza just finished.

Psalm 5

In this psalm David was evidently living in Jerusalem and was free to worship in the tabernacle as usual. *"My voice You shall hear in the morning, O Lord; in the morning will I direct it to You, and I will look up"* (3). The word "direct" used here by David had the meaning in Hebrew of putting something in order. David had an order or pattern or purpose for his prayertime with God. Do you? Do you meet Him every morning on purpose, being careful not to let the day fill up with other demands before you have your planned time in God's presence? Christians have the right to come into God's presence because of the covenant they have with God through the blood of Jesus. Whether they have been good or bad, like David they can come into the Lord's house because of His mercy [that's *hesed* or covenant love] (7), and once there, they can receive guidance for the day: *"Make Your way straight before my face."*

What Happened to "Love Your Enemies"?

Psalm 5 is considered one of many ***imprecatory*** psalms. In verses 9 and 10 David asked God to *"pronounce them guilty"* and let his enemies *"fall by their own counsels"* because there was *"no righteousness* [covenant truth] *in their mouth."* Nellie Constance, founder and author of Explorer's Bible Study explained David's words this way: "David's prayer...was not malicious. David was not cursing his enemies, but he was jealous for the honor of his Master. He considered the wickedness of traitors as a rebellion against God and as more than the treason against his own earthly throne. His prayer was for the honor of God's name and the

imprecatory -calling down curses on a person

vindication of His justice. How important it is for us to love what God loves and hate what He hates. To hear His name taken in vain and a disregard for His Word should pierce our hearts like a sword. Pray that God will never allow us to get accustomed to sin. God hates sin and so must we. But always love and pray for the sinner. Joy, blessing and protection come to those who love God."

| penitential -expressive of repentance |

Psalm 6

This is an example of a **penitential** psalm. In it, David asked for forgiveness of his sins and for God's mercies. He described his physical suffering: aching bones, tearful nights, and utter exhaustion. Yet, he ended the psalm with confidence in the final verses because he knew God would forgive him and defend him from his enemies once more. What a relief it is physically, emotionally, and spiritually to confess our sins and receive forgiveness! Have you been honest with God in your prayers?

What a relief it is physically, emotionally, and spiritually to confess our sins and receive forgiveness! Have you been honest with God in your prayers?

Psalm 7

The historical background for this psalm is found in 2 Samuel 16 when David fled from Absalom and was cursed publicly by a bystander from the tribe of Benjamin. David's friends and followers wanted permission to kill the man who dared to curse the king, but David left him to God's judgment. Later, he put his feelings into this psalm: *"Save me from all those who persecute me; and deliver me, lest they tear me like a lion . . ."* David asked God to examine his heart; he believed he was innocent of the charges made by his enemies (3-5). David believed that his enemy would fall *"into the ditch which he made. His trouble shall return upon his own head . . .* (15,16). Instead of planning revenge, David gave his energies to praising the Lord who would defend him. We should, too.

Psalm 8

So far we have had psalms that spoke of the benefits of God's covenant with His people and one that described the Christ, but now the third theme is introduced, God as Creator. David praised God here for His name and *"glory above the heavens!"* After considering all of God's spectacular creation, David wondered at the unique position God had given man. You will find no evolutionary theories here. David recognized that God had thoughtfully and purposefully created man to have dominion over all the other things God had made. What mercy! David praised His excellent name.

Psalm 9 and Psalm 10

Older Bible manuscripts (ancient hand-written copies) have these two psalms as one continual alphabetic acrostic, with each stanza beginning with a subsequent letter of the Hebrew alphabet. Psalm 9 described what will happen when the nations who have hated Israel finally face God's judgment: *"The nations have sunk down in the pit which they made; In the net which they hid, their own foot is caught"* (15). Psalm 10 pointed out that the individual who hates God and oppresses God's people will face judgment as well: *"Lord, You have heard the desire of the humble; . . . You will cause your ear to hear, to do justice to the fatherless and the oppressed, that the man of the earth may oppress no more"* (17, 18). Both of these warnings still need to be heard. We might think that what our nation does goes unnoticed by God—mistakenly believing that politics are not His concern. However, God is very interested in what the people of a nation allow their national leaders to decide and act upon. Christians need to be involved in local and national decision-making. Also, individuals are certainly accountable to God. Citizenship in a certain nation, being born into a Christian home, or even church membership does not make someone a Christian. Each person must accept Christ into his life for himself, and his actions should reveal that the choice was sincere. Nations and individuals are still carefully watched by God.

> *Citizenship in a certain nation, being born into a Christian home, or even church membership does not make someone a Christian. Each person must accept Christ into his life for himself, and his actions should reveal that the choice was sincere.*

One More Comment Because this was an introduction to all the psalms, you probably thought that the questions covered ten psalms too quickly while the notes did not move quickly enough! However, some basic information had to be given here to get you ready to understand and enjoy the rest of the study. The next lesson should not be as overwhelming.

BIBLE QUEST

Questions

Study Procedure: Read the Scripture references before answering questions. Unless otherwise instructed, use only the Bible in answering questions. Some questions may be more difficult than others but try to answer as many as you can. Pray for God's wisdom and understanding as you study and don't be discouraged if some answers are not obvious at first. Do not read the study notes for this lesson until AFTER you have completed your questions.

Day One: Review

1. Vocabulary Review. Fill in the vocabulary word that matches the definitions below:

ACROSS

1. soaked completely
7. continually increasing in extent or severity
8. the husks of grain separated from the seed; worthless matter

DOWN

1. expressing or implying the same meaning
2. expressive of repentance
3. characterized by mocking or ridiculing
4. to call down curses on a person
5. one who maintains a doubting attitude
6. located, placed, fixed

Day Two: Read Psalm 11 and 12.

 MEMORY: PSALM 12:6-7

1. In Psalm 11, the writer was responding to the advice of another to run away from his present difficulties. What were his reasons for not running away? _____

_____

_____

2. What verse(s) reminds the reader that God is always aware of what is happening to people and can be trusted to act? _____

3. Which characteristics are those of the Lord's words and which are those of the ungodly person?

The ungodly _____

The Lord's _____

    a) idle   b) flattering   c) hypocritical   d) proud   e) pure   f) like purified silver

4. What makes sin and sin's vile actions increase? _____
_____

5. Read the following passage from the epistle written by James from the New Testament. Comment in the space following it on any of its observations about the human tongue that you also have noticed in your experience so far in life.

3:1 My brethren, let not many of you become teachers, knowing that we shall receive a stricter judgment. (2) For we all stumble in many things. If anyone does not stumble in word, he is a perfect man, able also to bridle the whole body. (3) Indeed, we put bits in horses' mouths that they may obey us, and we turn their whole body. (4) Look also at ships: although they are so large and are driven by fierce winds, they are turned by a very small rudder wherever the pilot desires. (5) Even so the tongue is a little member and boasts great things. See how great a forest a little fire kindles! (6) And the tongue is a fire, a world of iniquity. The tongue is so set among our members that it defiles the whole body, and sets on fire the course of nature; and it is set on fire by hell. (7) For every kind of beast and bird, of reptile and creature of the sea, is tamed and has been tamed by mankind. (8) But no man can tame the tongue. It is an unruly evil, full of deadly poison. (9) With it we bless our God and Father, and with it we curse men, who have been made in the similitude of God. (10) Out of the same mouth proceed blessing and cursing. My brethren, these things ought not to be so.

_____
_____
_____
_____
_____

Day Three: Read Psalm 13 and 14.

1. What two-word phrase was repeated four times in the opening verses of Psalm 13?
_____

2. Have you ever used that phrase with God? If so, what were the circumstances? _____
_____
_____

3. What caused the change of attitude in the psalmist between the first and last verses of this psalm? _____
_____

4. Read Psalm 14. What are the characteristics of a fool? _____
_____
_____
_____

5. Read Romans 3: 9-12. What can a person do to be saved from being a fool? _____

_____

MEMORY: PSALM 15:1-3

Day Four: Read Psalm 15, 16, and 17.

1. In Psalm 15:1, David asked God what was required if a person really wanted to live in a close relationship to God or *"abide in Your tabernacle"* (v. 1). Read God's response in verses 2-5 and then pick the best phrase below to summarize those thoughts.
   To have a close relationship with God, a person must:
   a) be faithful in regular worship
   b) be a careful student of the Scriptures
   c) love his neighbor as himself
   d) be careful with his words

2. Compare your answer to Romans 13:9 and comment below about what you discover.

_____

_____

_____

3. Psalm 15 has been called the "gentleman's psalm" because it gives wonderful guidelines for having the best manners in all situations. With Christ's help, we should all have good manners! List some that you find in this psalm that you would like to see more often in your daily life.

_____

_____

_____

4. Psalm 16 was prophetic of the coming Messiah. In the New Testament, Peter quoted it as a proof that Jesus was the real Messiah because He fulfilled this prophecy of rising from death without His body decomposing. Read Acts 2:22-33 and then give the verses from Psalm 16 from which Peter quoted.

_____

_____

5. In Psalm 17, David spoke to God in a very personal way, referring to God as one having a physical body to use in behalf of His children. What did David ask God to do for him

with his ears_____

eyes _____

hand _____

and face _____

Day Five: Read Psalm 18. **CHALLENGE ASSIGNMENT**

1. In this psalm, David sang his gratitude to God for getting him through approximately ten years of being hunted and harassed by King Saul as well as through battles with other enemy groups. To understand what David had lived through, you need to read 1 Samuel 16 all the way through 1 Samuel 31. (Note: 2 Samuel 1-22 gives information about the rest of David's reign and would also be good reading at this point.) After you have read 1 Samuel 16-31, put the correct chapter numbers beside the incidents which occurred there.

    _____ a. Jonathan and David made a covenant and Jonathan gave David his clothes and armor.

    _____ b. David fought Goliath.

    _____ c. David married Saul's daughter.

    _____ d. David was anointed king by Samuel.

    _____ e. Saul tried to spear David while David was playing music for him.

    _____ f. David was allowed to eat the holy bread from the tabernacle.

    _____ g. Jonathan repledged his loyalty to David in covenant and made David promise kindness to Jonathan's descendants.

    _____ h. The men who followed David were distressed, in debt, and discontented.

    _____ i. David, after asking God for direction, fought the Philistines and won.

    _____ j. Saul had the priests and their families murdered for helping David.

    _____ k. David refused to kill Saul when Saul was relieving himself in a cave.

    _____ l. A fool had a smart wife.

    _____ m. Saul consulted a medium or witch for advice.

    _____ n. David spared Saul again.

    _____ o. David's people were captured by the Amalekites, but David succeeded in getting them back.

    _____ p. Saul and his sons died tragically.

2. Now read Psalm 18 and make a note below of a few of the verses you can relate to what you read about the life of David as recorded in 1 Samuel. Notice David's great love for God throughout as well as the absence of any specific mention of Saul who had so mistreated him.

    _____

    _____

    _____

    _____

    _____

    _____

3. Now take a few minutes and read the notes for this lesson.

Notes

Covenant Power   (Psalms 11-18)

Through faith in Jesus, we are connected to God who is all-powerful, yet still we must read His "directions" and then follow them obediently if we want to benefit from His power.

How Does It Work?

It would only take a storm to show us our limitations. With electricity in abundance, we forget that our homes, businesses, and personal comfort depend on a regular source of power. Let it be taken from us, and we would quickly realize our personal weakness. As Christians, we have a power source—God Himself—who is certainly dependable and constant. We are connected to Him or "plugged in" through covenant. Yet, just as an appliance or tool could be plugged in and ready to go, it would still not be of benefit until the one using it knew what its purpose was and how to use it. Through faith in Jesus, we are connected to God who is all-powerful, yet still we must read His "directions" and then follow them obediently if we want to benefit from His power. Psalms 11-18 are particularly helpful in emphasizing the need for *information* (knowledge of the Bible), *communication* (prayer), and *application* (obedience to God's will) in order to get the most from our covenant connection with God.

Psalm 11

In verse one David identified his source of power: *"In the Lord I put my trust."* However, others were telling him to run away like a bird from the wicked who were after him, those who were always ready to *"shoot secretly at the upright in heart"* (2). David did not take their advice. He knew that God's people had to stand up to evil, *"If the foundations are destroyed, what can the righteous do?"* (3). God's people must be aware that they do not live to please themselves; they must always consider how their actions will affect others. In covenant, God is with us and in us and we can stand firm against evil. A healthy family and a healthy society depend upon it. The power of God in David was obvious because David knew God personally. David knew the Holy Scriptures. He had the right information about God: *"The Lord is in His holy temple"* (4). God never falls off His throne because of the wickedness on earth. In fact, just as God was watching closely what was happening in David's life, He is still watching ours: *"His eyes behold, His eyelids test the sons of men"* (4b). In other words, God has narrowed His eyes in disapproval of the wickedness in the world. He *"tests the righteous"* but will punish the wicked. David knew that God wanted His people—the covenant ones, the righteous—to act according to His will. In the same way, when we take a stand for God's truth, refusing to run away, God sees and supports us because *"He loves righteousness"* (7).

upright -the Hebrew root of this word is *hesed* or covenant. An upright person is one who is in covenant with God. Such a person is always a target of the wicked, those outside the covenant.

One additional thought on this psalm. When a person takes a difficult stand, he will rarely end up standing alone. Many are just waiting for someone to take the first step and then they will quickly join in. Remember David's stand against Goliath in 1 Samuel 17? Once he faced and defeated that giant, all of the Israeli army eagerly joined in battle to defeat the Philistines who had moments before seemed so unconquerable. Follow David's example and get your information straight: if you are in covenant with God, you are on the winning side, or as someone said, "God plus one is always a majority!"

Psalm 12

This psalm illustrated one of the biggest differences between those walking in the power of the Holy Spirit and those who were not. This difference was revealed in the words that were spoken. David expressed his feelings at being in the minority: *"Help, Lord, for the godly man ceases!"* He then described the evidence that surrounded him: idle speech, flattering lips, and words from hypocritical hearts (2). Jesus warned in Matthew 12:34 that words spoken by a person revealed the real state of that person's heart: *"For out of the abundance of the heart the mouth speaks."* A common computer phrase expresses it this way: "garbage in, garbage out." In short, words only show what was inside the person all the time. In this psalm, the ungodly hearts of proud speakers went further to cause evil actions such as oppression of the poor and neglect of the needy (5). David concluded that such evil only increased when people accepted and encouraged it (8). An example of this acceptance of wicked words and actions can be seen in our response to current television, movie, music, and radio programming. What might have shocked our parents has become expected, accepted, and, sadly, even cheered and paid for by us.

Jesus warned in Matthew 12:34 that words spoken by a person revealed the real state of that person's heart: "For out of the abundance of the heart the mouth speaks." A common computer phrase expresses it this way: "garbage in, garbage out."

To wake us up to God's standard for speech and actions, this psalm presented the contrast of God's Word: *"The words of the Lord are pure words... purified seven times."* David stated what God had assured him, that God would certainly see that His Word was kept and preserved for those who would join Him through the covenant sealed by Jesus. Even though, like David, we might feel as if we were in the minority, we can be sure that God's Word known and obeyed will bring us victory. The wicked may *"prowl on every side"* (8) but God will certainly show His strength on behalf of those who belong to Him. Check yourself now: based on your words, to whom does your heart belong?

Feeling Forgotten (Psalm 13)

David had not asked God to single him out of his family and anoint him king of Israel (1 Samuel 16). He was the youngest of his father Jesse's eight sons and was not even

Have you also asked "how long?" in your prayers? David taught us something here even in his grief and frustration: take everything to God in prayer.

thought worthy to be called from the sheep herds when the prophet Samuel came to anoint God's choice from among them. Further, once anointed, things had become even more complicated. David was requested by King Saul to remain at his court to soothe the attacks of an evil spirit with music. However, not long afterward Saul returned his loyal service in court and on the battlefield with threats against David's life, which drove David to live as an exile for about ten years. This psalm's repeated question of *"How long, O Lord?"* is certainly understandable when we remember that David was sure of God's call on his life but confused about God's methods of preparation for the throne and timing for that move.

Have you ever felt that way? Have you known the leading of the Holy Spirit in your life to a certain course of action or particular job and then been set aside or even persecuted intensely? Have you also asked "how long?" in your prayers? David taught us something here even in his grief and frustration: take everything to God in prayer.

disposition -one's usual manner of emotional response; temperament

fatigue -physical or mental weariness or exhaustion

Notice the progress of the psalm: the physical position as well as the emotional **disposition** of David shifted upward. First, it was as if he were on his face in anguish and desperation, letting God know of his deep feelings of helplessness and **fatigue** (1,2). Next, he seemed to rise to his knees asking God specifically to reveal His will, clear David's confusion, and "enlighten" his eyes (3,4). Finally, it is as if, having let God know everything in prayer, he suddenly felt better, ready to dry his tears, stand up, and declare boldly, *"But I have trusted in Your mercy; my heart shall rejoice in Your salvation. I will sing to the Lord, because He has dealt bountifully with me"* (5,6). What had changed? Not his situation—he was still being pursued by enemies, but through prayer he had changed his focus, from his problems to his Protector. Through prayer, too, we are changed and made ready to receive the power of God for the problems of life. Suddenly we find that we can hold on a bit longer—certain that God has not forgotten and will never forget or abandon us.

What had changed? Not his situation— he was still being pursued by enemies, but through prayer he had changed his focus, from his problems to his Protector.

No Fun for Fools (Psalm 14)

The word *fool* used in the opening verse (*"The fool has said in his heart, 'There is no God.'"*) did not mean someone who was uneducated or mentally slow, but one who opposed and mocked God's standard of what was good and right and true. In 1 Samuel 25:25 the man who was so ungrateful to David for the protection David and his men had provided for the surrounding areas was named Nabal, the same word used here meaning "fool." His wife Abigail, in her grateful actions toward David and his men, provided quite a contrast to the foolish actions of her husband. God does not give His power to ungodly fools, *"for God is with the generation of the righteous"* (5). Yet, without the gift of new life and the Holy Spirit whom we receive through faith in Jesus, we all would be classified as fools.

This truth was made even more clear by Paul in Romans 3:9-12 where this psalm was quoted: *"What then? Are we better than they? Not at all. For we have previously charged both Jews and Greeks that they are all under sin. As it is written:'There is none righteous, no, not one; there is none who understands; there is none who seeks after God. They have all turned aside; they have together become unprofitable; there is none who does good, no, not one.'"*

In the final verses, the psalmist wrote longingly of what the righteous hoped would cure all the world's fools: *"that the salvation of Israel would come out of Zion!"* We recognize that same salvation in Jesus who was born in Zion (Israel) to be our Savior. However, many still refuse to believe in Him and stubbornly cling to their foolishness. When He returns to fulfill His promises to Israel and bring back *"the captivity of His people,"* those who have denied His first coming will not join believing Jacob and Israel in their rejoicing (7). Today is the day to receive Him and His gift of new life and to leave all foolishness behind!

Good Behavior (Psalm 15)

Benjamin Franklin dubbed this the "gentleman's psalm" because he felt that it described the proper behavior of a gentleman. However, the question the psalmist asked in the opening verse was not "How do I improve my manners?" but "How can I stay close to God?" Surprisingly, the Lord's response in verses 2-5 did not focus on proper worship of Himself but, instead, on loving treatment of other people: walk in honesty and holiness, speak truthfully and kindly, demonstrate kindness to neighbors, discourage evil, encourage holiness, fulfill what is promised, and do not be ruled or try to rule others with money. The Bible summarized this elsewhere with *"love your neighbor as yourself"* (Lev. 19:18; Rom. 13:9; Gal. 5:14; James 2:8). The practical side of this behavior was explained in 1 John 4: 20: *"If someone says, 'I love God,' and hates his brother, he is a liar; for he who does not love his brother whom he has seen, how can he love God whom he has not seen?"* Do you want to improve your fellowship with God? Begin right where you are by giving kind attention to those who touch your life today.

Do you want to improve your fellowship with God? Begin right where you are by giving kind attention to those who touch your life today.

A Song of the Messiah (Psalm 16)

In the introduction to this study of Psalms it was explained that three common themes run throughout: Creation, Covenant, and Christ. Psalm 16 falls into the last category; it was written as if Christ Himself were praying to His

Father in heaven. First, He asked to be protected as He went about His Father's business: *"Preserve me, O God…."* Then, just as Jesus claimed later to do nothing apart from His Father (John 5:19,30 and 8:28), verse 2b stated *"My goodness is nothing apart from You."*

The saints of verse 3 who were called *"excellent ones"* were those people who had entered covenant with God. Like *godly* and *upright* noted earlier, *saints* had as its root the Hebrew word *hesed* also. Those who were outside of the covenant and who followed other gods were not to expect Messiah's recognition of them, while the saints could be assured of God's delight. The gratitude continued in verse 5-8 as God was praised for giving a *"good inheritance"* as well as counsel and instruction. The New Testament recorded many times when Jesus went apart to pray to His Father for such counsel.

Sheol -the place of the dead

The final verses (9-11) offered a preview of Jesus' resurrection after His crucifixion and burial: *"For You will not leave my soul in **Sheol**, nor will You allow Your Holy One to see **corruption**. You will show me the path of life; in your presence is fullness of joy; at Your right hand are pleasures forevermore."* We do not have to guess that this spoke of Jesus' resurrection; the Holy Spirit led Peter to see it and explain it in Acts 2:25-31. Peter showed that the fulfillment of this passage was a valuable proof that Jesus was the Messiah whom the nation of Israel had believed would come. After all, David, the author of this psalm, had died and his body had decayed; they could look at his bones even at that time, Peter reasoned. So the psalmist was prophesying of someone else, greater than David, who would overcome death with a resurrected body untouched by the rottenness of the grave. In what greater power can we trust than the One who can even overcome death?

corruption -decay, disintegration

We, too, can know God in such a personal way that we can ask Him to use His ears, eyes, lips, and hands to help us.

A Very Personal Kind of Praying (Psalm 17)

The Bible says of God that He is Spirit (John 4:24) and that no man has seen God (John 1:18), and yet David prayed to God as if He were visible to him, often referring to the parts of God's "body." This was an amazing kind of closeness to the Creator of all expressed by one of His mere "creatures"! Yet, even before Jesus came into our world with a human body, David understood through the covenant he had with God that God desired to be clearly revealed to and known by His covenant partners. We, too, can know God in such a personal way that we can ask Him to use His ears, eyes, lips, and hands to help us.

This psalm mentioned human body parts, too. It described the difference between the one who tried to please God with a pure heart (3), honest lips (3), and faithful feet (4), and the wicked and deadly enemies who *"closed up their fat hearts"* and opened up their proud mouths against God's people. The ones pleasing God could expect His attention and lovingkindness (*hesed*) and even protection (6-9). The psalmist dared to ask for the protection reserved for God's own eye. The *"apple"* of God's eye mentioned in verse 8 had an interesting origin. In Hebrew it meant "little man" and referred to the pupil of the eye because then, as now, when a person looked closely in the eyes of another, he could see himself—a "little man"—reflected there. The cornea of the eye which covers that area has a larger concentration of nerve endings than anywhere else in the body. It is extremely sensitive in order to be highly protective of anything threatening to damage a person's vision. So, in asking God to protect him as the *"apple"* of His eye, the psalmist was praying for maximum protection!

This psalm ended with a statement of hope about not only "seeing" God but also bearing a "family" resemblance: *"As for me, I will see Your face in righteousness; I shall be satisfied when I awake in Your likeness"* (15). The apostle John agreed with that hope when he wrote this centuries later: *"Beloved, now we are children of God; and it has not yet been revealed what we shall be, but we know that when He is revealed, we shall be like Him, for we shall see Him as He is"* (1 John 3:2).

> *"Beloved, now we are children of God; and it has not yet been revealed what we shall be, but we know that when He is revealed, we shall be like Him, for we shall see Him as He is" (1 John 3:2).*

A Good Ending (Psalm 18)

David had been aggravated by enemies throughout his life. Before he was allowed to serve as king, he was chased and threatened by Saul. After he was king, the trouble continued. He endured criticism from his own countrymen, a rebellion led by his son Absalom, and wars started by foreign nations. Yet, through it all, David knew that God had been faithful. This psalm was a psalm of praise and thanksgiving for a life protected and directed by a mighty God.

Verses 1-3:   God was praised as David's strength, rock, fortress, deliverer, shield, horn, stronghold, and rescuer.

Verses 4-19:   Here David summarized his many experiences with dangerous enemies and God's faithful and supernatural response to his calls for help.

Verses 20-30:   David described the way his relationship with God worked. Because David was in covenant with God, and so grateful for God's mercy, David was determined to obey God's will and Word. Such obedience pleased God then, and still does!

exalt -to lift up, to raise in position, to elevate

Knowing His Word, asking for His help, and obeying His will make it possible for His power to flow in and through our lives just as surely as it did through the life of David.

Verses 31-45: Here was a list of the many wonderful things God had done for David in his lifelong battles with enemies. The main focus was on God's greatness. (Note how many times "You" and "Your" were used.)

Verses 46-50: This last stanza of gratitude began *"The Lord lives! Blessed be my Rock! Let the God of my salvation be exalted."* That was David's whole purpose. He did not dwell on his enemies: Saul, Absalom, Ahithophel, or any of the others were never called by name. David only wanted to *exalt* the name of God. He did a great job of it in this psalm and in all the psalms of this lesson.

Closing Thought

The psalms of this lesson reminded us of the rich blessings of our covenant life with God. God is our Source for all help and power. Knowing His Word, asking for His help, and obeying His will make it possible for His power to flow in and through our lives just as surely as it did through the life of David.

Questions

Study Procedure: Read the Scripture references before answering questions. Unless otherwise instructed, use only the Bible in answering questions. Some questions may be more difficult than others but try to answer as many as you can. Pray for God's wisdom and understanding as you study and don't be discouraged if some answers are not obvious at first. Do not read the study notes for this lesson until AFTER you have completed your questions.

Day One: Vocabulary Review: Choose the best definition of each word.

_____1. upright   a) standing still   b) has *hesed* as its root; honest   c) loving

_____2. Sheol   a) a type of rock   b) an ancient shovel   c) the place of the dead

_____3. disposition   a) usual attitude or temperament   b) process of churning
                          c) lowest position on a job

_____4. fatigue   a) obesity   b) physical or mental weariness   c) disgust

_____5. corruption   a) decay   b) bumpiness   c) explosion

_____6. exalt   a) to leave   b) to quit   c) to lift up

Match each thought, theme, or quotation with the psalm from which it was taken.

_____a) the "gentleman's psalm"

_____b) In this psalm, you will find a description of a fool.

_____c) This psalm contains a prophecy about resurrection.

_____d) *"Keep me as the apple of Your eye."*

_____e) A warrior-king praises God for a lifetime of protecting love.

_____f) The words spoken out loud reveal the condition of the heart inside.

_____g) Don't urge me to run when God has called me to stand!

_____h) *"How long, O Lord?"*

7. Ps. 11   8. Ps. 12   9. Ps. 13   10. Ps. 14   11. Ps. 15   12. Ps. 16   13. Ps. 17   14. Ps. 18

MEMORY: PSALM 19:1, 14; 20:7

Day Two: Read Psalms 19, 20, and 21.

1. According to Psalm 19, God revealed Himself to mankind in two distinct ways. Identify them in the blanks provided.

Verses 1-6: _____

Verses 7-11: _____

2. Draw lines to match the following synonyms for the Word of God with their effects on the hearer.

law   clean and enduring forever

testimony   right and rejoicing the heart

statutes   true and righteous altogether

commandment   perfect and converting the soul

fear   pure and enlightening the eyes

judgments   sure and making wise the
                                                           simple

3. Read Psalm 20 with the idea that it was probably prayed as a congregational or group prayer for Israel's king before going to war. List the requests that were made to God for that leader.

Verse 1: _____

Verse 2: _____

Verse 3: _____

Verse 4: _____

Verse 5: _____

Verse 9: _____

4. What verses confidently spoke of their faith in God at such a time? _____

_____

_____

5. Read Psalm 21 with the idea that it may have been a "thank-you" psalm for the answers to the prayers of Psalm 20 for their king and nation as well as a preview of what the Messiah King would experience. List below the good things God had given this king as well as the future plans of God.

Good things: _____

_____

_____

_____

_____

Future plans: _____

_____

_____

_____

_____

Day Three: Read Psalms 22, 23, and 24.

1. Carefully read Psalm 22 which has been called the "Psalm of the Cross" since it details much of the suffering that the Messiah would endure centuries later. List the verses from this psalm that you can relate to what you know from the New Testament accounts of Jesus' arrest and crucifixion. Use Matthew 27:27-56 and John 19:28 for your New Testament references.

   Verses from Psalm 22   Fulfillment in Matthew or John

   _____

   _____

   _____

   _____

   _____

   _____

2. Psalm 23 is so familiar that there is a danger of missing its precious praise for God's covenant provision. Because the Lord is our Good Shepherd, just what can we expect?

   _____

   _____

   _____

CHALLENGE MEMORY: PSALM 24:1-10

3. Read Psalm 24.

   a) Which verses stated that everything and everyone belong to God?_____

   b) Which verses described the inward qualities of those blessed by God?_____

   c) List those inward qualities: _____

   _____

   d) Which verses described the coming of the King of Glory into a walled city? _____

   _____

Day Four: Read Psalms 25, 26, and 27.

1. Psalm 25 is an alphabetic acrostic in which each of its twenty-two verses begins with a different letter of the twenty-two letter Hebrew alphabet.

   a) In which verses did the writer ask God to forgive or forget his sins? _____

   b) What phrases are used to describe God? (Give references) _____

   _____

   _____

   c) What are the blessings and benefits for the one who fears the Lord in verses 12-15?

   _____

   _____

d) In verses 2, 3, and 20 the psalmist mentioned a desire not to be ashamed. Have you ever been concerned with that? Did you know you could pray about that? _____

_____

_____

2. Read Psalm 26. Write the verse which mentions the "good behavior" of the psalmist listed below:

a) Your lovingkindness is before my eyes. _____

b) I have walked in Your truth. _____

c) I have not sat with idolaters or hypocrites. _____

d) I maintain innocence and worship regularly. _____

e) I tell others about Your greatness. _____

f) I walk in integrity. _____

g) I stand firmly in a secure place._____

3. Even though the writer of Psalm 26 lived very obediently to God's will, what did he still need? (see verse 11)

a) time and money

b) friends and neighbors

c) mercy and redemption

4. Read Psalm 27. From verse one, why did David not have to be afraid? _____

_____

5. Matthew 6:33 states: *"But seek first the kingdom of God and His righteousness, and all these things shall be added to you."* Write down the verses in Psalm 27 that showed that the Holy Spirit had taught this truth to the people of the Old Testament, too. _____

_____

_____

_____

6. Which of the final verses described the hope that helped the psalmist get through tough times?

_____

_____

Day Five: Read Psalms 28 and 29.

1. In which half of the psalm does the writer make requests and in which half does he rejoice?

_____

_____

2. In Psalm 28, what can you learn about the wicked? _____

_____

_____

3. Read Psalm 29 and then match each section below with the summary of its message about God and what He does.

Verses 1 and 2: _____

Verses 3 through 10: _____

Verse 11: _____

      a) He gives peace   b) He deserves praise   c) He has unequalled power

4. Now take a few moments and read the notes for this lesson

Notes

God Does Not Hide From Us   (Psalms 19-29)

Two Sources of Information about God (Psalm 19)

Through the marvelous works of creation, God declares to every living being, "I am here!" Psalm 19 began: *"The heavens declare the glory of God;"* and then continued with *"the firmament shows...; ...day utters...night reveals."* There is no language barrier with the creative Word: *"There is no speech nor language where their voice is not heard"* (3). The sun's regular appearance is an assurance of His faithfulness (5,6); the darkness of the night allows the **vastness** of His expansive universe to be seen (2). However, the creative Word is only the beginning, a **prelude** to much, much more.

> **vastness** -a great extent or area; hugeness

"The law of the Lord is perfect, converting the soul" (7). Creation stirs the emotions but it takes the written Word of God to convert the soul. Creation proves that God exists and that He is all-powerful, but it is the written Word of God that tells us that God loves each of us and wants to be in covenant with us.   When we realize that He exists, we should desire to know more about Him. That is when the Scriptures are needed.

> **prelude** -a preliminary to an action, event, or work of higher importance

In verses 7-11, many synonyms for the Scriptures are used by the psalmist: law, testimony, statutes, commandment, and judgments. The written Word is precious and sweet and brings warning and reward to those that love it (10,11).

The last section began with *"Who can understand his errors? Cleanse me from secret faults."* The Bible shows us God's will for us and if studied, will help us see our sins. God uses that same Word to clean us up so we can start over. Like the psalmist, we must pray for God's help in applying His Word to our lives, to break the power of sin, and then we can be *"blameless"* and *"innocent of great transgression."*

> *Creation proves that God exists and that He is all-powerful, but it is the written Word of God that tells us that God loves each of us and wants to be in covenant with us.*

Since the creative Word and the written Word of God are so powerful, it makes sense that our words should line up with them: *"Let the words of my mouth and the meditation of my heart be acceptable in Your sight, O Lord, my strength, my Redeemer"* (14). It would be wonderful to make this your regular, daily prayer.

Prayer before Battle (Psalm 20)

As king, David was not only a brave warrior, but he also placed great emphasis on careful planning of group worship (See 1 Chronicles 15:16). This psalm of David addressed to "the Chief Musician" was typical of a congregational worship song. In it, the group asked God for His help and strength for the coming battle. It was evidently written to follow after the appropriate offerings were made, since they prayed, *"May He remember all your offerings, and accept your burnt sacrifice"* (3). The focus of their prayers was not just for a victory for their nation but for God to be given full credit for that victory. They promised *"in the name of our God we will set up our **banners**"* (5).

banners -the flags of a country, army, or troop

Years before David was king, when Israel asked God to replace their judges with a king like other nations had, God had granted their request but warned them of its cost (1 Samuel 8:11-18). Remaining sensitive to God's warning about ambitious kings, David had written, *"Some trust in chariots, and some in horses; But we will remember the name of the Lord our God"* (7). Our nation would do well to return to the truths revealed in this psalm and seek God's help for national problems.

"Let the words of my mouth and the meditation of my heart be acceptable in Your sight, O Lord, my strength, my Redeemer" (14). It would be wonderful to make this your regular, daily prayer.

A "Thank You" Psalm (Psalm 21)

This psalm seemed logically placed after Psalm 20 since its theme was gratitude for giving the king his heart's desire for victory over enemies prayed for there. Yet, like many psalms, it could also be prophetic of the "blessings of goodness" to come to Israel's future King Messiah. Jesus Himself said in the following passage that the Old Testament Scriptures, which included the Psalms, had reference to Himself: *" 'O foolish ones, and slow of heart to believe in all that the prophets have spoken! Ought not the Christ to have suffered these things and to enter into His glory?' And beginning at Moses and all the Prophets, He expounded to them in all the Scriptures the things concerning Himself "* (Luke 24:25-27).

Verses 3 through 7 are rich with references to the Second Coming of Christ. No longer a *"man of sorrows and acquainted with grief "* (Isaiah 53), Psalm 21 predicted: *"You set a crown of pure gold upon his head. He asked life from You, and You gave it to him—length of days forever and ever. His glory is great in Your salvation; honor and majesty You have placed upon him. For You have made him most blessed forever...."*

The next section (8-12) promised God's permanent judgment on the wicked, again a role explained in the New Testament as belonging uniquely to Jesus: *"And He commanded us to preach to the people, and to testify that it is He who was ordained by God to be Judge of the living and the dead"*(Acts 10:42). When Jesus returns, those who had opposed Him and His people will realize that they had *"devised a plot which they are not able to perform"*(11); God will show His power and answer the prayers of His people. That was how Psalm 21 ended—with hopeful praise that God would do just that: *"Be exalted, O Lord, in Your own strength! We will sing and praise Your power"*(13).

Psalm of the Cross (Psalm 22)

Some Bible students believe that Jesus had memorized this psalm and quoted it while hanging on the cross. The Matthew 27:46 recorded Jesus' quotation of the opening verse, *"My God, My God, why have You forsaken Me?"* The rest of the psalm continued from the viewpoint of a godly person in great torment, who had asked for and yet wondered at the delay of God's requested help. The physical pain described matched perfectly with the known sufferings caused by a death by crucifixion; however, crucifixion as used by the Romans in Jesus' day, approximately a thousand years later, had not yet been invented or introduced into the area of Israel at the time this psalm was written. The Holy Spirit certainly was at work inspiring the psalmist to predict in **minute** detail what Messiah would be required to suffer in our place. A careful reading of this psalm provided details of **taunting** mockery, great thirst, unbroken bones pulled out of joint, pierced feet and hands, gambling over clothing, and a broken heart. Two direct quotations from the scene at the cross can also be found: Verse 1, spoken by Jesus and verse 8 spoken by His enemies.

Appropriately, the psalmist used animals to describe those heartless enemies. The sufferer was surrounded by people acting like bulls(12) a roaring lion (13), dogs(16), and wild oxen (21). Yet the victim himself felt like a worm (6). The Hebrew word for worm was *tola*, a small yet valuable worm which was crushed to provide juices to make a very expensive scarlet dye, affordable only by the very rich. Jesus was crushed, indeed, that we might be clothed in the splendor of God's righteousness and blessing.

A reference to God's plan of resurrection for Jesus, the **subsequent** carrying of the gospel message throughout the world, and Jesus' return as Ruler of all nations could be seen in the closing verses 22 through 31. Psalm 22 has been called the "Psalm of the Cross" but its writer made clear that God's plan for this Sufferer did not end there.

The physical pain described matched perfectly with the known sufferings caused by a death by crucifixion; however, crucifixion as used by the Romans in Jesus' day, approximately a thousand years later, had not yet been invented or introduced into the area of Israel at the time this psalm was written.

minute (mi-noot') - extremely small

taunting -provoking by sarcasm or insult; malicious teasing

subsequent -coming later or after

The Psalm of the "Crook" (Psalm 23)

The curved "crook" was standard equipment for the Eastern shepherd and so was used for the title above. The trio of psalms in this section, 22, 23, and 24, dubbed "The Cross," "The Crook," and "The Crown," gave interesting details about the Messiah promised to Israel through the line of David. This psalm, Psalm 23, described the loving care of the *"great Shepherd of the sheep"*(Hebrews 13:20). Using illustrations that were commonly understood in his culture, David catalogued the covenant care he enjoyed. An excellent book by Philip Keller entitled *A Shepherd Looks at the Twenty-third Psalm* explained David's illustrations for those not familiar with the care of sheep. Brief summaries from that book follow:

Like sheep, we have a thirst for the spiritual and without our Shepherd, we might drink from polluted and ungodly sources in search of meaning and fulfillment. Our Shepherd leads us to the pure, still source of His Word made clear to us through the Holy Spirit.

1. *"I shall not want"* meant that the sheep was contented. A sheep could claim no credit for that; the sensitive help of a good shepherd made that possible.

2. *"He makes me lie down in green pastures."* A sheep would not lie down unless four things had occurred: any source of fear had been removed, friction within the flock had been calmed, flies or other pests had been stopped from irritating them, and sufficient food had been provided. Psalm 23 gave praise to God who had done it all so that the sheep could *"lie down."*

3. Another thing sheep required was that the water they drank be from a peaceful source; however, they were not very particular about the purity of it. Since sheep required a large amount of water daily, a shepherd had to know where the sources of pure water were and lead them there so that his sheep would not in desperate thirst drink from potholes or disease-infested pools. A shepherd had to spend quite a bit of energy on just this one requirement. Like sheep, we have a thirst for the spiritual and without our Shepherd, we might drink from polluted and ungodly sources in search of meaning and fulfillment. Our Shepherd leads us to the pure, still source of His Word made clear to us through the Holy Spirit.

4. *"He restores my soul."* Even well-cared-for sheep often got themselves into trouble. One particular problem was "casting." This occurred when a sheep lay down but could not get back up. Sometimes it was because the ground was too soft, its wool was too heavy, or it was too fat. Any of those things would make it get out of balance, shift its center of gravity, and cause it to be unable to get up. A good shepherd had to constantly watch for this problem because unhelped, a sheep would soon die. Like sheep, we need restoring, too, when we choose the easy, soft way too long or become weighted down with worldly, wooly cares. Some sheep just need to get on a better spiritual diet and get more exercise in godly service to lose the fatness that endangers them. The wise shepherd helps his sheep avoid such dangers.

5. *"He leads me in paths of righteousness for His name's sake."* Keller wrote: "The difficult point is that most of us don't want to come. We don't want to follow…. We actually prefer to turn our own way even though it may take us straight into trouble. The stubborn, self-willed, proud, self-sufficient sheep that persists in pursuing its old paths and grazing on its own polluted ground will end up a bag of bones on ruined land" (p.75).

6. *"Your rod and Your staff, they comfort me."* The rod was for protection against anyone or anything threatening the sheep while the staff, a long pole with a crook on the end, was for bringing sheep nearer to the shepherd or to the group when they wandered away.

7. The prepared *"table"* was necessary because sheep might eat poisonous plants if the shepherd were not careful.

8. The anointing oil would help heal wounds or keep pestering insects away.

9. The contented sheep could sing, *"Surely goodness and mercy shall follow me all the days of my life."* That same joy should show in our lives and overflow in love to the "sheep" around us. This will bless us but will also please our Shepherd who gave Himself so completely to meet our every need.

> *"Surely goodness and mercy shall follow me all the days of my life." That same joy should show in our lives and overflow in love to the "sheep" around us.*

The Crown (Psalm 24)

The first coming of Christ was in sacrifice and service as depicted in Psalms 22 and 23, while His second coming according to Psalm 24 would be as *"King of glory"* (7). He owned everything: *"the earth is the Lord's, and all its fullness"* (1), and only *"clean hands"* and *"pure"* hearts could approach Him (3,4). The very gates of Jerusalem would open at His presence (7,8,9). This was a psalm describing the glorious return of the Messiah.

"Let Me Not Be Ashamed!" (Psalm 25)

Have you ever worried that you would do something that would really embarrass or shame you or those you loved? Did you pray about it? The writer of this psalm did and offered some guidelines for those wanting God's help: glorify Him (1,2); wait for Him (3,21); ask Him (4,5); confess your own sins (6,7,16-22); submit everything to His care (8-15).

"Doing All I Can" (Psalm 26)

In this psalm the singer had done his best to do what was right in God's eyes and avoid what was wrong: *"…I have walked in Your truth. I have not sat with idolatrous mortals, nor will I go in with hypocrites"* (3,4). He invited God to inspect him (2), and recognize his good intentions. Yet, at the end, the psalmist admitted that his good works could never be adequate. He intended to keep trying, but he knew only God could really make him good: *"…I will walk in my integrity; redeem me and be merciful to me"* (11).

Excited about His Faith (Psalm 27)

So many of the verses from this psalm are familiar ones. Grieving loved ones at funerals are still comforted by *"The Lord is my light and my salvation; whom shall I fear? The Lord is the strength of my life; of whom shall I be afraid?"* (1). Those wanting to *"seek first the kingdom of God"* refocus with this: *"One thing I have desired of the Lord, that will I seek: that I may dwell in the house of the Lord all the days of my life…"* (4). Those feeling abandoned might repeat this: *"When my father and my mother forsake me, then the Lord will take care of me"* (10) or this: *"I would have lost heart, unless I had believed that I would see the goodness of the Lord in the land of the living"* (13). The final lines urged patience because God could be trusted no matter how difficult the circumstances appeared: *"Wait on the Lord; be of good courage, and He shall strengthen your heart; wait, I say, on the Lord!"* (14).

"Blessed be the Lord, because He has heard the voice of my supplications . . . my heart trusted in Him, and I am helped . . ." (6, 7). When you are in trouble, try prayer!

Request, then Rejoice! (Psalm 28)

In verses 1-5, David cried for help so that he would not be destroyed as if he did not belong to the Lord. Just letting God know how he felt through prayer evidently made him feel better immediately, because the mood changed from desperation to delight. In verses 6-9 he praised God for hearing: *"Blessed be the Lord, because He has heard the voice of my supplications…my heart trusted in Him, and I am helped…"* (6,7). When you are in trouble, try prayer!

Superior to the Storm (Psalm 29)

Psalm 29 returned to the theme introduced in the beginning of Psalm 19, that the creative Word of God goes out to all the world. First, in verses 1 and 2, a call was made for everyone to worship God as He deserved. Then, the psalmist described the unequalled power of the *"voice of the Lord"* in the common occurrence of a thunder storm. That *"voice"* could break cedars, divide flames of fire, shake the wilderness, make deer give birth, and strip forests bare. However, the Lord Himself sat undisturbed even during the Great Flood, and still *"sits as King forever,"* able to *"give strength to His people"* and bless them with peace (10,11). We would do well to appreciate the evidence in nature of God's awesome power and to praise Him for making it available to us.

Summing Up

From the psalms in this study we learned that creation proclaims Him, while Scripture explains Him! His power gets our attention, but His Word explains His loving plan for our individual lives. That plan included the coming of a unique King from the line of David: first as a sacrifice for our sins, but later as the King of glory to rule over eternity. How wonderful that God recorded His plan for us even in the music of these beloved psalms!

BIBLE QUEST

Questions

Study Procedure: Read the Scripture references before answering questions. Unless otherwise instructed, use only the Bible in answering questions. Some questions may be more difficult than others but try to answer as many as you can. Pray for God's wisdom and understanding as you study and don't be discouraged if some answers are not obvious at first. Do not read the study notes for this lesson until AFTER you have completed your questions.

Day One: Vocabulary Review: Fill in the blanks below with the correct vocabulary word from this list:

minute   prelude   banners   taunting   subsequent   vastness

1. The army's colorful _____ were not yet torn and dirty from battle.

2. God cares about even the _____ details of your life.

3. David's enemies were _____him about his present troubles.

4. The _____ of the universe should make us praise God.

5. God's help in the past was a _____ to more help in the future.

6. Faithfulness in a person's present circumstances is often the best preparation for

   _____ challenges.

7. In which psalm can you find a description of the two ways God has revealed Himself to us, in creation and through Scripture. _____

8. Which psalm described the future crucifixion of Jesus? _____

9. Which psalm described the loving care of God, comparing it to the love of a shepherd for his sheep?_____

10. Which psalm described a trust in God instead of in chariots and horses? _____

11. Which psalm was an alphabetic acrostic? _____

12. Which psalm stated, *"When my father and my mother forsake me, Then the Lord will take care of me"*?

> MEMORY: PSALM 31:23-24; 32:1-2

Day Two: Read Psalm 30, 31, and 32.

1. Read Psalm 30. When a covenant was made between partners, the needy partner could expect help from the other. What help did David receive from God because of their covenant? (Fill in the blank and give verse)

   a) "I cried out . . . and You _____." (____)

   b) "You _____that I should not go down to the pit."(____)

   c) "Weeping may endure for a night, but _____." (____)

   d) "You have turned my mourning into _____." (____)

2. Read Psalm 31. This psalm may have been written when David had been forced into hiding by his enemies. He let God know of his trust in Him but also made clear his current troubles. Divide the psalm verse by verse into these two categories.

Trust	Troubles
_____	_____
_____	_____
_____	_____
_____	_____
_____	_____
_____	_____

3. Read 2 Samuel 11 and 12. Contrast David with Uriah. _____

_____

_____

_____

4. Now read Psalm 32 which described how David felt during the year he did not confess his sin of adultery and murder to God.

a) How did he suffer physically? _____

_____

b) What brought him relief? _____

_____

MEMORY: PSALM 34:1, 4, 19

Day Three: Read Psalm 33, 34, and 35.

1. Read Psalm 33. Draw a line to match the following with the correct answer.

a) How were the heavens made?   "on those who fear Him" (v. 18)

b) What is full of the goodness of the Lord?   "the earth" (v. 5)

c) Why is a nation blessed?   Yes (v. 4)

d) On whom does God keep His eye?   because God is their Lord (v. 12)

e) Can armies and horses be trusted to save a king?   No (v. 16)

f) Is the word of the Lord always right?   "by the word of the Lord" (v. 6)

2. Read 1 Samuel 21:10-15 and 1 Samuel 22:1, 2 for the background information on this psalm.

a) Why was David in danger? _____

_____

b) Who joined David in hiding? _____

_____

3. Now read Psalm 34 which is another alphabetic acrostic of praise to God for His help to David in that dangerous situation. Write down some of your favorite verses from this psalm. Many of them are probably familiar to you.

_____

_____

_____

_____

4. Read Psalm 35. There are three ways we can react to the troubles that come our way. Give the verses from this psalm that could illustrate these ways:

a) evil for good (Satan's way) _____

b) evil for evil; good for good (the human or "natural" way) _____

c) good for evil (the godly or Christian way)_____

MEMORY: PSALM 37:4-5, 23-24, 39

Day Four: Read Psalm 36, 37, and 38.

1. Read Psalm 36. From verses 1-5 and 11-12, summarize the characteristics of a wicked person.

_____

_____

_____

_____

2. From Psalm 36:5-10, fill in the blanks with David's rich praise of God for blessing the righteous.

a) Your mercy, O Lord, is _____.

b) Your faithfulness reaches _____.

c) Your righteousness is like the _____.

d) Your judgments are a _____.

e) They are abundantly satisfied with the _____.

f) And You give them drink from the _____.

g) For with You is the _____.

h) In your light we see _____.

3. Read Psalm 37. Write down what you learn about "fretting" which comes from a Hebrew word meaning "to boil" or "to stew." _____

_____

_____

4. Write down some of the verbs used to describe what a person in trouble should do instead of fretting.

_____

_____

_____

5. Read Psalm 38 and then pick the best summary of it from those given below: (Be prepared to defend your answer.)

a) It is wonderful to be loved by You, O Lord!

b) The consequences of sin can really make life miserable!

c) When sick, ask God for healing.

d) Loneliness can just about kill a person.

e) (Write your own here.) _____

Day Five: Read Psalm 39, 40, and 41.   **MEMORY: PSALM 40:1**

1. Read Psalm 39. What is the general mood of this psalm? _____

_____

2. Read James 4:13-17. James evidently knew what David was talking about. What advice, do you think, would James have given him for coping in such a situation? _____

_____

_____

3. Read Psalm 40. Someone entitled this psalm "From the Mire to the Choir." What verses inspired such a title?_____

_____

4. Write down some verses that described how David told others about God. _____

_____

5. Read Psalm 41. What was causing so much hurt to David in this psalm? _____

_____

6. What verse in Psalm 41 described something that Jesus Himself would experience? _____

_____

7. Now take a few minutes and read the notes for this lesson.

Notes

No Secret Sin   (Psalms 30-41)

Remember in covenant, sorrows as well as joys are shared. One partner's need is the other's opportunity to serve and save.

Help from His Covenant Partner (Psalm 30)

The heading for this psalm mentions that it was used at a dedication of David's house. Whether David's own house (2 Samuel 5:11) or the place David had prepared for the ark of the Covenant (2 Samuel 6:17) was meant is not certain. Anyway, this psalm celebrates the covenant help that God had given David in his recent circumstances. Remember in covenant, sorrows as well as joys are shared. One partner's need is the other's opportunity to serve and save. Notice all the contrasts.

1. I was down, but God *"lifted me up."* Literally, that means like drawing up a bucket from a deep well. (30:1)

2. I was near the grave, but you *"kept me alive, that I should not go down to the pit"* (30:3). David praised God for this healing help.

3. *"For His anger is but for a moment, His favor is for life"* (30:5a).

4. *"Weeping may endure for a night, but joy comes in the morning"* (30:5b).

5. *"You have turned my mourning into dancing"* and exchanged my sackcloth, symbolizing grief, with a garment symbolizing gladness (30:11).

An important part of this psalm is the confession of sin in verse 6. Covenant partners should never try to hide anything from one another. Since they are bound to help the other in time of need, they should be kept informed of anything that might require action on their part, even the personal sin of the other partner. David confessed that he had become over-confident, full of pride, thinking that nothing bad would happen to him, *"I shall never be moved."* Yet, soon after, some serious problem did occur, and his earlier words shamed him. Still, God helped—even when he was to blame—and David praised God for this loyal rescue. The lesson for us to remember here is to confess our sins, not only to God, who knows everything, but to our parents, friends, or spouses, if married, if they are in covenant with us and expected to be on call to help us. A person can be a better help if he has time to prepare. Confession helps the person hearing it to understand and more quickly forgive. Hiding sin causes big problems.

> *If you have ever been miserable and lonely because other people were gossiping about or criticizing you, you will recognize the pain mixed in with the praise of this psalm. "In You, O Lord, I put my trust . . . Bow down Your ear to me . . ." (31:1, 2).*

Into Your Hand I Commit My Spirit (Psalm 31)

If you have ever been miserable and lonely because other people were gossiping about or criticizing you, you will recognize the pain mixed in with the praise of this psalm. God is called on as the only source of real help and the giver of loving understanding: *"In You, O Lord, I put my trust....Bow down Your ear to me..."* (31:1,2). What should a person do when under attack by others?

1. Draw nearer to God. Tell Him all about it in prayer. Praise Him for who He is and what He has done already for you. David said, *"You are my rock and fortress"* (31:3). Ask for His help: *"Lead me and guide me, pull me out of the net which they have secretly laid for me, for You are my strength"* (31:3,4).

2. If you have sinned in any way, making the problem worse, confess it. It did not sound like a very big sin, but David confessed that at one point he had given up hope, *"For I said in my haste, 'I am cut off from before Your eyes'"* (31:22). Confession of sin is necessary if we are to receive the help we need. It is an act of humility to admit that you, too, have been wrong.

3. Remember that others have gone through it, and you can, too. *"Be of good courage, and He shall strengthen your heart, all you who hope in the Lord"* (31:24).

More physical and emotional problems than we realize are caused by a failure to confess our sins and receive God's forgiveness. Learn from David's dangerous delay; humble yourself daily and confess your sins to God.

Confession of David's Sin with Bathsheba (2 Samuel 11-12; Psalm 32)

Years ago there was a commercial jingle for some medicine that boasted, "Relief is just a swallow away!" When we sin, relief is just a confession away! From 2 Samuel 11 and 12 we find that after David had become king, there was a season of war when he decided to stay at home instead of leading his men in battle. It was during this leisure time that he looked out from his palace to the roof of a house where a beautiful woman named Bathsheba was bathing. He ordered her brought to him, knowing the command of the king would be obeyed, and had sexual intercourse with her, even though she was a married woman and he was a married man. After the act, he sent her home only to hear from her later that their union had left her pregnant. Instead of confessing the sin, David tried to cover it up by sending for her husband, who was one of his best soldiers in battle, to come home. David hoped that if the man went home to his wife while back in Jerusalem, it would be thought that the pregnancy was caused by their normal husband-wife relationship. However, the husband Uriah was more honorable than David and would not enjoy the pleasures of sex even with his own beautiful wife while his men were still in battle. So, David sinned in an even worse way by having his general Joab put Uriah in the next battle where he would certainly be killed. This happened, and after a brief period of **mourning**, David sent for Bathsheba to come live with him as his wife. For about a year, David lived this lie without confessing his terrible sin. Psalm 32 tells of the physical suffering such guilt caused him: *"When I kept silent, my bones grew old, through my groaning all the day long....My **vitality** was turned into the **drought** of summer"* (32:3,4). Only after Nathan the prophet came and told him a parable that showed the pain caused when one man took what was another's, did David confess his sin. What a relief! *"I acknowledged my sin to You, and my iniquity I have not hidden...And you forgave the iniquity of my sin"* (32:5).

How hard will God have to deal with you to get you to confess your sin? Will he have to squeeze you dry like a sponge (4)? Bridle you like a horse (9)? Or, will you humble yourself immediately and let him *"instruct you and teach you"* (8)? More physical and emotional problems than we realize are caused by a failure to confess our sins and receive God's forgiveness. Learn from David's dangerous delay; humble yourself daily and confess your sins to God.

mourning -grieving, a sadness over a loss

vitality -an energy or force characteristic of life

drought -dry period

Pure Praise (Psalm 33)

One of the big activities in the life of a Christian should be praising God, but how can we keep praise fresh and interesting? David used two different subjects to inspire praise in this psalm and so can we.

One of the big activities in the life of a Christian should be praising God, but how can we keep praise fresh and interesting?

God's Word:

"Rejoice in the Lord....For the word of the Lord is right..." (33:1,4).

"By the word of the Lord the heavens were made... (33:6).

"For He spoke, and it was done... (33:9).

God's Works:

"And all His work is done in truth..." (33:4b).

"He gathers the waters of the sea together as a heap..." (33:7).

"The Lord brings the counsel of the nations to nothing..." (33:10).

"He fashions their hearts individually..." (33:15).

"Behold the eye of the Lord is on those who fear Him...to deliver their souls from death, and to keep them alive in famine" (33:18,19).

Another Alphabet of Praise (Psalm 34)

This is an alphabetic acrostic describing the happy results of trusting in God. The background is given in 1 Samuel 21:10-15 where a rather embarrassing situation was described. David was still running from Saul and went to the land of the Philistines, Israel's long-time enemies. They recognized him as one who had fought against them, and he became frightened. To protect himself, he acted as if he were mentally ill, and they left him alone. However, there is no note of embarrassment in this psalm—just sheer relief at being safe again: *"I sought the Lord, and He heard me, and delivered me from all my fears."* (4) God does not want us to be afraid of our enemies, but to "fear" or reverence Him. David told of the promise of help: *"The angel of the Lord encamps all around those who fear Him, and delivers them"* (7), and again, *"Oh, fear the Lord, you His saints! There is no want to those who fear Him. The young lions lack and suffer hunger; but those who seek the Lord shall not lack any good thing"* (9,10).

Let God Be Your Avenger (Psalm 35)

In this psalm, David is asking God to take action against those who seek his life without a reason: *"Plead my cause, O Lord, with those who strive with me"* (1). Some see in this and many other of its emotional pleas the inner thoughts and silent prayers of Jesus when He was on trial before Pilate, Herod, and the Jewish leaders. Whether you hear David or Jesus as the speaker, however, the lesson is the same: revenge does not belong to us, but to God. If we are in covenant with Him, He can be trusted to defend us. We need more prayers and less angry glares when we are criticized, accused, or attacked. There are three ways to react in any situation—the human way, the demonic

"Prayer is never lost: If it does not bless those for whom intercession is made, it will bless the intercessors. Clouds do not always descend in showers upon the same spot from which the vapors ascended, but they do come down somewhere. In some place or other prayers yield their showers of mercy."

way (like Satan would), or the divine way (like Jesus would). Human nature left to react on its own will return good for good and evil for evil (See 35:1-8 and 27 where David asks God to get them back for hurting him and reward those who support him). When Satan is allowed to influence us, the demonic response is evil for good (See 35:11,12). Only when the Holy Spirit directs us can we consistently give good for evil (See 35:13,14 where David showed real concern for his enemies' problems and pain). Think about how you most often respond to others. If it is not the divine way, you are going the wrong way. Praying for enemies—instead of verbally slaying enemies, is something that we must practice even if we do not see results right away. In his devotional book on Psalms, Charles Spurgeon reminded us, "Prayer is never lost: If it does not bless those for whom intercession is made, it will bless the intercessors. Clouds do not always descend in showers upon the same spot from which the vapors ascended, but they do come down somewhere. In some place or other prayers yield their showers of mercy...."

Safe in the Shadow (Psalm 36)

This psalm contrasts the wicked with the godly. The wicked do not fear God but instead flatter themselves. They have lost any wisdom they had about right and wrong and spend their time planning evil The godly ones, who are in covenant with God, are not living by themselves in their own sinful world. They are protected *"under the shadow"* of His *"wings"* (7), fed at His table (8), given drinks from *"the river"* of His *"pleasures"* (8), and enlightened by His *"light"* (9). The benefits of godliness are wonderful! Don't settle for less!

Delight - Don't Fret (Psalm 37)

This is another alphabetic acrostic psalm, but it offers advice to its readers instead of the usual praise to man's Maker. What is that advice? Exercise self-control: "...*the meek shall inherit the earth, and shall delight themselves in the abundance of peace"* (11). Meekness is not weakness, but instead it is the power of the Holy Spirit under the control of the Holy Spirit. When we are born-again, God gives us the "fruit" of self-control, the ability to not give in to what we naturally want to do, in order to wait for God's will to be done. The psalm begins with and then repeats one of our favorite "natural" responses to problems, "fretting." The Hebrew for that word means "to stew" or "to boil." We are told not to fret because *"it only causes harm"* (8), but instead to turn our thoughts to God and wait for His help. To stop fretting, the psalmist tells us to "change channels" in our thoughts to trusting and doing what we know is good (3); to committing everything to God (5); resting in Him and waiting for Him (7); to stop giving in to anger (8); and to depart from evil (27). Verses 12-40 emphasize the difference in the righteous and the wicked. God will protect and bless the righteous even when it appears that the wicked might overpower them: *"But the salvation of the righteous is from the Lord; He is*

Meekness is not weakness, but instead it is the power of the Holy Spirit under the control of the Holy Spirit.

their strength in the time of trouble. And the Lord shall help them and deliver them; He shall deliver them from the wicked, and save them, because they trust in Him" (39, 40).

Double Trouble (Psalm 38)

This psalm makes the reader feel the pain of David on two fronts: first, he is suffering emotionally and physically because of God's displeasure over his personal sin (1-10), and secondly, he is miserable over the absence of his friends and loved ones during this time of trouble (11-14). God is his only hope and comfort, and so he cries out, *"Do not forsake me, O Lord; O my God, be not far from me! Make haste to help me, O Lord my salvation!"* (21,22).

People rarely get into trouble for what they do not say, but often for what they do say.

Taking It like a Man (Psalm 39)

In this psalm David was being disciplined by God and kept his mouth shut about it, "I was mute, I did not open my mouth, because it was You who did it." That is a very wise example for us, too. People rarely get into trouble for what they do not say, but often for what they do say. It was not easy to hold back his comments at such a difficult time, especially while his enemies were watching; in fact, his unspoken words burned inside him: *"I was mute with silence, I held my peace even from good; and my sorrow was stirred up. My heart was hot within me; while I was musing, the fire burned"* (1-3). After holding back, at last he spoke to God, not in anger but in humility, asking for His help to understand what was happening: *"Lord, make me to know my end....what do I wait for? My hope is in You"* (4-7). One of the hardest things for us to do is to quietly endure. Jesus did it when He was innocent (see Matt. 26:63), and He will give us the grace to do it even in our guilt. When we do speak, it should be only, like David, to ask God to show us what we need to learn from the situation. Everyone of us needs correction from time to time. When it comes, take it like a man!

When we do speak, it should be only, like David, to ask God to show us what we need to learn from the situation. Everyone of us needs correction from time to time. When it comes, take it like a man!

From the Mire to the Choir (Psalm 40)

This psalm begins *"I waited patiently for the Lord...and [He] heard my cry...He...brought me...out of the miry clay, and set my feet upon a rock,...He has put a new song in my mouth—Praise to our God; many will see it and fear, and will trust in the Lord"* (1-3). The waiting urged in Psalms 37 (don't fret), Psalm 38 (do pray), and Psalm 39 (don't complain) paid off here as God acted on David's behalf, taking him (as Warren Wiersbe described it in his book <u>Prayer, Praise, and Promises</u>) "from the mire to the choir!" David praised God for His help and encouraged others to trust God, too. The benefits of such trust *"are more than can be numbered"* (5).

Another way to study this psalm is to see in it a description of the attitude of Christ the Messiah when He came centuries later to lay down His life for us. Verses 7 and 8 especially apply to Him: *"Then I said, 'Behold I come; In the scroll of the book it is written of me. I delight to do Your will, O my God, 'and Your law is within my heart.'"* And these words sound familiar, too: *"I have proclaimed the good news of righteousness....I have declared Your faithfulness and Your salvation..."*(9,10).

viper -poisonous snake

Whether from the point of view of a sufferer in this present world, or from Christ's position as suffering for us, this psalm urges us to continue to trust in God, praying honestly about our needs, and waiting for His saving help.

venomous -poisonous

Gossip and Grace (Psalm 41) One of the most painful things we experience is the unkind and often untrue words others say about us. David was sick and suffering, and instead of getting help from those around him, he was made to suffer more as he heard them wishing for his death. David described the worst pain of all: *"Even my own familiar friend in whom I trusted, who ate my bread, has lifted up his heel against me"* (9). Charles Spurgeon in his devotional book on the Psalms commented on the problem of gossip and slander described in this psalm: "David's enemies spoke evil of him; the **viper** fastened on Paul's hand; the better the man the more likely he is to be attacked and the more **venomous** the

slander -to utter damaging reports about a person

slander. Evil tongues are busy tongues and they are never truthful. Jesus was completely misrepresented, although no offense was in Him…. How far people will go to publish their slanders! They would gladly write their falsehoods in the sky. A little fault is magnified, a slip of the tongue is a **libel**, a mistake a crime, and if a word can have two meanings, the worse is always given to it." Jesus was betrayed by one of His own disciples just as David was

libel -any written, printed, or pictorial statement that damages a person by making his character appear evil or exposes him to ridicule

betrayed by a close friend. (See 2 Samuel 15:1-12.) Yet both were able to rejoice in God's ultimate victory: *"By this I know that You are well pleased with me, because my enemy does not triumph over me. As for me, You uphold me in my integrity, and set me before Your face forever. Blessed be the Lord God of Israel from everlasting to everlasting"* (11-13).

Questions

Study Procedure: Read the Scripture references before answering questions. Unless otherwise instructed, use only the Bible in answering questions. Some questions may be more difficult than others but try to answer as many as you can. Pray for God's wisdom and understanding as you study and don't be discouraged if some answers are not obvious at first. Do not read the study notes for this lesson until AFTER you have completed your questions.

MEMORY: PSALM 41:1

Day One: Vocabulary Review: Circle the best definition.

1. drought: work horse   dry period   an order to join the army

2. vitality: liveliness   courage   hair oil

3. venomous: dangerous   bloody   poisonous

4. viper: snake   a flute player   an insect

5. slander: spoken criticism without proof   under-weight   a female goose

6. libel: freedom   an ancient tool   any written criticism without proof

7. From the notes on lesson 12, what should a person do when under verbal attack by others?

_____

_____

_____

8. What were the two subjects of David's praise in Psalm 33? _____

_____

9. What did you learn about the life of David in the last lesson?_____

_____

_____

_____

_____

Day Two: Read Psalms 42, 43, 44, and 45.
MEMORY: PSALM 42:1-2

1. Read through Psalms 42 and 43. What refrains (or repeated verses) are shared by both psalms?

_____

_____

2. Match the summaries below with the verses in Psalms 42 and 43 to which they relate.

   a) He is out of his home territory and longs to go back to worship God at the tabernacle in Jerusalem.

   _____

   b) His homesickness is made worse because his enemies ridicule him for not having God's favor, and

   their words have made him begin to doubt. _____

   c) He gives himself a pep-talk, making himself focus on his future hope. _____

   d) He calls on God Whom he knows to be his only real hope._____

        (1) 42:5, 11 and 43:5   (2) 42:9, 10; 43:1, 2   (3) 43:3, 4   (4) 42:1-4, 6-8

3. Read through Psalm 44 and fill in the correct answers with your own words.

   a) In the past, God had_____

   b) We still trust in _____

   c) But now _____

   d) Even though_____

4. Read the following New Testament passages and then answer, "Can a nation or group of people

   suffer without deserving it?" _____

   Romans 8:35: *"Who shall separate us from the love of Christ? Shall tribulation, or distress, or*

   persecution, or famine, or nakedness, or peril, or sword?"

   2 Timothy 3:12: *"Yes, and all who desire to live godly in Christ Jesus will suffer persecution."*

5. Psalm 45 is a song of love and praise to a great king on his wedding day. Many see this as a psalm

   describing the future glory of Christ Messiah when He returns for His Bride, the Church. Which

   verses seem to you to describe Christ? _____

   _____

   _____

6. Read Hebrews 1:1-9. Which verses there quote Psalm 45 about Jesus? _____

   _____

   _____

Day Three: Read Psalms 46, 47, and 48.   *MEMORY: PSALM 46:1, 10; 48:1*

1. Read the wonderful words of Psalm 46. Just how much power does the psalmist think God really

   has? (Give verses to support these answers.)

   a) Enough to protect us even if the world, as we know it, ends_____

   b) Enough to protect Jerusalem even if the whole world attacks her _____

c) Enough to rule over the whole earth, stopping all war forever _____

2. Read Psalm 47. Which verses describe how far-reaching His kingdom really is?

_____

_____

3. From Psalm 47, were the Israelites always supposed to be quiet in their worship of God? List some ways the people were encouraged to celebrate the eternal King? _____

_____

_____

4. Read Psalm 48.

   a) What city is being described here? _____

   b) How long will it exist? _____

   c) Who protects it? _____

Day Four: Read Psalm 49 and 50.

MEMORY: PSALM 50:10, 15

1. Read Psalm 49.

   a) What can money not buy? _____

_____

   b) What do the rich sometimes do to try to prolong their fame? _____

_____

   c) Why should you not envy the rich person? _____

_____

2. Read Psalm 50. This is a psalm that describes the dramatic appearance of God as a righteous Judge. Read the following statements about Psalm 50 and mark them either True or False.

   a) _____ When God gets ready to judge the earth, He will do it quietly and privately.

   b) _____ God depends on people to help Him out by bringing their offerings.

   c) _____ God wants His people to be thankful and to do what they have promised to do.

   d) _____ God will help those who call on Him.

   e) _____ Because God kept silent about the sins of the wicked, it showed He overlooked them.

   f) _____ If repentance is real, and the wicked change their conduct, God will show His salvation to them.

Day Five: Read Psalm 51.

MEMORY: PSALM 51:10

1. Psalm 51 is a favorite of many because it:

    a) Is full of praise

    b) voices the deep emotion of one who knows the pain of sinning, but desires the relief of forgiveness

    c) can be memorized quickly

    d) none of the above

2. David realized that although sinning may hurt many people, including the sinner himself, at its root all sin is really against _____.

3. According to this psalm, when did David believe sin began in his life? _____

4. What did he ask God to do for him? _____

   _____

5. When is a person able to help others find the way out of sin? _____

   _____

6. What does God really want from us? _____

   _____

7. David finished this psalm with a prayer for what? _____

   _____

8. Now take a few moments and read the notes for this lesson.

Notes

Rebellion to Obedience   (Psalms 42-51)

Have you ever been homesick? There's nothing quite like it. Even if you are with family or friends, there can come up in you a painfully intense hunger for the familiar sights, sounds, even smells of home.

The Sons of Korah

This section (42-51), which begins Book 2 of the Psalms, contains several psalms written by the sons of Korah. Korah was a man in Moses' time who rebelled against Moses' and Aaron's authority. He was punished by God for his rebellion (see Numbers 16). However, some of his descendants evidently returned to proper obedience and generations later were still serving God in worship as temple doorkeepers (1 Chronicles 9:19), temple singers, and musicians (1 Chronicles 6:31-37).

Homesick (Psalms 42-43)

Have you ever been homesick? There's nothing quite like it. Even if you are with family or friends, there can come up in you a painfully intense hunger for the familiar sights, sounds, even smells of home. In Psalm 42 and 43, which may originally have been one psalm since they share a refrain (42:5, 11; 43:5), the writer describes a serious "thirst" for God: *"As the deer pants for the water brooks, so pants my soul for You O God"* (42:1). He even recalls the old routine he enjoyed there:

"For I used to go with the multitude; I went with them to the house of God, With the voice of joy and praise, With a multitude that kept a pilgrim feast" (42:4). Something else besides just the distance, however, has added to his pain. Enemies have taunted him by asking *"Where is your God?"* (42:10) trying to make him believe he has been abandoned. In an effort to get his thinking straight, the psalmist repeatedly questions himself and then gives his own advice about what he knows to be true: *"Why are you cast down, O my soul?…Hope in God; For I shall yet praise Him, the help of my countenance and my God"* (42:11).   In Psalm 43 the same homesickness lingers. Here, which is good advice for anyone suffering, the psalmist speaks openly to God about what he needs to feel better. Here are the two things he requests: help with the present trouble that keeps him away from home (*"Deliver me from the deceitful and unjust man!"* 43:1) and clearer thinking about the whole situation (*"Oh, send out Your light and Your truth! Let them lead me…."* (43:3). The best thing to do when you find yourself where you don't want to be is to pray to God about it. Like the psalmist here, maybe even try writing down how you feel. Tell God everything and expect Him to help. *"Hope in God…"* (43:5). This will clear your thinking and help you let go of fear and worry. Even if the troubles do not immediately stop, you will be better able to cope while you wait for God's full answer to your needs.

deceitful -false, lying

The best thing to do when you find yourself where you don't want to be is to pray to God about it. Even if the troubles do not immediately stop, you will be better able to cope while you wait for God's full answer to your needs.

Help Us Again (Psalm 44)

The writer of this psalm is well-acquainted with the record of God's help for Israel in the past (1-3) and knows that in her present predicament—perhaps war—she needs Him to help again(4-8).   However, she is seeing none of the miraculous help she has heard about. Israel is losing and being captured and enslaved (9-12). The surrounding nations hate her and do not see God's power (13-26). If Israel had turned away from God or broken His covenant, they could understand what was happening, but their *"heart has not turned back, nor have our steps departed from Your way….Yet for Your sake we are killed all day long; we are accounted as sheep for the slaughter"* (17-22). The psalm ends with a plea for God to wake up and come back to her to help her *"for [His] mercies' sake."*

Bad things do happen to God's people and life does not always seem to have a happy ending. We might have to change schools or jobs, or we might be suddenly injured or become ill. We do not like to think about that, and yet, while there are many, many Bible promises for our everyday life, we also know that we may be called on to suffer when we are not at fault or simply because we are Christians, and never get everything "fixed" in this earthly life. The famous "Hall of Faith" in Hebrews is often quoted for its description of the heroes of the Bible who experienced God's great power while they lived, but the end of that chapter, which is not so often quoted, describes something different: *"Still others had trial of mockings and scourgings, yes, and of*

Bad things do happen to God's people and life does not always seem to have a happy ending. We might have to change schools or jobs, or we might be suddenly injured or become ill.

chains and imprisonment. They were stoned, they were sawn in two, were tempted, were slain with the sword. They wandered about in sheepskins and goatskins, being destitute, afflicted, tormented--of whom the world was not worthy" (Hebrews 11:36-38). Even though God can get us out of great troubles, He might choose to give us power to just get through them. Either way, talk to Him about your needs and your pain and trust Him to do the best thing for you and His kingdom.

messianic -having to do with the expected coming of the King of the Jews, Jesus Christ

commemorates -honors the memory of

Even though God can get us out of great troubles, He might choose to give us power to just get through them. Either way, talk to Him about your needs and your pain and trust Him to do the best thing for you and His kingdom.

alludes-refers to something indirectly

A Royal Wedding (Psalm 45)

We do not have to guess about whether or not this psalm is **messianic**. The writer of Hebrews quoted it to describe Jesus, *"Your throne, O God, is forever and ever; A scepter of righteousness is the scepter of Your kingdom"* (Hebrews 1:8,9 and Ps.45: 6,7). Specifically, the psalm **commemorates** a special event in the King Messiah's life, a wedding! In the New Testament the believers in Christ—the Church—are described as Christ's bride (Eph. 5:22-32 and John 3:29). And, when Jesus told the disciples before His crucifixion that He was going to prepare a place for them and would certainly return to take them with Him, He was using the familiar language of a groom to His betrothed bride (John 14:1-3). When all preparations were ready for their permanent life together, a prospective groom would return, suddenly, for his waiting bride. Psalm 45 describes the public adoration of King Messiah, the "groom": *"You are fairer than the sons of men; grace is poured upon Your lips; therefore God has blessed You forever" (2)*. The bride is described, too: *"The royal daughter is all glorious within the palace; her clothing is woven with gold. She shall be brought to the King in robes of many colors; the virgins, her companions who follow her, shall be brought to You. With gladness and rejoicing they shall be brought"* (13,14 and also 2 Cor. 11:2).

What did it cost this bride to come to her king? Psalm 45 **alludes** to it: *"Listen, O daughter….forget your own people also, and your father's house"* (10). In a similar way, when a person comes to Christ, she must leave her old life and enter the family of God. God must from then on be first in her loyalty and love. Is it worth it? Will the bride have what she needs if she leaves her old world behind? Psalm 45:12 says that *"the daughter of Tyre will be there with a gift; the rich among the people will seek your favor."* Tyre, at the time this psalm was written, was the richest commercial city around. Once the bride became the wife of the King, she would have everything else she needed. So, we are told to *"seek first the kingdom of God, and His righteousness, and all these things shall be added…"* (Matt. 6:33). Just as entering the marriage covenant entitles a bride to all her husband has, so when we enter the covenant of Christ, we share in all he has. Psalm 45 is right in celebrating with beautiful language the wedding of the King of Kings.

What's the Worst that Could Happen? (Psalm 46)

Martin Luther's famous hymn *A Mighty Fortress Is Our God,* was inspired by this psalm. The word for refuge in verse 1 means shelter, fortress, or stronghold. With God as our fortress, of whom or of what should we be afraid? The psalmist colorfully describes the worst possibilities:

1. (2,3) The end of the world as we know it, with the earth being moved and mountains broken and carried to the sea. Even in that event, we are still safe with God who created and can re-create it all.

2. (4-6) Attacks focused on Jerusalem and the Jewish place of worship. God could stop that instantly: *"He uttered His voice, the earth melted."*

3. (8,9) Wars all over the world. God can stop those, too: *"He makes wars cease to the end of the earth...."*

This psalm could have the events of 2 Kings 19:32-35 and Isaiah 36-37 as its historical inspiration, where God stepped in miraculously to deliver Israel from the Assyrians. However, its truths are eternal. *"If God is for us, who can be against us?"* (Romans 8:31). What should our response be, then, to our troubles? Psalm 46:10 answers with *"Be still and know that I am God."* Try it. Let His peace replace your worry and fear.

> *What should our response be, then, to our troubles? Psalm 45:10 answers with "Be still and know that I am God." Try it. Let His peace replace your worry and fear.*

Make Some Noise! (Psalm 47)

This psalm must have been written to celebrate another great act of help or mercy by God for Israel. He is praised as all-powerful, worthy of notice and worship. The people are encouraged to worship Him enthusiastically with clapping and shouting and singing. Many, many people go wild with enthusiasm at sporting events but sit like *zombies* in worship services. This psalm tells us that there are times when we must come alive and express our joy over such a wonderful God, who owns all the *"shields of the earth"* and *"reigns over the nations"* (8,9). Does this advice apply to you?

> **zombies** -persons resembling the walking dead

> *The people are encouraged to worship Him enthusiastically with clapping and shouting and singing. Many, many people go wild with enthusiasm at sporting events but sit like zombies in worship services.*

A Special City (Psalm 48)

Jerusalem is mentioned often in the Bible, and although God loves people in cities everywhere, He has said some unique things about Jerusalem. Verse 8 states that *"God will establish it forever."* What a promise! Thousands of cities have come and gone, but God has promised to keep Jerusalem going. Zion is sometimes used as a synonym for Jerusalem since Mt. Zion is an area very near to the city. Jerusalem became the center of worship under David's rule but was given special notice even in the time of Abraham when he was greeted by Melchizedek, who was an early king of that city and area (Genesis 14:18-20). Judgments have fallen on Jerusalem as the prophets foretold, one of the most devastating being when it was overrun and its temple destroyed by the Romans in 70 A.D. Jesus had been sad over the people of Jerusalem not accepting Him and warned of that particular attack. (Luke 19:41-44).

sects -parts or divisions of something larger

There has been no temple for central worship since that time. Although its name means "peace" ("salem" has the same origin as "shalom"), it is a city that remains at the center of controversy. Today Jews, Christians, and Muslims, as well as various **sects** of those three religions, claim a right to worship there. However, no matter how often Jerusalem has been attacked, God has preserved her. This psalm reminds us of God's trustworthiness. What He has promised, just as with Jerusalem, He will certainly do.

What Money Cannot Do (Psalm 49)

This psalm sounds like some of the chapters in Proverbs. The writer here is giving very practical advice about placing too much emphasis on money. That is still a problem in our time. One preacher gave a sermon about what the world thinks about money and substituted "money" for "love" in the famous passage from 1 Corinthians 13. Think about it. Too often, if a person has plenty of money, he is excused from all sorts of personal faults. Psalm 49 wakes the reader up to just what money cannot do.

Money is a tool to use to help others as well as ourselves in this present life, but only God is to be worshiped and completely trusted. Money will run out in life or be left behind at death, "But God will redeem my soul from the power of the grave, for He shall receive me" (15).

1. (5-9) Money cannot purchase salvation for a "brother." The price of eternal life is out-of-reach except by Jesus who paid it for us.

2. (9-20) Money cannot keep a person from dying at some time. When that happens, even the rich have to leave everything behind. They may try to buy fame by calling *"their lands after their own names,"* but their memory will still not remain for long: *"Death shall feed on them...; and their beauty shall be consumed in the grave."*

Money is a tool to use to help others as well as ourselves in this present life, but only God is to be worshiped and completely trusted. Money will run out in life or be left behind at death, *"But God will redeem my soul from the power of the grave, for He shall receive me"* (15). Can you make that statement?

Here Comes the Judge (Psalm 50)

The small print above this psalm attributes it to Asaph, a man who lived at the time of David and was in charge of one of the twenty-four groups which participated in the musical service for worship in Jerusalem. Asaph, who has twelve psalms included in this book, was mentioned in 1 Chronicles 25:1-31; and 2 Chronicles 29:30.

What is being described in Psalm 50 is a very dramatic appearance of God as Judge of the world: *"Our God shall come, and shall not keep silent; a fire shall devour before Him, and it shall be very tempestuous all around Him, He shall call to the heavens from above, and to the earth, that He may judge His people: 'Gather My saints together to Me, those who have made covenant with Me by sacrifice.'...for God Himself is Judge"* (3-6).

Have you ever dreaded getting a report card or a test paper back? If you did, it was probably because you were not sure of how you had done or if you had done enough. When God "judges" His own people, they will not have to fear execution or hell because they have not "done enough," because Jesus' sacrifice has met all of God's requirements. However, God does care about what we have done in our lives since we have come into covenant with Him. The psalm emphasizes some things God is quite serious about. First, church attendance and personal quiet time should not be done mechanically, out of habit, and without sincere feeling. God does not need our gifts and activities—He owns *'the cattle on a thousand hills"* (10). But He knows that giving and serving help us mature as we should. Secondly, He does want us to have thankful hearts toward Him and to carry out what we have vowed or promised Him. Also, He wants "heart-felt" not "canned" prayers: *"Call upon Me in the day of trouble; I will deliver you, and you shall glorify Me"* (15).

Who should fear the judgment of God, if His own children will be disciplined but not damned? Verses 16-21 answer this. Anyone who talks about God's statutes and covenant without really believing and obeying them better watch out. God can see through any religious "act" that is done publicly while sins like stealing, adultery, and gossip continue secretly. He has withheld judgment, desiring that every sinner would repent, but some have thought His delay was His "okay." God sets the record straight: *"You thought I was altogether like you; but I will reprove you, and set them in order before your eyes"* (21).

God wants His children to be honest in their worship and service, and He wants the wicked who really do not know Him to repent and turn to Him while there is still time.

The psalm ends with a marvelous reminder that this awesome Judge still longs to show mercy: *"Now consider this, you who forget God…Whoever offers praise glorifies Me; and to him who orders his conduct aright I will show the salvation of God"* (22:23). God wants His children to be honest in their worship and service, and He wants the wicked who really do not know Him to repent and turn to Him while there is still time. One day the opportunity for repentance and salvation will be withdrawn.

Have Mercy Upon Me (Psalm 51)

The background for this psalm can be found in 2 Samuel 11 and 12. There David's sins of adultery and murder are described as well as his refusal to confess them to God for almost a full year (see notes on Psalm 32, page 102). Psalm 32 came out of this same historical background and revealed the pain and suffering of trying to hide something from God, as well as the great relief and healing that follows a complete confession. Psalm 51 is one of the best-loved psalms because it outlines the heartfelt prayer of David for God's mercy and forgiveness. David had quit hiding and was being open and honest about the deadly consequences and far-reaching pain caused by sin.

While it is true that we hurt many, many people when we sin, the real tragedy is that we have rebelled against a holy God. We demanded our way and our will instead of His.

(1-3) *"Have mercy….Blot out….Wash me thoroughly…."* Only God can make us clean again when we have sinned. *"Against You, You only, have I sinned."* While it is true that we hurt many, many people when we sin, the real tragedy is that we have rebelled against a holy God. We demanded our way and our will instead of His.

(5-6) Here is the real problem. We are born with a sin nature. Yet, God wants a pure nature. Unless He changes us completely, we cannot know Him or please Him.

(7-10) The shame and pain of sin were so deep that David cried out again for washing and healing and a return to the joy he once knew with God. Sometimes it is hard for us to believe that God is willing to forgive us of some of the terrible things we have done, and we find ourselves repeatedly pleading with God, as David did here.

(10-11) *"Create in me a clean heart, O God, and renew a steadfast spirit within me."* This is the result of the knowledge of verses 5 and 6. We know we need an "inside-out" renewal.

(12-13) *"Restore to me the joy of Your salvation….Then I will teach transgressors Your ways…."* Sometimes the kindest and most helpful teachers are those who have experienced God's forgiveness and help in overcoming their own sins. David certainly was such a teacher.

Sin may knock us down, but it should never knock us out of God's service. Do not let past sins keep you from present usefulness.

(14-17) *"The sacrifices of God are a broken spirit, a broken and contrite heart…."* Humility and honesty are what God can use and bless in His people.

(18-19) *"…Build the walls of Jerusalem."* After we get our personal lives straight, we should begin to be concerned for others. We must spend time searching our hearts and confessing our sins, but then we must get up and get at the business of obedience and service once more. Sin may knock us down, but it should never knock us out of God's service. Do not let past sins keep you from present usefulness.

 BIBLE QUEST   LESSON 14

Questions

Study Procedure: Read the Scripture references before answering questions. Unless otherwise instructed, use only the Bible in answering questions. Some questions may be more difficult than others but try to answer as many as you can. Pray for God's wisdom and understanding as you study and don't be discouraged if some answers are not obvious at first. Do not read the study notes for this lesson until AFTER you have completed your questions.

Day One

1. Vocabulary Review: Scan the notes for the words that these phrases define.

    a) _____ false, lying

    b) _____ having to do with the expected coming of the King of the Jews, Jesus Christ

    c) _____ honors the memory of

    d) _____ refers to something indirectly

    e) _____ persons resembling the walking dead

    f) _____ parts or divisions of something larger

2. Review of Psalms 42-51: Match the verse to the psalm from which it was taken.

_____a) "Clap your hands, all you peoples!"

_____b) "God is our refuge and strength, a very present help in trouble."

_____c) "In the city of our God: God will establish it forever."

_____d) "Why are you cast down, O my soul? . . . Hope in God . . ."

_____e) "Yet for Your sake we are killed all day long. We are accounted as sheep for the slaughter."

_____f) "Your throne, O God, is forever and ever; a scepter of righteousness is the scepter of Your kingdom."

_____g) "They shall call their lands after their own names."

_____h) "Offer to God thanksgiving, and pay your vows to the Most High."

_____i) "Create in me a clean heart, O God."

    44:22   48:8   42:5, 11   43:5   47:1   46:1   51:10   50:14   49:11   45:6

Day Two

1. Read 1 Samuel 21:1-9 and 22:9-23 and then identify the following men:

    a) Ahimelech _____

    _____

    b) Doeg _____

    _____

c) Goliath _____

_____

d) Saul _____

_____

e) Abiathar _____

_____

2. Now that you know the historical background, read Psalm 52. Which verses described Doeg, the herdsman-turned-executioner? _____

3. Which verses described David, God's beloved? _____

4. Read Psalm 53. See if you can find out which psalm from an earlier lesson is almost exactly like it. (Hint: if you have a reference Bible, there will probably be a reference given in the center or side column.) _____

5. The background for Psalm 54 can be found in 1 Samuel 23:1-13 and 19. David had been betrayed by some people whom he had helped earlier.

   a) Which verse in Psalm 54 recognizes that the people who betrayed him were not following God as David was? _____

   b) Which verses show David's continuing faith in God even when men failed him? _____

Day Three: Read Psalm 55, 56, and 57.   *MEMORY: PSALM 56:3-4, 11*

1. Read Psalm 55:1-11 and summarize David's problem and what he wishes he could do.

_____

_____

2. Read Psalm 55:12-23 and then select the summary statement(s) below that fit(s) that passage:

   a) What makes all this so terrible is that it is not a stranger who is attacking me but one of my closest friends.

   b) No matter what, I will continue to call on God and trust Him to handle this terrible situation. He will never break covenant with me. He can be trusted.

   c) I am going to quit everything. I give up.

   d) Let me tell you about my old friend. He was a smooth talker and I thought he loved me, but he was hiding all his hate in his heart even then.

   e) I am ready to forgive my enemies, no matter what they have done to me.

3. Read Psalm 56. David had been tormented by enemies, but he continued to turn to God.

   a) How did he cope with the fear? _____

   _____

   b) What did he say about his tears? _____

   _____

   c) What work of God did he repeatedly praise? _____

   _____

   d) What had God done with David's feet? _____

   _____

4. Read Psalm 57. Where did David intend to stay until his present storm of trouble was over?

   _____

5. Select some of the "praise phrases" from this psalm that you liked best and write them down

   below. _____

   _____

   _____

Day Four

1. Read Psalm 58. In the opening verses the judges or rulers of the land are addressed. What

   kind of job have they done in their position?

   a) they have upheld the Word of God

   b) they have acted very wickedly

   c) they are ignorant of their responsibilities

   d) they have helped the poor

2. What does David want God to do about them? _____

   _____

3. Why do you think he responded like this? _____

   _____

   _____

4. Read 1 Samuel 19:1-12 for the background for this psalm. Then explain why verses 3 and 4 are

   correct statements. _____

   _____

   _____

5. David compared his enemies to what kind of animal? (Give verses) _____

   _____

Day Five: Read Psalms 60, 61, and 62. *MEMORY: PSALM 61:1-2; 62:1-2*

1. Read Psalm 60, then use the words in the box to fill in the blanks:

   a) You have shown Your people_____. (v. _____)

   b) You have given this to those who fear You _____. (v._____)

   c) Ephraim is this_____. (v. _____)

   d) Moab is this_____. (v. _____)

   e) This kind of help is useless_____. (v. _____)

   f) Through _____ we will do valiantly. (v. _____)

   > God's helmet
   > God's washpot
   > a banner
   > God
   > man's
   > hard things

2. Read Psalm 61. List as many "word pictures" as you can find that describe God's protection. (Hint: the first one is in v. 2 "the rock that is higher than I.")_____

   _____

3. Think of some word pictures of your own that describe what God's love and protection is like for you. _____

   _____

4. Read Psalm 62. The image of God being a "rock" of refuge or safety is used in this psalm as it has been in earlier ones. Try to find out why rocks would have been so significant as places of shelter or safety in that part of the world. Write down what you find out below. _____

   _____

   _____

   _____

5. According to Psalm 62, where should a person and where shouldn't a person place their trust?

   _____

   _____

6. Now take a few moments and read the notes for this lesson.

Notes

Go Up Higher   (Psalms 52-62)

> **They Won't Get Away with It!**
> **(Psalm 52)**

treachery -disloyalty or deceptiveness

informant -one who supplies information which should remain secret

The background for this psalm is found in 1 Samuel 21:1-9 and 22:9-23 where David's request to a priest named Ahimelech for bread and a weapon while hiding from Saul were detailed. The priest's kindness was reported by an observer named Doeg to Saul as **treachery**. Saul reacted with violence and ordered all the priests of that place killed as well as the townspeople. Only the **informant**, Doeg, would obey such a senseless order, and when the news reached David in hiding, he was overwhelmed with grief that an action of his had resulted in the executions of innocent people.

The psalm opened with a question, *"Why do you boast in evil, O mighty man?"* (1). That term "mighty man" was probably **sarcastic**--how much "might" did it take to kill unarmed priests, women, and children? David found comfort in the truth that evil men like Doeg would not continue unstopped forever. The wicked were like shallow-rooted trees which God would soon pluck out of their places while the righteous watched. David compared himself to a *"green olive tree in the house of God,"* secure in the mercy and protection of the Lord forever. Olive trees were known for their long life span and continued productivity. So, a man of God could not be stopped permanently by the wickedness of others.

> **sarcastic** -meant to mock or insult

A Rerun (Psalm 53)

This is very similar to Psalm 14 except that the Hebrew word for *God* translated here is *Creator God* (*Elohim*) instead of *Covenant God* (*Jehovah*). This is an interesting difference because in Romans 1:18-32, Paul explained that **atheism** began with people denying that God created everything, which led to their refusing to give Him thanks, praise, and obedience. God, then, responded by withholding His help from them and leaving them to the consequences of their evil behavior. What a person believes about God affects everything else.

> **atheism** -the belief that there is no God

This psalm points out that everyone needs God; none can make it on his own: *"They have together become corrupt; there is none who does good, no, not one"* (3). There is no safety for the person who denies God and hurts God's covenant people--*"who eat up my people as they eat bread and do not call upon God"* (4). Their bones will be scattered when God acts in judgment (5). The psalm ends with a heartcry for God to bring to pass His plans for Israel which will include judgment on all the ungodly who have opposed her.

> *Instead of griping and grumbling about how we have been mistreated, we need to simply tell God our needs in prayer and then thank Him for handling it for us. He will do a better job defending us than we can ourselves.*

Tattletales (Psalm 54)

While in the wilderness to avoid being killed by Saul, David often defended people who were under attack by others (1 Samuel 23:1-5). He did not abuse defenseless folks in the area where he camped. However, his good behavior did not keep those he helped or others from trying to turn him in to King Saul. In 1 Samuel 23:19, the Ziphites reported his position and David had to flee again. Psalm 54 is David's prayer to God for help in facing undeserved oppression from the ungodly: *"Hear my prayer, O God; ...For strangers have risen up against me,...they have not set God before them"* (2, 3). David names God as his "helper" and turns his energies to praising Him instead of moping over the actions of others. This should be a model for us, too. Instead of griping and grumbling about how we have been mistreated, we need to simply tell God our needs in prayer and then thank Him for handling them for us. He will do a better job defending us than we can ourselves.

betrayal -disloyalty or unfaithfulness

The Pain of Betrayal (Psalm 55)

This is another psalm describing the pain of **betrayal**, but this time David has been betrayed by a covenant partner, someone in very close relationship to him, and not by a stranger as in Psalm 54. This pain is much worse. This is a psalm that would speak to victims of divorce or abuse, those surprised by the dishonesty of a trusted business partner, or immorality of a Christian leader. Anguish and heartbreak bleed through almost every line. He just wants to escape, to run away from it all, to *"fly away and be at rest"* (6). David explains the terrible pain this way: *"For it is not an enemy who reproaches me; then I could bear it. Nor is it one who hates me who has exalted himself against me; then I could hide from him. But it was you, a man my equal, my companion and my acquaintance. We took sweet counsel together, and we walked to the house of God in the throng"* (12-14).

There is no pain like that of betrayal by one who was loved and trusted. What can be done to get through such deep suffering? "As for me, I will call upon God, and the Lord shall save me. Evening and morning and at noon I will pray, and cry aloud, and He shall hear my voice."

Many see foreshadowed here the betrayal of Jesus by one of the twelve men before whom He had lived sinlessly and devotedly for three years: *"He has put forth his hands against those who were at peace with him; he has broken his covenant. The words of his mouth were smoother than butter, but war was in his heart..."* (20, 21). There is no pain like that of betrayal by one who was loved and trusted. What can be done to get through such deep suffering? David explained what he did: *"As for me, I will call upon God, and the Lord shall save me. Evening and morning and at noon I will pray, and cry aloud, and He shall hear my voice. He has redeemed my soul in peace from the battle that was against me..."* (16-18). Our Lord knows the pain of betrayal, disloyalty, broken promises, and shattered dreams. He offers a remedy: *"Cast your burden on the Lord, and He shall sustain you..."* (22). And He will also deal with those who have hurt you! (For the probable historical background, see 2 Samuel 15:31 and 2 Samuel 16:15-17:14,23 where one of David's most trusted counselors Ahithophel left David to help Absalom overthrow him. Sadly, David would inflict this same pain of betrayal on a trusted soldier in 2 Samuel 11.)

Enemy Territory (Psalm 56)

The background for this and Psalm 34 is found in 1 Samuel 21:10-15 where David was recognized as an enemy while hiding in Gath, a city of the Philistines. Hunted by Saul and the army of Israel and now recognized in Gath, what could he do? He prayed to the only help he had, *"Be merciful to me, O God, for man would swallow me up..."* (1). David spoke helpful words for us about what he did when in danger: *"Whenever I am afraid, I will trust in You, in God (I will praise His word)"* (3). He trusted in God and found comfort in God's Word. Even when everyone was against him, he knew God saw his tears and wanderings and even recorded them in a book (8, 9). The psalm ended with a reference to the importance of keeping vows to God and statements of praise for protection and direction.

Concert In a Cave (Psalm 57)

David was cornered, unable to sprout wings and fly away, so he trusted in God's wings: *"...in the shadow of Your wings I will make my refuge, until these calamities have passed by"* (1). David calls God what Abraham had called Him—*"Most High."* David was in a cave, but he knew God was not only near, but able to act. He was *"Most High"* and free to send help from heaven itself (2, 3). David described his problems in verses 4 and 6, but then he changed his focus to praise: *"Be exalted, O God, above the heavens; let Your glory be above all the earth"* (5). Giving a wonderful concert in his cave of trouble, David sang: *"I will sing and give praise. Awake, my glory! Awake, lute and harp! I will awaken the dawn"* (8). The mercy and truth of God were expected and praised by David in verses 3 and 10. His mercy or covenant love (Hebrew: *hesed*) still saves us while His truth trains us for His service. David expected God to help him and so was able to sing while he waited. Can we?

Unjust Judges (Psalm 58)

The opening line *"Do you indeed speak righteousness, you silent ones? Do you judge uprightly, you sons of men?"* seems to be directed to those judges or leaders who should have been using their authority to carry out God's will. Instead, they were silent when they should have spoken. They are idle when they should have acted. David asked God to *"break their teeth"* and let them melt *"like a snail which melts away as it goes"* (6-8). Earlier church leaders have thought that such psalms should not have been included in the Bible. They are called *imprecatory* psalms and seem to contradict what Jesus taught about loving our enemies. However, they were included, and so evidently have something to teach us still. C. S. Lewis, an English *theologian* of this century, commented on the repeated cursings of their enemies by Israel: "If the Jews cursed more bitterly than the pagans this was, I think, at least in part because they took right and wrong more seriously. For if we look at their *railings* we find that they are usually angry not simply because these things have been done to them but because these things are manifestly wrong, are hateful to God as well as to the victim." We would do better to hate what God hates and not try to cover up so many of our personal and national sins. The old advice of "hate the sin and love the sinner" is still good. In our day and age we seem to err on the side of loving the sinner and overlooking the sin completely. David did not. He wanted evil and unrighteousness to stop, and he called on God to judge those who were opposing God's work and will. If you, too, are tired of the failures of those in authority, pray for them (1 Timothy 2:1,2). Then, remember, this world is not our permanent home. The righteous Judge will some day return to put things right (11).

We would do better to hate what God hates and not try to cover up so many of our personal and national sins. The old advice of "hate the sin and love the sinner" is still good.

imprecatory -to call down a curse upon

theologian -one who studies the nature of God

railings -bitter, harsh, or abusive talk

Under Surveillance (Psalm 59)

The background for this psalm in 1 Samuel 19:1-18 places this at an early time in David's career, when, while married to a daughter of Saul named Michal, he had to escape a plot by the king to have him captured at home. David, as Jonathan pointed out to the angry Saul, had done nothing but be loyal to the king. Michal helped David escape, but weakened under the questioning of her father and did not defend David's good character. This psalm includes David's prayer for help: *"Deliver me….For look, they lie in wait for my life;…They run and prepare themselves through no fault of mine"* (1-4). David compared his enemies to growling dogs (6, 14) which pursued him everywhere. Another imprecatory psalm, it included David's plea for God's judgment on all of them. It ended, though, not with a curse, but with a great statement of faith, characteristic of David's understanding of God's covenant with him: *"…I will sing aloud of Your mercy in the morning; for You have been my defense and refuge in the day of my trouble"* (16).

Broken but Believing (Psalm 60)

David and his "general" Joab were leading the armies of Israel against two enemies in the north when a third enemy invaded in the south (2 Samuel 8). How often it still happens—one or two problems get solved and a third appears! The new challenge left David confused: *"O God, You have cast us off; You have broken us down"* but still hopeful: *"Restore us again!…You have broken it; Heal its **breaches**, for it is shaking"* (1, 2). David reminded God of His promises to Israel (6, 7) which were physical (ownership of the land) and political (its control—helmet and lawgiver) as well as His prophecies for their enemies (v. 8—washpot and servant). David knew that the *"help of man is useless"* and only *"through God we will do valiantly"* (11, 12). When we do not understand why something is happening to us, we can still trust the "Who" who is in charge! We will fail if we forget we are completely dependent on God for every victory.

breaches -broken places in a wall or line of defense

When we do not understand why something is happening to us, we can still trust the "Who" who is in charge! We will fail if we forget we are not completely dependent on God for every victory.

The Rock that Is Higher (Psalm 61)

David prayed and praised in this psalm. When feeling overwhelmed, he asked God to take him to a place of refuge and shelter, *"to the rock that is higher"* than he was (2). Rocks and high places might not seem too significant in your life and location, but to David who spent so many years in the dry wilderness, without trees for shade or cities for safety, every big rock or high place had the potential power for shelter, shade, defense, or observation of the enemy. God, to him, had been *"a shelter"* and *"a strong tower from the enemy,"* (3) and under that protection David intended to remain. An interesting New Testament reference described the rock of the wilderness known by the Israelites during their exodus as representing Christ Himself (1 Cor. 10:4). David knew his Lord to be such a rock of safety and provision as well.

Wait on the Lord (Psalm 62)

When a person waits on God as his only salvation and defense, no matter what happens, he will not be *"greatly moved."* Events in our lives may often shock and rattle our emotions, but the encouragement of this psalm is that we do not have to be ruined by them—faith in God prevents us from being *"greatly moved."* The familiar description of God as the rock of help is repeated here. Some false sources of help are described in verses 9 and 10: (1) men of low degree, those who could be paid or made to act in a certain way, but could not be trusted without payment or **coercion**; (2) men of high degree, those who seem to have influence or power but are really *"lighter than vapor"*; (3) oppression, the use of violence; (4) robbery, stealing from others; and (5) riches, buying freedom or protection. All those are false hopes for help; true power only belongs to God (v. 11). And, mercy is only His, too—and that is something we always need.

When a person waits on God as his only salvation and defense, no matter what happens, he will not be "greatly moved."

coercion -force used to restrain or dominate someone

BIBLE QUEST

LESSON 15

Questions

Study Procedure: Read the Scripture references before answering questions. Unless otherwise instructed, use only the Bible in answering questions. Some questions may be more difficult than others but try to answer as many as you can. Pray for God's wisdom and understanding as you study and don't be discouraged if some answers are not obvious at first. Do not read the study notes for this lesson until AFTER you have completed your questions.

Day One: Review.

1. Vocabulary Review. Fill in the vocabulary word that matches the definitions below:

ACROSS

3. bitter, harsh, or abusive talking
6. broken places in a wall or line of defense
7. call down a curse upon
8. disloyalty or unfaithfulness
9. force used to restrain or dominate someone

DOWN

1. one who studies the nature of God
2. the belief that there is no God
4. one who supplies information which should remain secret
5. meant to mock or insult

Review of Psalms 52-62: Matching

_____ 1. What a fool says.

_____ 2. Good times to pray according to Psalm 55.

_____ 3. Where tears go.

_____ 4. Doeg

_____ 5. Whose teeth David wanted broken.

_____ 6. The enemies seemed to growl like dogs in this psalm.

_____ 7. God's washpot.

_____ 8. Where to go when overwhelmed (Psalm 61).

_____ 9. This belongs to God (Psalm 62).

a) the mighty man (Ps. 52)

b) Psalm 59

c) power

d) evening, morning and at noon

e) the rock that is higher than you are

f) There is no God.

g) Moab

h) in God's bottle

i) unrighteous judges (Ps. 58)

Day Two: Read Psalms 63 and 64.

1. In Psalm 63, David was in the wilderness away from Jerusalem and the formal worship of his people. Write down the phrases that showed that he longed to return to that kind of worship.

    _____

    _____

2. Without organized singers and musicians and priests to offer animal sacrifices,

    a) what did David use to worship where he was? _____

    _____

    b) what other spiritual actions did David take even though he was in the wilderness?

    _____

    _____

    c) when you are away from your home church, do you worship anyway? _____

3. In Psalm 64, what are the weapons of the enemy? _____

4. How will God defeat them? _____

    _____

5. Have you used such "weapons" to hurt others? _____

Day Three: Read Psalms 65 and 66.

1. Psalm 65 praises God for His dealings in the following areas: (Give the verses for each)

    a) hearing prayer and providing atonement _____

    b) calling individual worshipers _____

    c) exercising worldwide influence _____

    d) taking care of the earth _____

2. Fill in the blanks from Psalm 66:1-7.

    a) Make a joyful _____ to God . . .

    b) Sing out the _____ of His name.

    c) Say to God, "How _____ are Your works!"

    d) Come and see the _____ of God . . .

    e) He rules by His _____ forever.

3. Great suffering is described in verses 8-12, but how did it all end? _____

    _____

4. Can you describe a time in your life where you suffered only to have God bring you through it as a better person or to a better place? _____

    _____

5. From verses 13-20, what can keep a person's prayers from being heard and answered? (pick one)

    a) failure to keep a vow

    b) offering imperfect sacrifices

    c) dull praise

    d) unconfessed sin

MEMORY: PSALM 67:1-7

Day Four: Read Psalms 67, 68, and 69.

1. Read Psalm 67. When "all the peoples" praise God what happens

    a) to the earth? _____

    b) to God's people? _____

    c) to people all over the world? _____

2. Read Psalm 68. From verses 1-6, list some of the things God does. _____

_____

_____

3. What verse(s) from Psalm 68 did Paul quote in Ephesians 4:8 to describe Christ's triumph after

    the cross? _____

4. Read Psalm 69 carefully.

    a) Write down the verses that remind you of the suffering of Jesus. _____

_____

_____

    b) **Challenge:** Now write down some verses that do not match what you know of Jesus' suffering

       on the cross _____

_____

Day Five: Read Psalms 70, 71, and 72.

MEMORY: PSALM 71:1

1. Read Psalm 70. What phrases show that David needed help immediately? _____

_____

2. Read Psalm 71. Write out or summarize the verses that talk of God's help

    a) at birth _____

_____

    b) in youth _____

_____

    c) in old age _____

_____

3. Read Psalm 72.

   a) Who is given credit as the author of this psalm? _____

   b) Read 1 Kings 4:32. How many others did he write? _____

4. This psalm is considered messianic, meaning that it described Christ, the Messiah. Which event is described here, His first or second coming? (Support your answer with verses from this psalm. Hint: if it is not true now after His first coming, it must point toward a future fulfillment at His second.)_____

   _____

   _____

   _____

   _____

   _____

5. Now take a few moments and read the notes for this lesson.

Notes

Holy Zeal   (Psalms 63-72)

What Is Zeal? *Zeal* has the same root as "jealousy" and is a passionate enthusiasm for a person or cause. The Hebrew root word for it means "to boil." Christians should have a zeal for God, but how can they get it? As in a delightful human friendship, the "zeal" appears automatically at the beginning. No one has to make us tell about the one we love—what we feel just comes bubbling out in our words and expressions. God enjoys such enthusiasm or zeal in us. Jesus even described it in Revelation 2:4 as *"first love"* and urged believers to return to it. The psalms in this lesson should help us do just that.

zeal -great interest or eagerness

Take Time to Remember (Psalm 63) Psalm 63 was written while David hid from Saul in the wilderness of Judah. David missed the beautiful worship he had enjoyed in Jerusalem. He took time to think about what he was missing and wrote down how he felt: *"My soul thirsts for You; my flesh longs for You in a dry and thirsty land where there is no water. So I have looked for You in the sanctuary, to see Your power and Your glory"*(1, 2). What did David do with the memories? He used them to spur him to private and personal worship. He praised God with his own lips and lifted up his hands to bless God in the absence of the "wave offerings" of grain or animal sacrifices. He found his wilderness worship as satisfying as the marrow and fatness of the offerings he had made in the past. He did not put God and happier times out of his mind. All during the night, when the guards would have relieved each other from their "watches," David remembered God's past help and was certain of His future help. David did not lose his *"first love"* or holy zeal even while suffering, and neither should we.

No one has to make us tell about the one we love— what we feel just comes bubbling out in our words and expressions. God enjoys such enthusiasm or zeal in us.

We must make definite efforts to remember God and His goodness. A prayer journal, calendar, or diary could help review God's help in our lives. Travelers to some places in Europe might be surprised to find benches scattered in odd places over the countryside inviting the traveler to sit and enjoy the view. In India there are "resting poles" complete with shelves to hold personal backpacks or baskets. A person is to lean against them to rest and think. We could use more solid reminders like those to cause us to pause and rest and remember. Busyness is an enemy to holy zeal because it does not allow a person to use his memory to praise God. Are you too busy to worship?

Fear Brings Failure (Psalm 64)

Zeal for God can be lost when we are afraid of what might happen to us physically, emotionally, spiritually, and even financially. So, fear must be dealt with if we are to function with enthusiastic faith. David told God about his fear: *"Hear my voice…. Preserve my life from fear of the enemy"* (1) There were times in David's life when people lied about him or met together to scheme against him. He knew the power of ungodly mouths. Such people *"sharpen their tongue like a sword, and bend their bows to shoot their arrows—bitter words"* (3). It seemed that David's fear dissolved as he continued in this psalm to tell God about it. The psalm ended in a confident statement about what God would do: *"But God shall shoot at them with an arrow;…so he will make them stumble over their own tongue"* (7, 8). With real enthusiasm this statement followed: *"The righteous shall be glad in the Lord, and trust in Him. And all the upright in heart shall glory."* The lesson for us is not to hide our fears. No one can help what he feels at any given moment, but every Christian has the ability to "let go" of a negative feeling like fear by confessing it to God. Then, like David, he must choose to focus on the power of God and what He can do. The fear will fade and faith will return.

The lesson for us is not to hide our fears. No one can help what he feels at any given moment, but every Christian has the ability to "let go" of a negative feeling like fear by confessing it to God.

Count Your Blessings (Psalm 65)

If we find ourselves taking someone for granted or maybe criticizing them for not acting in a certain way, it helps to stop and consider what that person has already done or been in our life—to count the blessings already received. Even David probably had times of feeling spiritually distant from God, but his words in this psalm could soon cure that. He specifically described God's work in several different areas.

1. **Personal**: Vows can be made to God, but should be made prayerfully and then carefully performed. God is the One who hears prayer and provides atonement for sin (1-3). Also, God communicates with people individually. He has chosen us—and draws us to Himself. When we respond, we *"shall be satisfied with the goodness of [His] house"* (4).

2. <u>International:</u> God's great deeds can be seen worldwide, to *"the ends of the earth, and of the far-off seas"* (5). His power is revealed in the realm of nature through movements in mountains and oceans. No one can miss seeing His power at work (6-8).

3. <u>Environmental:</u> God waters the earth, causes crops to grow, and lets animal life flourish, all for man's use and enjoyment. He should be praised! (9-13).

See how it works? Counting blessings makes us quit focusing on present delays and causes us to have hope for the future. God does not change. What He has done in the past, He is still able to do in the present and future.

In the joyful beginning, difficult middle, or satisfying end of our lives or activities, God can be called on to help if we will be honest before Him and confess our sins. When this is done, like the psalmist, we can rejoice: "Blessed be God, Who has not turned away my prayer, nor His mercy from me!" (20).

Tough It Out! (Psalm 66)

Often, the beginning of a relationship or a project is exciting and causes those involved to overflow with excitement. In this psalm *"all the earth"* is called to *"make a joyful shout to God"* for His help in defeating the enemies of Israel and, in the biggest miracle of the Old Testament, getting Israel out of Egypt across the Red Sea without getting wet (1-6). Yes, beginnings are wonderful. However, to get to the end of a project or to reach a goal, one often has to endure a tougher "middle" period. This is when many quit, as the older generation of Israel did in the wilderness. The psalmist described a difficult "middle" period: *"For You, O God, have proved us; You have refined us as silver is refined, You brought us into the net; You laid affliction on our backs. You have caused men to ride over our heads; we went through fire and through water..."* (10-12). Did they give up? No, they trusted God and toughed it out. The result? *"But You brought us out to rich fulfillment."* The zeal of the beginning might dwindle in the middle, but staying at the task to the finish will make it blaze once more.

In the final two sections, the psalmist promises to pay the vows he has made to God and plans to do them with great enthusiasm out of appreciation for the Lord who answers prayer (13-15). A very important point is made a few verses later about which prayers are heard. *"If I regard iniquity in my heart, the Lord will not hear"* (18). In the joyful beginning, difficult middle, or satisfying end of our lives or activities, God can be called on to help if we will be honest before Him and confess our sins. When this is done, like the psalmist, we can rejoice: *"Blessed be God, Who has not turned away my prayer, nor His mercy from me!"* (20).

When working through something difficult or time-consuming, it is helpful to consider what the end result will be—to think about reaching the end, meeting the goal, or winning the prize.

Eyes on the Prize (Psalm 67)

When working through something difficult or time-consuming, it is helpful to consider what the end result will be—to think about reaching the end, meeting the goal, or winning the prize. Psalm 67 is a song of praise for the future plans of God. There will be a time when His salvation will be known *"among all nations"*(2); when the Lord will sit as a righteous judge to govern the nations (3, 4); and when the earth will be free of pollution and erosion and *"shall yield her increase"*(5-7). Such events are worth waiting for!

Victory Parade (Psalm 68)

"Let God arise, let His enemies be scattered; let those who hate Him flee before Him, as smoke is driven away...." That line begins the praise parade with God on High honored like a returning hero. The psalmist seems to clear the roadways before the great name of God, calling out to everyone around to *"Extol Him who rides on the clouds"*(4). He then begins a *litany* of the great works of the Lord: *"a father to the fatherless"*; One who *"sets the solitary in families"*; one who helps the poor become prosperous; and punishes the rebellious (5, 6). Similar to Deborah's battle song in Judges 5:4, 5, the next part of the psalm recounts God's presence with Israel during the exodus and in the wilderness at Sinai (7-10). Then, God is praised for the conquest of the Promised Land in verses 12-14. The parade image grows with the announcement in verse 17 that God has thousands of thousands of chariots, and places His headquarters at *"Sinai, in the Holy Place."* The description of the Lord as *"ascended on high"* having led *"captivity captive"* and *"received gifts among men"* was quoted by Paul in Ephesians 4:8 to describe the ascension of Christ to His rightful place of power following the crucifixion, burial, and resurrection. This victorious Lord of ours *"daily loads us with benefits"* (19).

> **litany** -a prayer where the leader reads phrases and allows for a response from the congregation

The zeal of David in this psalm never fades. In 21-23, the defeat of all God's enemies is foretold. Verses 24-30 describe the *"procession"* of God into the sanctuary. The whole scene is quite festive with singers, instruments, and notable *dignitaries*. The final section promises that the world will recognize Him and honor Him with gifts. This God is worthy; He is more *"awesome than [His] holy places"* and it is He who gives *"strength and power to His people"* (31-35).

> **dignitaries** -a person of high rank, notability, or influence

Psalm 68 should motivate us to "stage" a parade of praise somehow in our place of worship. Consider participation in a church cantata or other musical program. Volunteer to help make banners or other special occasion decorations. We should go the extra mile frequently to be generous in our expression of praise to so wonderful a Lord. Psalm 68 may have been written to celebrate the return of the ark of the covenant to Jerusalem in 2 Samuel 6:12. A new song for a joyful occasion!

Much Suffering (Psalm 69)

This is a psalm that someone undergoing undeserved suffering could certainly understand. There are striking parallels in some verses to the sufferings of Christ at Calvary: *"I am weary with my crying; My throat is dry…"* (v. 3—John 19:28); *"those who hate me without a cause are more than the hairs of my head…"* (v. 4—John 15:25); *"…zeal for Your house has eaten me up, and the reproaches of those who reproach You have fallen on me"* (v. 9—John 2:17); *"But as for me, my prayer is to You, O Lord…"* (v. 13); *"do not hide Your face from Your servant"* (v. 17—Matt. 27:46); *"I looked for someone to take pity, but there was none;…They also gave me gall for my food…[and] vinegar to drink"* (vs. 20,21—Matt. 27:34).

Even if every person we know were to abandon us undeservedly or because of our sins, God would not.

On the other hand, there are many verses that Jesus would not have used. He prayed for God to forgive His enemies, not destroy them as the sufferer of Psalm 69 did (See verses 5,6, and 22-28). But we can still learn from this psalm in our own sufferings. Even if every person we know were to abandon us undeservedly or because of our sins, God would not. We can sing with this psalmist: *"…I am poor and sorrowful; let Your salvation, O God, set me on high…..The humble shall see this and be glad; and you who seek God, your hearts shall live. For the Lord hears the poor and does not despise His prisoners."* That is comforting.

More Suffering (Psalm 70)

This short psalm is almost identical to Psalm 40:15-17. Just as a new singer might revive an old song in our day, adding his particular style to its performance, so, long ago, psalms were revived and repeated. This one is a cry of a desperate soul to God for immediate help and relief from enemy attack, physical and verbal. *"Make haste to me, O God! You are my help and deliverer; O Lord, do not delay"* (5). It is a song that can be sung in any age since conflicts among people will never stop till the Peacemaker returns to rule and judge.

*There are phases of our lives in which our abilities, needs, physical **stamina**, and senses may vary. God does not expect the same work from us in every phase, but He does expect faithfulness at every stage of life.*

Problems of Aging (Psalm 71)

There are phases of our lives in which our abilities, needs, physical **stamina**, and senses may vary. God does not expect the same work from us in every phase, but He does expect faithfulness at every stage of life. We must not let aging stop us from being available to God. Christians may tire, but they do not get to retire! This psalm was written by one who knew the frustrations of a weakening body. Appropriately, he prayed to God about his fears, asking Him for the following help:

stamina -physical or moral endurance

1. **Stay close:** *"Be my strong habitation, to which I may resort continually"* (3).

2. **Don't abandon me now:** *"You are my trust from my youth. By You I have been upheld from birth..."*(5, 6)

3. **Make up for the strength I have lost:** *"Do not cast me off in the time of old age; do not forsake me when my strength fails"* (9).

4. **Keep teaching me so I can teach others:** *"You have taught me from my youth...Now also when I am old and grayheaded, O God, do not forsake me, until I declare your strength to this generation, Your power to everyone who is to come"*(17, 18).

> *Emotion is not our goal when we talk about renewing our zeal for God, but an awakening to the greatness of our God is! What a great God!*

This psalm can help us realize that even if we are not the ones facing old-age right now, we need to be sensitive to the changing needs of those who are. They need to remain useful in the Lord's work and not overlooked. The jobs may need to be adjusted to their changing abilities, but they still must be included. Age is no excuse for fading zeal, even if activities must be carried on at a slower pace.

He's Coming Back! (Psalm 72)

Emotion is not our goal when we talk about renewing our zeal for God, but an awakening to the greatness of our God is! What a great God! This psalm describes some of what will happen when God calls "Time's up!" and lets Christ return to finish all earthly battles and set up His righteous kingdom. Here are some of the things we can expect:

1. **True justice (1-4 and 12-14):** The way our present world operates cannot be called fair. There is so much suffering through injustice of governments, ignorance, abuse of power, and man's meanness to others that godly people get frustrated and tired of the struggle. However, when Christ returns, *"He will judge Your people with righteousness, and Your poor with justice."*

2. **Lasting peace (5-7):** *"In His days the righteous shall flourish, and abundance of peace, until the moon is no more."*

3. **Kingdom of God over all the earth (8-11):** *"Yes, all kings shall fall down before Him; all nations shall serve Him."* The earth will be renewed and become very productive **(16):** *"There will be abundance of grain in the earth, on top of the mountains...."*

> *To all those wonderful future happenings there needs to be an enthusiastic response. Here it is: "Blessed be the Lord God...Who only does wondrous things!"*

To all those wonderful future happenings there needs to be an enthusiastic response. Here it is: *"Blessed be the Lord God...Who only does wondrous things!"*

BIBLE QUEST

Questions

Study Procedure: Read the Scripture references before answering questions. Unless otherwise instructed, use only the Bible in answering questions. Some questions may be more difficult than others but try to answer as many as you can. Pray for God's wisdom and understanding as you study and don't be discouraged if some answers are not obvious at first. Do not read the study notes for this lesson until AFTER you have completed your questions.

Day One: Review.

1. Vocabulary Review: Draw lines to match the word to the correct definition.

dignitaries   great interest or eager enthusiasm

litany   persons of high rank, popularity, or influence

stamina   a prayer where the leader reads phrases, allowing
                               for the congregation to respond

zeal   physical or moral endurance

2. Review of Psalms 63-72. Fill in the appropriate answer from the clues given below: (Scripture references are in parentheses at the end of the clue. Example (63) refers to Psalm 63, etc.)

MEMORY:
PSALM 73:22-26

DOWN

2. Your _____ is better than life. (63)
3. Let God arise, Let His enemies be
   _____. (68)
4. Make _____, O God, to deliver me!
   (70)
5. Now also when I am old and _____,
   O God, do not forsake me. (71)
7. Praise is awaiting You, O God, in
   _____. (65)

ACROSS

1. Because _____ for your house has eaten me up. (69)
6. The arrows used by David's enemies _____ _____. (64)
8. What the people must do for the earth to "yield her increase" _____ _____. (67)
9. Blessed be the Lord God, the God of Israel, Who only does _____ things. (72)

135

Day Two: Read Psalm 73.

1. Read verses 1-3. What almost made the psalmist "slip"? _____

_____

2. What verses describe the appearance and actions of the wicked? _____

_____

3. At what point did the psalmist get his thinking corrected?_____

_____

4. Read verses 18-27 and then pick the best summary of their content from the sentences below.

   a) Even though I cannot see it now, I know you will bring judgment on the wicked while you preserve and guide my life.

   b) I give up. I have no where to turn. I have wasted my life. I will join the wicked.

   c) It was all a dream. Really this world is okay. People are all basically good.

5. From verse 28, write down what the psalmist decided he would do. _____

_____

Day Three: Read Psalm 74 and 2 Kings 25.

1. Psalm 74 seems to fit best at a time when Israel had just been defeated by the army of Babylon (also called Chaldeans). From Psalm 74:1-8, how much damage had the area sustained?

_____

_____

2. From 74:9-11, summarize what troubled them about God. _____

_____

_____

3. From verses 12-17, what had God done for them before? _____

_____

_____

4. If the problem was not with God -- He never loses His power -- the problem must have been with Israel. On what basis did they appeal for God's help anyway? Use verses 8-23.

_____

Day Four: Read Psalms 75, 76 and 77.   MEMORY: PSALM 75:1

1. From Psalm 75, what event does this psalm describe?

   a) the Crucifixion   b) the Last Judgment   c) the Second Chance

2. According to Psalm 75, when will this occur?

   a) when the fat lady sings   b) when God chooses the proper time   c) after the third trumpet blast

3. How will the earth be affected?

   a) it won't be   b) it will become new   c) it will be dissolved

4. What will God not tolerate forever?

   a) boastfulness and wickedness   b) lazy Christians   c) animals with horns

5. Read Psalm 76. In verse 1, what do Judah, Salem, and Zion have in common? _____

   _____

   _____

6. What are some of the reasons given for fearing the Lord? _____

   _____

   _____

7. Read Psalm 77.

   a) One word, or a form of it, is repeated five times in 77:1-12. What is it? _____

   b) What did this cause the writer to feel or think?_____

   _____

   c) Read verses 16-20. What event was the psalmist remembering here? _____

   _____

Day Five: Read Psalm 78.

1. Read Psalm 78:1-8. Why is it important to carefully teach children about God?_____

   _____

   _____

2. Read through the rest of this psalm carefully and write down a few examples for each of the categories below: (Give verse numbers.)

   a) God's miracles in Israel's behalf. _____

   _____

   _____

   b) Israel's sins in spite of God's help: _____

   _____

   _____

   c) God's patience and mercy with Israel:_____

   _____

   _____

3. Write down your favorite verse(s) from Psalm 78. _____

   _____

4. Now take a few minutes and read the notes for this lesson.

Notes

God Is in Charge   (Psalms 73-78)

A New Author

Asaph, founder of one of the temple choirs (1 Chronicles 25:1), was credited in the small print before each of the psalms of this section with being the author of them. Asaph was a contemporary of David and evidently was gifted by God to take a leadership role in praise and worship. Psalm 74, however, seems to cover an historical period after Asaph and David's time, and so perhaps Asaph's "school" of music produced this one, but gave the credit to Asaph as the original leader.

Temporarily Discouraged (Psalm 73)

This psalm does not hide its theme, but introduces it in the opening verses: *"Truly God is good to Israel,...But as for me, my feet had almost stumbled;...for I was envious of the boastful, when I saw the prosperity of the wicked."* The writer experienced what so many Christians have—frustration and discouragement at seeing people who hated God seeming to continue in a very happy life with no penalties for their wickedness. "What's the use?" the psalmist felt, if following God did not bring more immediate advantages to the godly than to the heathen. He observed that the wicked seemed to escape trouble (5) and have so much food that *"their eyes bulge with abundance"* (7). In contrast, the godly psalmist seemed to have cleansed his *"heart in vain...For all day long I have been plagued..."* (13,14). But, when he *"went into the sanctuary of God...[he] understood their end"* (17). They would indeed face God's judgment (18-20) while the godly would be safely held, guided, and received by God Himself in glory (21-24). "It's all worth it then," the psalmist must have decided about saying "no" to self and worldly sins to please God. He made a new commitment: *"I have put my trust in the Lord God, that I may declare all Your works."*

If the history of Israel from Solomon's rule up to the time of the destruction of the temple were reviewed, it would quickly be apparent that God had sent many, many prophets to warn the nation that her continual disobedience and disregard of God's covenant laws would not go unpunished forever.

Complaining, Yet Believing (Psalm 74)

This psalm was most likely written after the destruction of Solomon's temple by the army of Babylon in 2 Kings 25. The writer described the utter desolation of the once wonderfully beautiful structure (1-8). The shock was that God had not intervened to stop the attack (9-11) as He had so many other times in Israel's history (12-15). The very fact that there were still orderly patterns of night and day and the seasonal changes of summer and winter were evidence that Creator God was still in control (16-17), so why did He not help now?

If the history of Israel from Solomon's rule up to the time of the destruction of the temple were reviewed, it would quickly be apparent that God had sent many, many prophets to warn the nation that her continual disobedience and disregard of God's covenant laws would not go unpunished forever. He had repeatedly warned Israel, and then actually announced through Jeremiah that it was too late. He told them all to surrender, take their punishment, and one day He would let them return, with their land and structures spared. But they stubbornly refused and tried to fight the Babylonians, lost miserably, saw their leaders abused or executed, and witnessed the *demolition* of their holy place and cities. The psalmist spoke correctly when he said, *"There is no longer any prophet; nor is there any among us who knows how long"* (9). God had told them, but they were not familiar with Scripture. It would take Daniel, a godly captive in Babylon, many years later, to discover the truth and pray to God to let them return to Israel from Babylon.

| demolition -destruction |

"Have respect to the covenant," the psalmist cried (20), and God always does. He keeps His word to us when we are His, even when we fail to keep ours. Israel would be punished, but He would one day allow a *remnant* to return. Godly men like Ezra and Nehemiah would lead the efforts to rebuild what was lost, but it would not be done easily. Obedience to God is not something believers should turn on and off. Like a caring father, God always follows disobedience with discipline, and severe discipline will follow disobedience where there has not been repentance.

| remnant -a part, quantity or number remaining |

> *Obedience to God is not something believers should turn on and off. Like a caring father, God always follows disobedience with discipline, and severe discipline will follow disobedience where there has not been repentance.*

God Is Judge (Psalm 75)

In Psalm 73 the writer had wondered when God would judge the wicked, and in Psalm 74 the writer had wondered why God was already punishing Israel. This psalm described God's final judgment and pointed out that the righteous, those in covenant with God, will not face His fury, but the wicked and boastfully unrepentant people will. They will have to drink the *"fully mixed"* cup of wrath, right down to the *dregs* (6-8). God is now and has always been in charge. He will return as judge at the *"proper time"* and it will be quite dramatic because then *"the earth and all its inhabitants"* will be dissolved (2,3). When some claim that God will never judge this world, they are in error. 2 Peter 3:9 explained the delay: *"The Lord is not slack concerning His promise [of judgment], as some count slackness, but is longsuffering toward us, not willing that any should perish but that all should come to repentance."* Mercifully, God has not appeared as judge yet, wanting more people to repent and accept forgiveness through the blood of Christ, but He will finally return. Then, forever, *"the horns of the wicked"* will be cut off while the *"horns of the righteous shall be exalted"* (10).

| dregs -the sediment at the bottom of a liquor container; grounds, as in coffee |

| slack -slow, delayed |

Glorious and Excellent (Psalm 76)

This psalm seemed to celebrate a victory that God had brought to Israel. In 2 Kings 19:35-37 one such dramatic victory was recorded: *"And it came to pass on a certain night that the angel of the Lord went out, and killed in the* camp of the Assyrians one hundred and eighty-five thousand; and when people arose early in the morning, there were the corpses, all dead....." Verse 4-6 of Psalm 76 described such an event: "The stouthearted were plundered...And none of the mighty men have found the use of their hands, at Your rebuke, O God of Jacob, both the chariot and horse were cast into a dead sleep." This psalm praised the greatness of God and boasted: "Surely the wrath of man shall praise You." This meant that God can take the worst that man can do, and transform it for His use and His glory. The greatest example of this, of course, was at the Cross.

When you are troubled, stop counting your problems and start cheering God's power. He does care and will help. Praise Him while you wait.

A Change of Tune (Psalm 77)

If you have ever been troubled by sickness or worry, this psalm has some advice that might help you. At first, the writer was miserable, unable to sleep and too upset to even speak (4). Thoughts of God troubled him, as revealed by six questions he asked that voiced his doubts about God's ability or willingness to help (7-9). However, he suddenly made a decision that changed the tune of this psalm from one of self-pity to praise. Later, in the New Testament, Paul would describe this choice as *"bringing every thought into captivity to the obedience of Christ"* (2 Corinthians 10:5). The psalmist seemed determined to forget his troubles and think only about the great and good things that God had already done. The remainder of the psalm was a series of statements about the awesome power of God on behalf of Israel and in nature. The moral? When you are troubled, stop counting your problems and start cheering God's power. He does care and will help. Praise Him while you wait.

A Lesson to Teach (Psalm 78)

chronicled -recorded events in the order of time; wrote the history

This psalm, which is the second longest in the Psalter, gave a thousand-year history lesson to Israel. From Zoan, Egypt, to Zion, Israel, it **chronicled** God's miraculous care of Israel and Israel's repeated disobedience and ingratitude toward God. The purpose of the historical overview was given in the opening sections: *"For He...appointed a law in Israel, which He commanded our fathers, that they should make them known to their children; that the generation to come might know them...that they may set their hope in God, and not forget the works of God, but keep His commandments; and may not be like their fathers, ...a generation that did not set its heart aright..."* (5-8). The following events of Israel's history were described:

> (9-11) The cowardice of the tribe of Ephraim

> (12-16) The exodus from Egypt

> (17-55) The forty years in the wilderness

> (56-64) The years of the conquest and settlement of Canaan

> (65-72) The beginning of Israel as a kingdom

After reading this long psalm we need to ask ourselves, "Have we learned anything from the sins of Israel recorded here or the sins of our nation recorded in modern history?" Psalm 78 revealed that there are painful consequences for rebellious decisions made by God's people. God does not hide the unconfessed sins or embarrassing conduct of His children. Yet, in spite of their failure and faithlessness, God continues to be faithful. He disciplines them, sometimes severely, but He still longs for their return and an opportunity to show mercy and forgiveness. Let us learn from this history lesson and not be forced to re-learn its lessons ourselves.

God does not hide the unconfessed sins or embarrassing conduct of His children. Yet, in spite of their failure and faithlessness, God continues to be faithful.

 LESSON 17

Questions

Study Procedure: Read the Scripture references before answering questions. Unless otherwise instructed, use only the Bible in answering questions. Some questions may be more difficult than others but try to answer as many as you can. Pray for God's wisdom and understanding as you study and don't be discouraged if some answers are not obvious at first. Do not read the study notes for this lesson until AFTER you have completed your questions.

Day One: Vocabulary Review: Choose the best definition of each word.

_____1. demolition   a) an army squadron   b) a demonstration   c) destruction

_____2. remnant   a) the part that remains b) a traitor c) one who rents land

_____3. dregs   a) dirty kegs   b) the sediment at the bottom of a liquor container
c) lowest position on a job

_____4. slack   a) half a pair of trousers   b) stupid   c) slow, delayed

_____5. chronicled   a) wrote the history   b) checked the time   c) crowned the king

Review of Psalms 72-78. Matching:

_____ 6. Who was credited with writing these psalms?

_____ 7. Which psalm described the destruction of the temple by enemy invaders?

_____ 8. Which psalm discussed the troubling observation that the wicked seem to get away with their evil without punishment?

_____ 9. Which psalm described the judgment of the world by God?

_____10. Which psalm emphasized the importance of teaching children about God?

a. Ps. 78   b. Ps. 75   c. Asaph   d. Ps. 73   e. Ps. 74

Day Two: Read Psalms 79 and 80.

1. Between 597 and 587 B.C. the Babylonians conquered the southern kingdom of Israel called Judah and destroyed its capital in Jerusalem. From verses 1-4, describe just how awful the situation had become, according to the writer of this psalm.

_____

_____

_____

2. What verses indicated that the people of Judah saw the Babylonian invasion as a judgment from God? _____

3. On what grounds did the writer of this psalm ask for help and forgiveness for his nation?

_____

_____

_____

4. Read the following "Parable of the Vine" from Isaiah 5:1-7:

   5:1 Now let me sing to my Well-beloved a song of my Beloved regarding His vineyard: My Well-beloved has a vineyard on a very fruitful hill.

   2 He dug it up and cleared out its stones, and planted it with the choicest vine. He built a tower in its midst, and also made a winepress in it; so He expected it to bring forth good grapes, but it brought forth wild grapes.

   3 "And now, O inhabitants of Jerusalem and men of Judah, Judge, please, between Me and My vineyard.

   4 What more could have been done to My vineyard that I have not done in it? Why then, when I expected it to bring forth good grapes, did it bring forth wild grapes?

   5 And now, please let Me tell you what I will do to My vineyard: I will take away its hedge, and it shall be burned; and break down its wall, and it shall be trampled down.

   6 I will lay it waste; it shall not be pruned or dug, but there shall come up briers and thorns. I will also command the clouds that they rain no rain on it."

   7 For the vineyard of the Lord of hosts is the house of Israel, and the men of Judah are His pleasant plant. He looked for justice, but behold, oppression; for righteousness, but behold, a cry for help.

   Now read Psalm 80. What is the answer to the question the writer of the psalm asked God in verse 12? _____

   _____

   _____

   _____

5. Since psalms were meant to be sung, it should not be unusual to find a repeating "chorus" in Psalm 80 that described the writer's main request. What verses formed the repeating chorus and what were the words to it? _____

   _____

Day Three: Read Psalms 81, 82, and 83.

1. In Psalm 81, God described the judges or leaders as "gods." This word in Hebrew was *elohim*, or mighty ones, and was a common name for the one true God. Pick one of the following answers that best explains why leaders might have been called "gods" by God in this psalm.

   a) They needed an important title to get everyone's attention and obedience.

   b) They were to act in God's place in earthly matters of justice, but were to keep in mind that God was their final authority.

   c) God didn't want them to be different from other countries where many smaller gods were worshiped.

   d) None of the above. Here is my answer: _____

2. Think about this: ever since Cain killed Abel, violence, hate, and just plain meanness have existed among people. However, this psalm pointed out that the problem in Israel, as in our own nation, was that something had happened "at the top" of the civil order that caused evil to grow worse instead of being contained. What was it? _____

   _____

3. Read Psalm 83. Israel has suffered persecution from other nations since its beginning. What verse or verses from this psalm described just how much Israel was hated? _____

4. What did the psalmist want from God? _____

_____

Day Four: Read Psalms 84 and 85.

MEMORY: PSALM 84:1-2, 10-12

1. In Psalm 84, the joyful worshiper spoke out three "beatitudes" or "blessed" statements. Find them and write them out below, noting their verse numbers.

   a) Blessed are those who _____

   b) Blessed is the man whose _____

   c) Blessed is the man who _____

2. The writer of Psalm 84 was on his way, wanting to begin, or remembering fondly a pilgrimage to the tabernacle in Jerusalem. Find out what a *pilgrimage* was and write out the definition or explanation. _____

_____

3. Pick out your favorite descriptive phrase or verse from Psalm 84. _____

_____

_____

4. Read Psalm 85. This psalm might have celebrated the Jewish return to Israel after her seventy-year captivity in Babylon, but it could also be a prophecy of a future time of final peace for Israel. In the space below, write down the verses that could describe the feelings of people returning after captivity and those that could describe the state of things when all war is finally at an end and Jesus has returned to rule. Some verses might be used both places.

   Return from captivity: _____

   Return of the Lord: _____

Day Five: Read Psalms 86 and 87.

MEMORY: PSALM 86:15

1. Psalm 86 is the only psalm in this lesson thought to be written by David. It is a personal prayer for help, full of specific requests and marvelous expressions of praise.

   a) Briefly summarize several of David's requests. Give verses. _____

_____

_____

   b) Quote below at least three verses in which God is praised. _____

_____

_____

_____

2. David prayed in verse 11, *"Unite my heart to fear Your name."* Write down below some of the things that threaten "to divide" your heart and stop you from serving God completely and consistently. _____

_____

_____

3. Read Psalm 87 and then read the following verses. Zion or Mt. Zion is associated with what important city in Israel? _____

1 Kings 8:1: *Now Solomon assembled the elders of Israel and all the heads of the tribes, the chief fathers of the children of Israel, to King Solomon in Jerusalem, that they might bring up the ark of the covenant of the Lord from the City of David, which is Zion.*

2 Kings 19:21: *"This is the word which the Lord has spoken concerning him: The virgin, the daughter of Zion, has despised you, laughed you to scorn; the daughter of Jerusalem has shaken her head behind your back!*

2 Kings 19:31: *For out of Jerusalem shall go a remnant, and those who escape from Mount Zion. The zeal of the Lord of hosts will do this.*

4. From Psalm 87, how much does God care about Zion? _____

_____

5. Match the psalm from this lesson with an appropriate theme.

_____ Ps. 79   _____ Ps. 80   _____ Ps. 81   _____ Ps. 82   _____ Ps. 83   _____ Ps. 84   _____ Ps. 85   _____ Ps. 86   _____ Ps. 87

a) Our nation used to have your protection. Why have you removed it? Restore it again.

b) Israel wouldn't do things God's way, so He left them to suffer the consequences of their own stubborn hearts. However, He longed to bless and help them.

c) I have so many personal needs. Please help me. I love You! Help me follow You better than I have in the past.

d) Our enemies have ruined Jerusalem and have not even let us bury our dead! Please help us and give us another chance to obey.

e) You have failed to be the leaders I called you to be. Your judgment will come.

f) Someday the world will know worldwide goodness—when mercy and truth meet and righteousness kisses peace.

g) Zion is God's favorite city and He will watch over her.

h) I long to worship in Your tabernacle, to stay always in Your presence!

i) We have so many enemies! They have consulted together and formed a confederacy in hopes of destroying all of us. Please stop them, O Lord! For our sakes and Yours!

6. Take a few minutes and read the notes for this lesson.

Notes

The Uniqueness of Israel   (Psalms 79-87)

Always in the News

Have you noticed how often Israel is mentioned in the daily news media? Though a very small country, less than 200 miles long and 60 miles wide, with a population of about 4 million people, it is central to most world affairs. God called it the *"apple of His eye"* and made promises concerning its boundaries and capital city Jerusalem that still wait to be fulfilled. How did that nation start? Back in Genesis 12, God called a man named Abram to follow His directions and leave the established civilization he had known in Ur of the Chaldees (present day Iraq) to travel to another land several hundred miles to the west, bordering the Mediterranean Sea. Why did God pick Abram? Abram was a man who evidently had faith in the one true God, but there were certainly others elsewhere who did, too. God picked Abram because God could pick any one He wanted—He started with Abram and fulfilled His plan to use his descendants to "grow" a nation to whom He could show His covenant love, power, guidance, and future plans. That nation, in turn, would be responsible for taking the light of God's truth to the whole world.

Through them we have the Bible, our Messiah Jesus, and our place in God's family. God has blessings for all who are His, but Israel has some special promises that are set aside for her alone.

Israel has always been unique, set apart from other nations. While every Israelite has not loved and obeyed God, a remnant always has and through that group, God will bring to pass every promise that He has made to that nation. We must not be jealous of Israel. Through them we have the Bible, our Messiah Jesus, and our place in God's family. God has blessings for all who are His, but Israel has some special promises that are set aside for her alone.

It Happened as God Had Warned! (Psalm 79)

Psalm 79 was written after the Babylonians had overwhelmed Jerusalem, destroyed the temple, and slaughtered many people: *"The dead bodies of Your servants they have given as food for the birds of the heavens….We have become a reproach to our neighbors ….How long, Lord? Will You be angry forever?"* (2-5). Israel knew that if God had not protected them from their enemies this time, as He had so many times before, then God was angry with them—because He was certainly still able to have stopped the attack. For years Israel, or more accurately, Judah, the southern part of the nation—the northern part had already been conquered—had ignored the prophets whom God had sent and refused to repent and return in obedience to God's will [See Jeremiah 16:1-21]. The Babylonian attack and period of captivity were punishment for that refusal. *"Oh, do not remember former iniquities against us! Let Your tender mercies come speedily to meet us"* (8). When caught in sin, we want quick forgiveness and great mercy, too. We do not want to bear the

146

consequences of our sins. God, in His mercy, does forgive, but sometimes for our discipline, like Israel's, we must live through the results of what our choices have brought about. On the basis of the covenant—*"For Your name's sake"*—the psalmist asked God to help them, promising that this time they would give Him *"thanks forever"* (13), and then adding this bold promise, as well: *"We will show forth Your praise to all generations."* After seventy years in captivity, God did allow them to return to their own land.

Two Pictures of Israel (Psalm 80)

The opening line of this psalm called to God as the *"Shepherd of Israel."* One of the common descriptions of Israel was as God's "flock." The mention of God's dwelling between the cherubim was a reference to the two golden cherubim that appeared on the top of the ark's cover, the mercy seat. God's presence was described as dwelling there in a special way. Continuing the imagery of the ark, three tribes were named. These were the ones that always followed the ark of the covenant when it was carried in the wilderness: Ephraim, Benjamin, and Manasseh (Numbers 2:17-24).

This psalm must have been written at a time when Israel had suffered at the hands of enemies. As in songs today, it had a refrain or chorus which revealed its main thought: *"Restore us, O God of hosts, cause Your face to shine, and we shall be saved"* (3, 4, 19). The last half of the psalm (8-19) made reference to the other commonly used symbol for Israel—God's own vine, hand planted in His vineyard. This vine had been brought *"out of Egypt"* (8), carefully planted in Canaan from where it *"filled the land"* (9). The psalmist then asked, *"Why have You broken down her hedges"*—her barrier of security? (12). A beautiful, protected, nurtured vine that would not produce fruit for its owner (Isaiah 5:1-2) or whose trusted keepers would not obey the owner (Matthew 21:33-46) would not be allowed to take up space forever. Judgment had fallen on Israel for her fruitlessness and lack of obedience to God. The "root" of that vine, however, would bring forth growth again.

"Built-In" Reminders (Psalm 81)

The opening verses of this psalm were a call to worship for Israel. Seven holy events were to be remembered each year by God's people [See Leviticus 23]. Psalm 81 is thought to be a call to observe the Feast of Tabernacles, a seven-day period in which the nation was to gather in Jerusalem and "camp out," making temporary houses with branches, to remember the years God had taken care of them in the wilderness. It was a time for celebrating God's help in removing Israel's *"shoulder from the burden"* and hands from *"the baskets"* (6) of Egypt. The psalmist did not, however, leave out Israel's ungrateful response to God's help. Their grumbling over the water at Meribah (7) and their ignoring God's specific commandment to stay

When caught in sin, we want quick forgiveness and great mercy, too. We do not want to bear the consequences of our sins. God, in His mercy, does forgive, but sometimes for our discipline, like Israel's, we must live through the results of what our choices have brought about.

away from false gods (8-12) were mentioned. God had wanted to help and protect them, to feed them *"with the finest of wheat"* and to satisfy them with *"honey from the rock,"* but their rebellion against Him left Him no choice but to give *"them over to their own stubborn heart, to walk in their own counsels"* (12). G. Campbell Morgan, in his **exposition** of the Bible, commented on God's discipline this way: "It reveals a constant method of God with His disloyal and disobedient children. When they will not go His way, He lets them go their way. But this does not mean that He abandons them. It is rather that He permits them to learn by the bitter results of their own folly what He would have had them know by communion with Himself. How constantly the people of God have gone after the stubbornness of their own hearts only to find sorrow and anguish; and yet how constantly through that experience they have learned the perfection of the Divine way! This is so, because He is the God of all grace. Nevertheless, His choice for us is that we should **hearken** to Him, and so be saved, not merely through the bitterness of failure, but from it." Israel missed many blessings God had intended for them through unbelief and disobedience. Sadly, so have we.

> **exposition** -a commentary or interpretation

> **hearken** -listen carefully

When Leaders Fail (Psalm 82)

Like modern nations, ancient Israel had problems caused by ungodly leadership. Psalm 82 described how seriously God deals with evil in high places: *"He judges among the gods, how long will you judge unjustly, and show partiality to the wicked?"* The psalmist called the judges *"gods"* (1) and the children of the Most High *"gods"* (6). This word was *elohim* in Hebrew, and meant "mighty ones." It shocks us as we read it because it was also one of the names used for God. However, judges could be described as taking God's place, as those chosen to carry out His will on earth, and in that way of thinking the term was used here. Yet, how far from "gods" are so many who hold judgeships or exercise other legal authority today!--*"They do not know, nor do they understand; they walk about in darkness; all the foundations of the earth are unstable"* (5). When leadership does not lead people in the ways and will of God, then a whole nation can perish. How tragic is it? J. Vernon McGee, a longtime radio Bible teacher, illustrated the damage caused by bad leadership with this story: "What's worse than going to hell? The answer given by a great preacher in the South years ago was this: To go to hell and recognize the voice of your son and ask, 'Son, what are you doing here?' and hear him answer, 'Dad, I followed you!'" Where are you leading others?

> *Like modern nations, ancient Israel had problems caused by ungodly leadership.*

Persecuted (Psalm 83)

There has never been a very long period in Israel's history when it was not persecuted. Through Israel God gave the covenant, the Scriptures, and the Messiah, and so Satan has always stirred up hatred against Israel. Her Arab enemies today could be quoted as saying the same things spoken in this psalm long ago: *"Come and let us cut them off from being a nation, that the name of Israel may be remembered no more"* (4). In verses 5-12 a list of Israel's past enemies and God's dealings with them were given. The psalmist asked God for help to survive the persecution and overcome the attacks. The result of God's keeping His promises to Israel and letting them outlive all their enemies will be *"That they* [all those who hate Israel now] *may know You, whose name alone is the Lord...the Most High over all the earth."* Paul pointed this out in Romans 9-11 when he explained that God's faithfulness to Israel proves that God is righteous and to be trusted. Just as He kept and will fulfill every promise to Israel, He can be relied upon to keep every promise to us.

There has never been a very long period in Israel's history when it was not persecuted.

The Temple (Psalm 84)

For Israel, the tabernacle, and later the temple, at Jerusalem was the center for right worship. The writer of this psalm was familiar with its beauty, having even noticed the birds who nested in its supporting structure (3). To him, there was no better place to be than in that holy setting: *"For a day in Your courts is better than a thousand. I would rather be a doorkeeper in the house of my God than dwell in the tents of wickedness"* (10). How enthusiastic are you about spending time in God's presence?

The Past Gives a Glimpse of the Future (Psalm 85)

This psalm speaks gratefully to God for a recent deliverance. It could have been after the Babylonian captivity when, although glad to have returned, the people still faced much work and needed God's continued help: *"Restore us, O God of our salvation...Will You not revive us again, that Your people may rejoice in You?"* (4-6). However, if you really think about it, we could all sing this daily. He has always "just" delivered us from something, and we continually face difficult tasks of rebuilding certain areas of our lives. Yet for lasting change, like the psalmist, we must make up our mind to really listen to God and not go back to our old ways: *"I will hear what God the Lord will speak, for He will speak peace to His people and to His saints; but let them not turn back to folly..."* (8).

He has always "just" delivered us from something, and we continually face difficult tasks of rebuilding certain areas of our lives.

The last verses (10-13) described the hope of a brighter day for Israel : *"Mercy and truth have met together; righteousness and peace have kissed."* When Jesus came as Messiah, He made this happen. His presence revealed the truth about human sin, yet His mercy covered it forever. The righteousness of God required the sinner to be judged—yet Jesus took our place and gave us peace. However, many see in these last verses some future promises for the actual nation of Israel. At the Second Coming of Christ, the world will be set in its right order, and Israel will experience God's ultimate blessing: *"Yes, the Lord will give what is good; and our land will yield its increase. Righteousness will go before Him, and shall make His footsteps our pathway."*

Undivided Heart (Psalm 86)

This is the only psalm attributed to David in this section of Psalms. It makes use of quotations from several other psalms as it appeals to God for help in personal matters. The pronoun "I" is used at least thirty times. God loves Israel, but He also loves the individual citizen. One of the most powerful requests made by David was in verse 11: *"Teach me Your way, O Lord; I will walk in Your truth; unite my heart to fear Your name."* How often do we have "divided" hearts? How often do other interests or urges pull us away from God's will for us in the present? Twila Paris, a Christian singer/song-writer wrote these lyrics:

> "There have been days when I would die for You—and days when I would not die to me. There have been nights when I would cry with You—for the sins of the world and the pain in the city, but some nights I cried only tears of self-pity. I need a love that will always endure. Give me a love that is simple and pure. Chorus: **Give me an undivided heart. Place a new spirit in me. Give me an undivided heart—that I may fear Your name. Undivided, undivided heart.**
> Lord, You have seen me giving all I'm worth, but only to find me taking more. There are those times when I embrace the earth, when I rise to the need and I welcome the labor. And then I must fight to forgive my own neighbor. I need a love that will always endure—give me a love that is simple and pure...."

How often do we have "divided" hearts? How often do other interests or urges pull us away from God's will for us in the present?

Like David, we must pray about our "divided" interests: *"Give Your strength to Your servant"* (16). God hears and delights to answer such prayer.

Jerusalem - Glorious Things of Thee Are Spoken! (Psalm 87)

We know that God loves the nation Israel, but did you know that He has a favorite city there? Psalm 87 revealed it: *"The Lord loves the gates of Zion more than all the dwellings of Jacob. Glorious things are spoken of you, O city of God!"* (2, 3). Zion was one of the hills or mounts on which Jerusalem was built and was often used interchangeably with the name of the city in the Psalms. Isaiah prophesied about Jerusalem's future in Isaiah 2:2: *"And it shall come to pass in the last days, that the mountain of the Lord's house shall be established in the top of the mountains, and shall be exalted above the hills; and all nations shall flow to it."* Perhaps that is why there will be such honor associated with being born as one of its citizens: *"The Lord will record, When He registers the peoples: 'This one was born there'"* (6).

Present-day Jerusalem is the scene of daily violence and hatred. But this psalm promises that one day all that will change.

Present-day Jerusalem is the scene of daily violence and hatred. But this psalm promises that one day all that will change. The hymn-writer John Newton, inspired by Psalm 86, wrote of Jerusalem:

"Glorious things of thee are spoken, Zion, city of our God.
He whose word cannot be broken formed thee for His own *abode*.
On the Rock of Ages founded, what can shake thy sure *repose*?
With salvation's walls surrounded, thou mayest smile at all thy foes!"

abode -dwelling place, home

repose -rest, lying back comfortably

One More Comment

Where is your citizenship? It's the "second" birth that counts! Although Israel is promised some specific things like eternal ownership of a particular part of planet earth that Gentiles are not, we are offered citizenship in the Jerusalem that is above—in heaven (Galatians 4:26). Through Christ, we can share in spiritual blessings with Israel, if not in the physical ones. It is important, in the present, to remember Israel's unique place in God's plan. We must pray for her to recognize her Messiah Jesus. (See Romans 11:11-15.) We must pray for the peace of Jerusalem. We must never be part of any persecution against her as a nation or against Jews as individuals. After all, if it weren't for God's plan for Israel, we would not have the Scriptures we treasure or the Messiah we love!

Although Israel is promised some specific things like eternal ownership of a particular part of planet earth that Gentiles are not, we are offered citizenship in the Jerusalem that is above--in heaven.

BIBLE QUEST

Questions

Study Procedure: Read the Scripture references before answering questions. Unless otherwise instructed, use only the Bible in answering questions. Some questions may be more difficult than others but try to answer as many as you can. Pray for God's wisdom and understanding as you study and don't be discouraged if some answers are not obvious at first. Do not read the study notes for this lesson until AFTER you have completed your questions.

Day One

1. Vocabulary Review: Scan the notes for the words that these sentences define.

   a) _____ rest, lying back comfortably

   b) _____ dwelling place, home

   c) _____ a commentary or interpretation

   d) _____ to listen carefully

2. Review of Psalms 79-87: Locate and record the references for these quotations.

_____a) "You have brought a vine out of Egypt; You have cast out the nations, and planted it."

_____b) "But My people would not heed My voice. . . So I gave them over to their own stubborn heart, to walk in their own counsels."

_____c) "They have said, 'Come, and let us cut them off from being a nation. . .'"

_____d) ". . . I would rather be a doorkeeper in the house of my God than dwell in the tents of wickedness."

_____e) ". . . Unite my heart to fear Your name."

_____f) "Mercy and truth have met together; righteousness and peace have kissed."

_____g) "Oh, do not remember former iniquities against us! . . . For we have been brought very low."

_____h) "I said, 'You are gods . . . but you shall die like men.'"

_____i) "Glorious things are spoken of you, O city of God!"

Day Two: Read Psalms 88 and 89.

1. In the "small print" above each of these two psalms, find the names of the two authors called "Ezrahites" who served in the ministry of music for King David. Write their names here:

   _____

2. In Psalm 88, Heman was probably in his later years and suffering from a very serious physical illness. From verses 1-9, describe how he was feeling._____

   _____

   _____

   _____

3. Even though Heman did not find relief from his situation, he at least continued throughout Psalm 88 to call on his covenant God, with the name LORD, a translation of the Hebrew *Jahweh* or *Jehovah*. He evidently believed that his covenant LORD would deliver him through his suffering or from his suffering. Find the verses where LORD was used and write the verse numbers here.

_____

4. Read Psalm 89 again and match the following sections with a theme below.

_____a) A description of the blessings of the covenant God had made with David.

_____b) An explanation of the consequences of dishonoring the covenant made with David.

_____c) A complaint about the nation's present condition.

_____d) A request for mercy and forgiveness for the nation.

_____e) Praises to God from whom all blessings flowed.

MEMORY: PSALM 90:4, 12; 91:1-2, 11

Day Three: Read Psalms 90 and 91.

1. Psalm 90 was written by Moses, which makes this psalm the oldest in the book of Psalms. Read the psalm and then select <u>one</u> of the phases of Moses' life listed below which you think Psalm 90 described. Defend your choice with verses from the psalm.

a) His first forty years growing up in Egypt in Pharaoh's house. (vs. _____)

b) His forty years as a shepherd for his father-in-law in Midian. (vs. _____)

c) His forty years as leader of the children of Israel in the wilderness. (vs._____)

2. Using phrases from Psalm 90, contrast the length of God's existence with man's.

                 God   Man

_____

_____

3. Beginning with verse 12, list some of the things Moses asked God to do for Israel that you think would help you, your family, or your nation._____

_____

_____

4. According to Psalm 91, there are many benefits for the person who "dwells" in God's presence. Beside the following benefits, write down the verses from which they come.

a) safety and security _____

b) no fear _____

c) protection from evil and illnesses _____

d) help from angels _____

e) answered prayer _____

f) honor _____

g) satisfaction _____

h) salvation _____

MEMORY: PSALM 92:1-2; 93:1-2

Day Four: Read Psalms 92, 93 and 94.

1. One of the ways we "abide" with God is to keep our mind on Him by praising Him frequently and joyfully. For what does this psalmist praise God in the following verses?

   a) v. 2 _____

   b) v. 5 _____

   c) v. 8 _____

   d) v. 9 _____

   e) v. 15 _____

2. Put in your own words what, according to Psalm 92, must be done to "bear fruit in old age" and to remain "fresh and flourishing." _____

   _____

   _____

   _____

3. Read Psalm 93 carefully. What did the writer of this short psalm of praise ask God to do for him or his nation?

   a) Give them new clothes.

   b) Build a new throne for their king.

   c) Stop the flooding.

   d) Do nothing for him personally. It is a psalm of pure praise.

4. According to Psalm 94:1-7, the enemies of Israel did not think Israel's God was aware of what had been done to His people. What verses explained that God was very aware of everything?

   _____

5. Two questions were asked by the psalmist in verse 16: *"Who will rise up for me against the evildoers? Who will stand up for me against the workers of iniquity?"* From the remaining verses in Psalm 94, find the answer(s) to those questions and write them below.

   _____

   _____

   _____

MEMORY: PSALM 95:1-2, 6-7

Day Five: Read Psalms 95 and 96.

1. A really experienced "worship warrior" must have written Psalm 95!

   a) Which verses encouraged enthusiastic praise and why? _____

   _____

b) Which verses called for humility in worship? _____

c) Which verses warned of the dangers of not learning from past mistakes? _____

2. Read Psalm 96. From verses 1-10, find the phrases that encouraged worldwide praise for the greatness of God. Write them below along with their verse numbers. _____

_____

_____

_____

3. Such worldwide human praise will be joined by the rejoicing of the earth itself, when Christ returns to *"judge the world with righteousness."* From 11-13, list the specific parts of the natural world that were mentioned as participating in that praise. _____

_____

4. The coming of the Lord will mean joy for those who love Him but what will it bring for those who don't? _____

5. Does that information motivate you to act in some way? _____

_____

_____

_____

6. Now take a few minutes and read the notes for this lesson.

Notes

We Can Have God's Help   (Psalms 88-96)

Long-Term Praying (Psalm 88)

This psalm and Psalm 89 were written by two singers during David's time who were known for being very wise. [See 1 Chronicles 15:19 and 1 Kings 4:31.] The one named Heman, who was credited with Psalm 88, was evidently seriously ill and cried for God's help: *"For my soul is full of troubles, and my life draws near to the grave"*(3). How bad did he feel?—Like a dead man being buried (3-5), like a man pushed overboard being pounded with waves (6, 7), and like a man so wasted with illness that his friends could not stand to be around him (8, 9). He felt helpless, alone, and abandoned. He wondered out loud how his death could honor God: *"...Shall the dead arise and praise You? Shall your lovingkindness be declared in the grave?"* There was no answer from God or healing from heaven, and yet Heman kept praying. There was real **anguish** in his cries; he blamed God for his pain: *"Lord, why do You cast off my soul?...I suffer Your terrors; ...They came around me all day long like water..."*(13-18).

There was no answer from God or healing from heaven, and yet Heman kept praying.

anguish -great suffering from worry, grief, or pain

Is it all right to blame God—after all He could stop our pain, couldn't He? When a person is suffering terribly, he finds relief in speaking out his thoughts and fears, even when his reasoning is faulty and vision clouded. God can take it. He is strong. He allows us to vent our frustrations in prayer and air our **grievances**. The very fact that Heman prayed to God without seeing any immediate answer showed faith. Heman called God "Lord," which in Hebrew was *Jehovah*, the Covenant-Keeper. Like Job he knew that, even if the help he wanted was delayed or refused, he had nowhere else to go and no one else upon whom to call who could be more faithful than the Lord. So, the lesson for us is to continue to pray—regardless of the lack of evidence that we are being heard—because God has promised to hear and can be trusted to work things out for our good in His own perfect time.

> **grievances** -complaints of unfair treatment

> *Like Job, he knew that even if the help he wanted was delayed or refused, he had no where else to go and no one else upon whom to call who could be more faithful than the Lord.*

God Keeps His Promises (Psalm 89)

Ethan wrote this psalm and it revealed his knowledge of history. Ethan praised God for the covenant made with David (1-4), for the creative and controlling power at work in the universe (5-13), and for God's moral goodness and mercy shown to His people (14-18). But he placed special emphasis on God's covenant with David. [2 Samuel 7:7-17.] God had sworn to protect and help David, His anointed king, in the face of all enemies (19-23). He had promised a unique and eternal relationship with David: *"He shall cry to Me, 'You are my Father, My God, and the rock of my salvation,' also I will make him My firstborn, the Highest of the kings of the earth, My mercy I will keep for him forever, and My covenant shall stand firm with him, his seed also I will make to endure forever, and his throne as the days of heaven"* (24-29). However, Ethan also recorded, if any of David's sons did not walk in God's will and began to break His commandments, they would be punished severely by God. Yet His lovingkindness (covenant love from the Hebrew word *hesed*) would not "utterly" be taken *"from him...[David's] seed shall endure forever, and his throne as the sun before Me; it shall be established forever like the moon..."* (30-37).

It was at this point that Ethan changed tunes, so to speak. Although Ethan knew what God had done through David and in Solomon, Israel was presently suffering from the attacks of her enemies. To Ethan it appeared that God had gone back on His Word, His promise to David: *"You have renounced the covenant of Your servant...you have brought his strongholds to ruin...you have made all his enemies rejoice...and have not sustained him in the battle...You have covered him with shame"* (38-45).

This psalmist must have just witnessed the failure of Solomon's son Rehoboam (2 Chronicles 12:1-12), or some other descendant, to follow God's commands causing chaos in the nation. He cried, *"Lord, where are Your former lovingkindnesses, Which You swore to David in Your truth?"* (49). Even though many of David's descendants would fail to love and obey God and, consequently, would suffer God's punishment, His promise of continual blessing on the line of David would be fulfilled. As long as just one person of faith in David's line could be found—and there would always be some—God's word stood true. Poor Heman just had not lived long enough. The prince from David's line that would prove God true in every promise had not come yet. The Messiah would come, in spite of the failings of many, and God would be shown to be what He always has been—the God of all Truth, the Covenant-Keeper.

The prince from David's line that would prove God true in every promise had not come yet. The Messiah would come, in spite of the failings of many, and God would be shown to be what He always has been -- the God of all Truth, the Covenant-Keeper.

| **God Is Great Man Is Frail (Psalm 90)** | This is one of the psalms credited to Moses. He certainly knew the greatness of God: *"Even from everlasting to everlasting, You are God,"* as well as the **frailty** of man: *"You turn man to destruction [dust], and say, 'Return, O children of men"* (2, 3). God never has to worry about the clock: *"For* |

a thousand years in Your sight are like yesterday when it is past, and like a **watch** *in the night"* (4). In contrast, a human's life passes quickly, like a flash flood, a normal night's sleep, or grass that springs up quickly but withers in a few hours (5, 6).

Not only is life brief, but it is also full of sorrow, most of which is caused by human sin which requires God's judgment: *"You have set our iniquities before You, our secret sins in the light of Your countenance...for all our days have passed away in Your wrath..."* (7-9). Seventy years comprised the average lifespan, but even if ten more were added, they would be filled with *"labor and sorrow"* also. What was the remedy for such a short and miserable existence? Moses gave it in verse 12: *"Teach us to number our days, that we may gain a heart of wisdom."* Moses knew that if people realized that they needed to make everyday count, since life passed so quickly, they would spend their time obeying God and gaining His favor and blessing.

The good news of this psalm is that any person can start right now, no matter what age they are, to enjoy God's mercy. They can turn back to God and ask Him, as Moses did, to return his compassion and mercy to their lives. In verse 15, Moses boldly requested that God give them as many happy days as they had had *"afflicted"* ones. The final request, which can be ours today, too, was to let *"the beauty of the Lord"* be on their present lives and to let the work they were then doing last even after they were gone. The only way to have such work *"established"* (17) is to find out what God wants an individual to do and then do that with all his energies. Life is short and life can be painful, but it can also be **significant** if lived in line with God's will. That kind of living is satisfying for the individual as well as helpful to those who follow after.

frailty -weakness

watch -a definite period of time; Hebrew time was divided into "watches" which consisted of three hours each (see Judges 7:19)

significant -important, meaningful

The Greatest Dwelling Place (Psalm 91)

Many credit Moses with writing this beloved psalm. Vividly described here is the security of the one who "dwells" with God. That word implies more than an occasional Sunday visit. It means to live, to remain in God's presence. The one who dwells is one who can say, *"He is my refuge and my fortress"* (2). Dwelling requires first an awareness that God is good and that God wants to have us near Him so that we can look to Him for direction for our lives. Dwelling requires that we know Him and what pleases Him, knowledge that can only be gained by studying Scripture. Finally, it requires communication with Him through prayer that we might obey His plans for us.

Such nearness has benefits: *"Because you have made the Lord...your dwelling place"* you will have deliverance from evil, disease, lies, fear, and violence (3-10) while you enjoy angelic protection (12, 13). When we respond in love to God's love for us, He really blesses us. He will answer our prayers, help us in trouble, satisfy us with long life, and show us His salvation. Dwelling with God brings all these blessings. Do you need to change your address?

This is a psalm of pure praise—there is not a personal request in the whole thing! Every line causes the reader or listener to look up at a great God.

It Is Good to Give Thanks (Psalm 92)

This psalm was written to be used in the Sabbath service. With great energy and full musical accompaniment the people were encouraged to give thanks to God, morning and evening (1-4). The foolish or wicked person cannot know this joy in the Lord (6, 7). In God's presence the wicked just scatter or perish (8, 9) while the godly are promoted and freshly inspired (10). Like a healthy and beautiful tree, *"the righteous shall flourish"* and *"shall still bear fruit in old age,"* with energy enough to *"declare that the Lord is upright...and there is no unrighteousness in Him"* (12-15).

Evildoers continued their dirty work on God's people thinking that "the Lord does not see, nor does the God of Jacob understand." However, the psalmist knew better; God's delay was not denial . . .

Look Up! (Psalm 93)

This is a psalm of pure praise—there is not a personal request in the whole thing! Every line causes the reader or listener to look up at a great God. He *"reigns, clothed with majesty,...girded...with strength"* (1). A flood may rage below His throne, but He is unmoved because the *"Lord on high is mightier than the noise of many waters"* (2-4). As secure as His throne is the truth of His Word. Holiness "adorns" His dwelling. Praise Him!

Delay Is Not Denial (Psalm 94)

This psalm revealed the bold faith of the writer that God would help his nation. Secure that God would answer, he called on God to "shine forth" in vengeance and judgment on the proud and wicked. Evildoers continued their dirty work on God's people thinking that *"The Lord does not see, nor does the God of Jacob understand.'* However, the psalmist knew better; God's delay was not denial: *"He who planted the ear, shall He not hear? He who formed the eye, shall He not see? He who instructs the nations, shall He not correct?"* (8-11). God's blessings are reserved for the persons who submit to being taught by God's law. Godly people will rest safely while the *"pit is dug for the wicked"* (12-15).

The last half of the psalm described personal needs being met by God: *"Unless the Lord had been my help, my soul would soon have settled in silence…in the multitude of my anxieties within me, Your comforts delight my soul"* (16-18). The psalmist had been attacked by enemies but saw God defend him and become his refuge. To the wonderful Lord who protects whole nations, as well as needy individuals, this psalm gives praise!

A person does not have to kneel to pray or praise God, but that position often helps to remind us of our rightful position—below Him, at His feet.

Soft Hearts, Please! (Psalm 95)

Psalm 95 calls worshipers to come joyfully to sing and shout their thanks to God. He alone deserves it! *"In His hand"* (not ours) *"are the deep places of the earth; the heights of the hills are His also. The sea is His, for He made it; and His hands formed the dry land"* (1-5).

The physical position of humility is encouraged: *"Oh come, let us worship and bow down; let us kneel before the Lord our Maker. For He is our God, and we are the people of His pasture, and the sheep of His hand"* (6, 7). A person does not have to kneel to pray or praise God, but that position often helps to remind us of our rightful position—below Him, at His feet. The psalmist knew that we need to be reminded: *"Today, if you will hear His voice; do not harden your hearts, as in the rebellion"* (8). Israel had become proud even after God had delivered them so powerfully from slavery. Their rebellion grieved God for forty years. The result of their proud actions was that they also *"went astray in their hearts,"* missing God's *"rest"* (10-11). If your heart has hardened, try some physical therapy to bring about its softening: kneel regularly to praise the greatness and goodness of God.

advocate -a person who stands in favor of or in support of another; an attorney

Go Public (Psalm 96)

It is an amazing thing that some people will tell you all about their medical experiences, financial problems, and family history, but then claim that their faith is too personal to discuss! This psalm encourages every believer to go public with their praise of God! Forget the old boring methods: *"…sing to the Lord a new song!"* Forget just telling your friends and neighbors: *"Declare His glory among the nations"* (1-3). Our God is the real God—the rest are mere idols (5). The beauty and strength of God are to be described to the world, but also His plan to return to *"judge the peoples righteously"* (6-10). The whole earth—oceans, fields, and forests—will chime in on that day (11-13). However, to meet God as Judge without Jesus as *Advocate* will be terrible. The world needs to hear of our Savior, God's Lamb, before He returns as the Judge of all the world. Will anyone hear it from you?

It is an amazing thing that some people will tell you all about their medical experiences, financial problems, and family history, but then claim that their faith is too personal to discuss!

Questions

Study Procedure: Read the Scripture references before answering questions. Unless otherwise instructed, use only the Bible in answering questions. Some questions may be more difficult than others but try to answer as many as you can. Pray for God's wisdom and understanding as you study and don't be discouraged if some answers are not obvious at first. Do not read the study notes for this lesson until AFTER you have completed your questions.

Day One: Vocabulary Review.

1. Unscramble the following words to get the correct vocabulary word for the definitions:

   a) vocadate _____ a person who stands in favor or in support of another

   b) shiganu _____ great suffering from worry, grief or pain

   c) trailfy _____ weakness

   d) vancresieg _____ complaints of unfair treatment

   e) cantfingisi _____ important, meaningful

   f) chatw _____ a definite period of time

Review of Psalms 88-96.

2. In which psalm can you find the benefits of "dwelling" or "abiding" in the presence of God?

   _____

3. Which psalm was written by Moses, according to the small print at the beginning of it?

   _____

4. Which psalm was written by Ethan? _____

5. Which psalm was written by Heman? _____

6. Write down a few of the verses from this lesson that were most meaningful to you.

   _____

   _____

   _____

   _____

MEMORY: PSALM 98:1

Day Two: Read Psalms 97 and 98.

1. Psalm 97 described the awe-inspiring presence of God. Read the following description of God's meeting with Moses on Mt. Sinai from Exodus 19:16-20. Beside each underlined word, write down a verse from Psalm 97 that agrees with that description of the presence of God.

160

(16) Then it came to pass on the third day, in the morning, that there were thunderings and (a) lightnings v.____, and a (b) thick cloud v.____ on the mountain; and the sound of the trumpet was very loud, so that all the people who were in the camp trembled. (17) And Moses brought the people out of the camp to meet with God, and they stood at the foot of the mountain. (18) Now Mount Sinai was completely in smoke, because the LORD descended upon it in (c) fire v.____. Its smoke ascended like the smoke of a furnace, and the whole mountain (d) quaked v.____ greatly. (19) And when the blast of the trumpet sounded long and became louder and louder, Moses spoke, and God answered him by voice. (20) Then the LORD came down upon Mount Sinai, on the top of the mountain. And the LORD called Moses to the top of the mountain, and Moses went up.

2. Which verses warned about the foolishness of worshiping anything other than the Lord who obviously was far superior to all other gods? _____

3. From the last verses of Psalm 97, list the benefits of loving the Lord.

   _____

   _____

4. Psalm 98 is similar to Psalm 96 from the last lesson. Both call for the singing of a new song in thanksgiving for the wonderful works of God.

   a) List the instruments mentioned in vs. 4-6: _____

   _____

   b) List nature's noisemakers that were called to add their praises: _____

   _____

Day Three: Read Psalm 99, 100, and 101.   MEMORY: PSALM 100

1. What was emphasized three times in Psalm 99 about God and used as a summary of each section? _____

   _____

2. Match each section of Psalm 99 with its "time" reference below:

   a) God in the Present, all powerful _____

   b) God in the Past, faithful to speak to His people Israel _____

   c) God in the Future, fulfilling His promise of justice for Israel _____

3. Fill in the blanks of these familiar lines from Psalm 100. Try to do it without peeking!

   a) v. 1 Make a _____ noise to the LORD, all you lands!

   b) v. 2 Serve the LORD with gladness; Come before His presence with _____

   c) v. 3 Know that the LORD; He is _____; it is He who has made us, and not we ourselves; we are His people and the _____ of His pasture.

d) v. 4 Enter into His gates with _____, and into His courts with _____.
Be thankful unto Him and bless His name.

e) v. 5 For the LORD is _____; His _____ is everlasting, and His
_____ endures to all generations.

4. In Psalm 101, King David had set a standard for good behavior for himself and those around him.
From verses 1-4, list his personal goals. _____
_____
_____

5. Using David's words in Psalm 101:5-8 write a "help wanted" ad that he might have used to
locate suitable employees or counselors.
_____
_____
_____
_____
_____

MEMORY: PSALM 103:1-5, 11-14

Day Four: Read Psalms 102 and 103.

1. Psalm 102 is classified as a penitential psalm, a psalm that contains sorrowful expressions of
pain and sadness put in prayer form before the Lord. Find the verses in which these problems are
listed:

a) burning bones _____   e) sleeplessness _____

b) weak heart_____   f) bothered by enemies _____

c) no interest in eating _____   g) abandoned by God _____

d) weight loss _____

2. At what verse does the "tune" change from sadness to praise and why? _____
_____
_____

3. Answer the following from verses 12-28.

a) What verses could be called "messianic" because they describe the coming Christ?
_____
_____
_____

b) What verse mentions a future condition of the heavens and earth? _____

4. Read Psalm 103. In it, David urges the reader to *"forget not all His benefits."* List below, giving the references, several of the benefits we enjoy as God's children. _____

_____

_____

_____

Day Five: Read Psalms 104 and 105.

1. Read Psalm 104. It has been described as a creation hymn, praising God as the Creator of all. Beside each item listed below, find one or more verses that describe its creation or preservation by God.

   a) The heavens—planets, sun, moon, stars _____

   b) The atmosphere—clouds, wind, and rain _____

   c) The oceans and other bodies of water _____

   d) The vegetation on earth_____

   e) Land animals _____

   f) Man _____

   g) Sea creatures_____

2. The psalmist is so excited about the wonders of creation that he even calls on God to rejoice with him. Find the verse that describes that. _____

3. If Psalm 104 were a "Hymn of Creation," Psalm 105 might be called a "Hymn of History." Read through it carefully. Write beside each section of verses anything new to you or something you want to know more about.

   a) vs. 7-12 _____

   _____

   b) vs. 13-15 _____

   _____

   c) vs. 16-22 _____

   _____

   d) vs. 23-25 _____

   _____

   e) vs. 26-36 _____

   _____

   f) vs. 37-41 _____

   _____

   g) vs. 42-45 _____

   _____

4. Now take a few minutes and read the notes for this lesson.

Notes

God Is Great! (Psalms 97-105)

First Impression (Psalm 97)

It is a common belief that first impressions are important. Psalm 97 describes God's first meeting with Israel on Mt. Sinai, and what an impression He made on them there! [See Exodus 19.] They had been given three days' notice to get prepared and then warned not to come too close. God came down, and the mountain caught fire. It was soon covered with smoke, and the lightning and thunder resounded so that the ground actually shook and trembled with God's presence. The people were in such awe that they wanted Moses to do the talking: *"You speak to us and we will hear; but let not God speak to us lest we die."* And Moses said to the people, *"Do not fear; for God has come to prove you, and that the fear of him may be before your eyes, that you may not sin"* (Exodus 20:19 and 20). Psalm 97:2-6 described all this, and the psalmist pointed out the main lessons. First, God alone is to be worshiped: *"Let all be put to shame who serve carved images…For You, Lord, are most high above all the earth"* (7-9). The second point the psalmist made was that if we love God, then we should hate evil (10). The benefits God awarded for those two actions were deliverance from the hand of the wicked, light for the feet, and gladness for the heart (10, 11). For all that, the psalmist urged: *"Rejoice in the Lord, you righteous, and give thanks at the remembrance of His holy name"* (12).

It is a common belief that first impressions are important. Psalm 97 describes God's first meeting with Israel on Mt. Sinai, and what an impression He made on them there!

A New Song (Psalm 98)

Even God must get tired of the same old thing. Several psalms, like this one, have encouraged God's people to *"sing to the Lord a new song!"* [See Psalms 33:3; 40:3; 96:1; 144:9; 149:1.] What makes a song new? It becomes new when it is put in your own words or sung with a recent example of God's goodness in your mind. Freshness would be a good definition of "new." What has following God meant in your life recently? Praise Him for that.

In the early verses of Psalm 98 the psalmist gave examples of the *"marvelous things"* God had done. He had brought Israel to victory and made known His salvation and righteousness to the whole earth. In verses 4-8 the call was given to *"all the earth"* to *"break forth in song"* to the Lord. That was a strange invitation. Can the earth praise its Creator? Well, according to Romans 8:19-22, it can surely make noise: *"For the earnest expectation of the creation eagerly waits for the revealing of the sons of God… because the creation itself also will be delivered from the bondage of corruption into the glorious liberty of the children of God. For we know that the whole creation groans and labors with birth pangs together until now."* The psalmist wanted the earth to

Even God must get tired of the same old thing. Several psalms, like this one, have encouraged God's people to "sing to the Lord a new song!"

change its groan to a grin so that the sea would roar while the river clapped in anticipation of what the Lord would do next. And what was that exactly? The Lord was going to return to judge the earth. For those who loved Him, that would be great news. At last, real justice and lasting peace would come to all civilizations. But for the ungodly, it would be tragic. For in the presence of a holy God, unholiness would not go unnoticed or unpunished. That is a truth that still needs to be told. Too many do not know that a judgment awaits the enemies of God.

God Is Holy (Psalm 99)

Psalm 99 has a repeating line: *"God is Holy."* In verses 1-3, He is described as holy right now and always! Verses 4 and 5 depict a future revelation of His holiness as He fulfills His promises to Israel. The last section, verses 6-9, looks back to the past where He showed His holiness and the people responded with obedient hearts. Three men were named who exhibited personal holiness in their willingness to pray—Moses, Aaron, and Samuel. None were perfect in the sense of being sinless (8), but their lives could be described as "holy" because, as the word "holy" meant, they were willing to be separate, apart from worldly attachments, to be available for God's use. "Holy" also shares a meaning with "wholly" and can mean "complete" or "healthy." God is holy because He is complete, needs nothing, and is distinct from all others. He calls us to be holy as His followers, unattached to the world and available for His purposes. Could your life be described as holy?

God is holy because He is complete, needs nothing, and is distinct from all others. He calls us to be holy as His followers, unattached to the world and available for His purposes.

The Greatest Praise (Psalm 100)

This psalm is frequently sung in churches and called "The Great Doxology." "Doxology" comes from two words meaning "words" (*logos*) of "praise" (*doxa*). To praise (*doxa*) means literally *"to show forth."* How do we show the people around us and express to God Himself that we think He is wonderful? Three ways are mentioned here:

1. *"Serve the Lord with gladness"* (1-2). Going cheerfully about the duties of the day will certainly get the attention of others and please the One being served!

2. Submit (3) *"Know that the Lord, He is God; it is He who has made us, and not we ourselves; we are…the sheep of His pasture."* The second way to show forth God's greatness is to willingly submit to His plans and purposes. When we cheerfully submit, others see that we believe God is worthy of our obedience and that we think He has the wisdom to be trusted to direct our lives.

When we cheerfully submit, others see that we believe God is worthy of our obedience and that we think He has the wisdom to be trusted to direct our lives.

3. Say it (4, 5). *"Enter into His gates with thanksgiving, and into His courts with praise."* Put what you feel in words and tell God privately and others

publicly about God's great goodness, mercy, and truth. People will not automatically know what makes your life meaningful just by watching how you live. They must also hear from you about the source and cause of your joy and peace.

> *People will not automatically know what makes your life meaningful just by watching how you live. They must also hear from you about the source and cause of your joy and peace.*

Personal Choices (Psalm 101)

The determination of David in Psalm 101 to express his dedication to the will of God was emphasized with the repeated use of "I will" and "I shall." Much different than what we see in public leadership today, David knew that he must get his personal life in line before he could be the king God intended him to be in public life. He said in verse 2, *"I will behave wisely in a perfect way."* To be perfect before the Lord does not mean never to sin, but it does mean to be sincere and without **pretense**. The Apostle John called it *"walking in the light"* (1 Jn.1:5-10). How do we stay *"in the light"* of what pleases God? Here is the advice of this psalm:

pretense -a deceptive or false action or appearance

1. Be careful about what you let your eyes see (3). How appropriate this is in our day when almost no movie, video, television program, stage, or computer screen is safe from overexposure to violence, **vulgarity**, or nudity.

2. Be careful about what your ears hear (5). Allowing others to speak slander of your neighbors without stopping them is far from "perfect" living. This also could be applied to listening to ungodly music lyrics or any other source of unwholesome language.

3. Be careful in picking your friends (6, 7). David declared that he would be selective about his close associations. There is truth in the statement, "You become like those you are around."

vulgarity -indecency; showing of poor taste or manners

Surrendered, Yet Suffering (Psalm 102)

From the beginning, the psalmist made clear he was in trouble: *"Hear my prayer, O Lord, and let my cry come to You...Do not hide your face from me...answer me speedily."* He physically suffered: *"My heart is stricken...my bones cling to my skin...I lie awake"* (3-7). He suffered emotionally, feeling persecuted and abandoned: *"My enemies reproach me all day long;...for You have lifted me up and cast me away"* (8-11). Then, suddenly, he looked up, *"But You, O Lord, shall endure forever"* (12). He looked past his present pain to a future hope: *"For the Lord shall build up Zion; He shall appear in His glory, He shall regard the prayer of the **destitute**, And shall not despise their prayer."* No suffering in the life of a child of God lasts forever. Paul wrote: *"For I consider that the sufferings of this present time are not worthy to be compared to the glory which shall be revealed in us"* (Romans 8:18). The psalmist realized that it was important to write down the hope he had realized: *"This will be written for the generation to come, that a people yet to be created may praise the Lord"* (18). What was that future hope that

destitute -extremely poor

comforted him? He saw the coming of Messiah to soothe prisoners, save the dying, and bring unity to the world (19-22). There was a brief return to present pain, however; which was not unusual since we can only momentarily escape continuing pain: *"O my God, do not take me away in the midst of my days"* (24). The psalmist reasoned that since God was not limited by time, He did not have to cut short the life of one of his own. After all, God laid the foundation of the earth and would one day roll it up like an old garment and change it (25-26). Such a God could certainly be trusted to continue His care of one sick servant! Looking beyond present suffering to the goal ahead and our God who cares can help us endure what we must in the present.

One of the most wonderful gifts of God is forgiveness.

More Gratitude (Psalm 103)

"Bless the Lord, O my soul," David began. The word "bless" came from the Hebrew *bahrack* which meant "to kneel" in order to show **homage** or honor to someone. *"Forget not all His benefits,"* the psalm continued (2). The positive side of "forget not" is "to remember," and David was great at remembering. Here is David's list of some of the benefits of being in God's family:

(v. 3) Forgiveness of all sins; healing of all diseases

(v. 4) Rescue from destruction; being crowned with mercy

(v. 5) Satisfaction of appetite and renewed strength

homage -expression of high regard, honor

One of the most wonderful gifts of God is forgiveness. *"The Lord is merciful and gracious…He has not dealt with us according to our sins, nor punished us according to our iniquities"* (8-10). Isn't that great news! How much mercy can we have? *"For as the heavens are high above the earth, so great is His mercy toward those that fear Him"* (11). How far away has He removed our sins? *"As far as the east is from the west, so far has He removed our transgressions from us"* (12). For such great love and mercy, David needed extra help to express his praise. He called on the angels to help along with *"all His works"* to *"bless the Lord!"* (20-22).

How far away has He removed our sins? "As far as the east is from the west, so far has He removed our transgressions from us";
↑

Creation Hymn (Psalm 104)

In another acknowledgment of God as the Creator of all that exists, this psalm described that early work. *"O Lord my God, You are very great"* (1). How great? He stretched *"out the heavens like a curtain."* That was an interesting description in light of the discovery in recent years that the universe is still expanding—very much like a curtain being stretched. Next, the vast power of God to lay the foundations of the earth and to set boundaries for the oceans was praised (3-9). How loving of God to provide a water supply throughout the earth so that every wild beast and bird of heaven could be satisfied! (10-13). The staples that man would need—wine, oil, and bread—were likewise gifts from God (14, 15). For the marking of seasons and organizing of daily work God created the moon and sun to move with mathematical **precision** (19-23). Like the psalmist we should shout: *"O Lord, how manifold are Your works! In wisdom You have made them all"* (24). From the smallest fish to the largest dinosaur [See the description of Leviathan in Job 41.], they all depend on God to *"give them their food in due season"* and determine their life-span (27-30).

precision -exactness; accuracy

At this point, the psalmist was so overwhelmed that he expressed his hope that God Himself would *"rejoice in His works"* (31)—which we can be sure He does! A lifetime is not long enough to express praise for such a God, but like the psalmist, let us make every effort to use the time we have to do just that! (33-35).

manifold -many

The Covenant-Keeper (Psalm 105)

As Psalm 104 praised God as Creator, Psalm 105 praised God as the Covenant-Keeper: *"He is the Lord our God...He remembers His covenant forever"* (8). The covenant to which he referred was the covenant with the nation Israel that began with God making a covenant [serious pledge or promised agreement] with Abraham. This covenant was to apply to the descendants of Abraham, too, and so the psalmist mentioned Isaac, Jacob, and Joseph. He recounted the beginning of that family line, the promise of the special land (9-12), protection from enemies (13-15), and the famine that caused the growing family to go down to Egypt where Joseph had been set up, in spite of the evil intent of his brothers, as the one who would save his whole family, as well as Egypt, from starvation (16-23). Egypt later forgot the help of Joseph and enslaved that family, but God still did not forget His covenant with them. He sent Moses and Aaron to perform signs to gain their release (26-36). His covenant favor was so great that they left Egypt with riches and health, protected from the harsh elements of the desert and *"satisfied with the bread of heaven"* till at last they came into their promised land among the Gentiles (37-44). The psalmist's last statement emphasized the simple request that God had made to His people in return for all His covenant-care: *"That they might observe His statutes and keep His laws."* Though often they failed in their part—*"Praise the Lord!"* (45)—He never failed in His!

A lifetime is not long enough to express praise for such a God, but like the psalmist, let us make every effort to use the time we have to do just that!

Pulling It Together

This lesson began with Psalm 97 which described God's first appearance to Israel. The psalms that followed detailed the characteristics of God revealed there: holiness, righteous judgment, creative greatness, and covenant love. The other psalms made clear what our response should be to such greatness: thanks, praise, humility, and obedience. Ask God to show you which ones you need to practice.

BIBLE QUEST

Questions

Study Procedure: Read the Scripture references before answering questions. Unless otherwise instructed, use only the Bible in answering questions. Some questions may be more difficult than others but try to answer as many as you can. Pray for God's wisdom and understanding as you study and don't be discouraged if some answers are not obvious at first. Do not read the study notes for this lesson until AFTER you have completed your questions.

Day One: Vocabulary Review: Fill in the blanks below with the correct vocabulary word from this list:

> homage   destitute   manifold   precision   pretense   vulgarity

1. For all his smooth talking and expensive dressing, he still seemed a man full of _____, not to be trusted.

2. She found the child wandering in the street, dirty, cold and _____.

3. The wonders of God are, _____, all around us.

4. The movie was filled with such violence and _____ that we had to leave.

5. When handling the word of God, she worked with _____ and respect.

6. To God alone is due our total _____.

Review of Psalms 97-105.

7. Which psalm urged us to "*sing a new song*" to God—to be fresh and spontaneous in our praise? _____

8. Which psalm described God as "the God-Who-Forgives"? _____

9. Which psalm talked of the need to walk "in a perfect way"? _____

10. In which psalm did this appear: "*He has not dealt with us according to our sins, nor punished us according to our iniquities*"? _____

11. Which psalm could be called the "Hymn of Creation"? _____

> **MEMORY: PSALM 106:1; 107:1-2; 108:3-4**

Day Two: Read Psalms 106-109.

1. Overlapping a bit with Psalm 105, Psalm 106 continued the history of Israel with the emphasis on Israel's national sins, which are still the sins of our day. Write down the verses that describe these sins.

   a) forgetfulness _____   f) child sacrifice _____

   b) envy _____   g) impatience _____

   c) idolatry _____   h) lust _____

   d) rebellion _____   i) unbelief _____

   e) disobedience _____

2. Read Psalm 107. Write down the verse numbers for this psalm's refrain or chorus as well as

   the words to it. _____

   _____

   _____

3. Write down the verses from Psalm 107 that described situations in which God helped and for
   which the people should have been grateful.

   a) wilderness wanderers_____   d) sea travelers _____

   b) prisoners _____   e) farmers _____

   c) foolish sinners _____

4. Read Psalm 108. This psalm was made up of two earlier psalms. If you can find out which

   ones, write their numbers down here. _____

MEMORY: PSALM 111:1-3

Day Three: Read Psalms 109-111

1. Read Psalm 109. Finish the statements below from what you read in the psalm.

   a) They have _____

   _____

   b) I have _____

   _____

   c) I want You to _____

   _____

   d) I will _____

   _____

2. Read Psalm 110. This psalm of David announced the future reign of Messiah and described

   some of His duties or titles. Locate the verses that describe these:

   a) David's Lord and King _____

   b) Eternal Priest _____

   c) Warrior-Judge _____

3. Read Genesis 14:18-20 which records the one and only appearance of Melchizedek and also
   Hebrews 7:1-7 for a reference to him. Then, answer these questions:

   a) From where did he come? _____

   b) Who were his parents? _____

   c) What were his titles or jobs? _____

d) What did he do for Abraham? _____

e) What did Abraham do for him?_____

4. Read Psalm 111. The psalm praises God for "who He is" as well as for "what He does." Make two columns and list the examples from the psalm for each category.

Who He is	What He does

Day Four: Read Psalms 112-115.

MEMORY: PSALM 111:10

1. Read Psalm 112 and

   a) give at least five things that a person *"who fears the Lord"* and *"delights greatly in His commandments"* can expect to have done for him in his lifetime: _____

   _____

   b) at least three things that he will do for others during his lifetime: _____

   _____

2. Psalm 113 began a group of psalms called the *Egyptian Hallels* which were sung during the season of Passover to praise God for the deliverance of Israel from Egypt. Which verse(s) described the personal involvement of God in the affairs of His creatures? _____

3. Read Psalm 114. How did creation respond to God's plan to free Israel from slavery?

   _____

   _____

4. Read Psalm 115. Then read Isaiah 44:12-20. Why is it foolish to worship idols?

   _____

   _____

   _____

   _____

5. In contrast to the powerlessness of idols, what can God do? (use vs. 9-16) _____

_____

_____

_____

MEMORY: PSALM 116:1-2; 118:6, 8, 14, 24

Day Five: Read Psalms 116-118.

1. Read Psalm 116. Why is the psalmist so overwhelmed with love for God? What had happened to

    him? _____

    _____

2. What did the psalmist plan to do in gratitude to God? _____

    _____

    _____

3. Psalm 117 is the shortest psalm, but it had a big purpose. What was it? (Choose one)

    a) To try to get the Jews and Gentiles to quit fighting.

    b) To try and get the peoples of the world to praise the Lord.

    c) To try to tell the Gentiles that they could serve God, too.

4. Read Psalm 118. This was the last of the *Egyptian Hallels* and would have been sung by Jesus

    Himself during the final week of His life in Jerusalem at Passover. Which verses would have

    reminded Jesus of His mission? _____

    _____

    _____

5. Pick out any other familiar verse from this psalm or one that was meaningful to you.

    _____

    _____

    _____

    _____

6. Now take a few minutes and read the notes for this lesson.

Notes

God Still Cares (Psalms 106-118)

Short Memories (Psalm 106)

Psalm 106 gave the history of Israel with an emphasis on Israel's many sins against God. Even though God had repeatedly helped them in miraculous ways, they would sooner or later turn back to very sinful behavior. Before we get too harsh in our judgment of them, we need to pause and consider how many times we have forgotten all that God has done for us, and instead, we have insisted on our own ways. The blessings of God are continual for *"those who keep justice, and he who does righteousness at all times!"* (3). **Consistency** in doing justice and being righteous was as much a struggle for the children of Israel as it is for us today, but is something we need to strive for in our daily lives.

The psalmist identified with his sinning ancestors: *"We have sinned with our fathers"* (6). The psalmist recalled that Israel rebelled by the Red Sea, even after God's ten spectacular miracles in getting them out of Egypt: *"Nevertheless He saved them for His name's sake, that He might make His mighty power known"* (8). *"...Then they believed His words; they sang His praise"* (12); however, *"they soon forgot His works; they did not wait for His counsel,..."* (13). And so the pattern of Psalm 106 continued: God's mercy, Israel's sin, God's discipline, Israel's repentance, and God's mercy. One horrible example of sin was in their participation in child sacrifice after they failed to stay separate from the heathen nations around them. That caused severe punishment from God: *"And He gave them into the hand of the Gentiles, and those who hated them ruled over them"* (41). After the history was finished, the psalmist pleaded, *"Save us, O Lord our God, and gather us from among the Gentiles, to give thanks to Your holy name, to triumph in Your praise."* (47) Yes, we can use this psalm as we plead for mercy for our nation, too, with its history of blessings by God answered with rebellion and unbelief: *"Save us, O Lord our God!"*

Yes, we can use this psalm as we plead for mercy for our nation, too, with its history of blessings by God answered with rebellion and unbelief: "Save us, O Lord our God!"

consistency -similarity in repeated actions; staying the same throughout

Say "Thank You"! (Psalm 107)

Someone wrote that ingratitude was like stealing. Think about that. The writer of Psalm 107 would have agreed, as we can see from the refrain or chorus he placed in this psalm: *"Oh, that men would give thanks to the LORD for His goodness, and for His wonderful works to the children of men!"* (8, 15, 21, 31). We need to regularly acknowledge what God has done, for, when we don't, it is as if we have stolen the blessings from God. In fine poetic language, the psalmist described various kinds of problems into which God brought help and relief:

In fine poetic language, the psalmist described various kinds of problems into which God brought help and relief . . .

1. <u>**Lost people**</u>: *"He led them forth by the right way…"*(7). Has God helped you when you were lost, abandoned, or confused? Did you thank Him?

2. <u>**Prisoners**</u>: *"He brought them out of darkness and the shadow of death, and broke their chains in pieces"*(14). Out of what "prisons" has He freed you? Did you thank Him?

3. <u>**Fools**</u>: In Proverbs are described several kinds of fools. One type continually ignores the wisdom of God that is available to him. In His mercy, God even helps the fool out of the trouble he himself caused: *"He sent His word and healed them, and delivered them from their destructions"* (20). From how many foolish things has God saved you? Did you thank Him?

The passionate feelings of betrayal and injustice felt by David were evident, and he wanted God to do something severe about such treachery.

4. <u>**Sailors**</u>: *"He calms the storm, so that its waves are still"*(29). Has the Lord said *"Peace, be still"* to the winds and waves in your life? Did you thank Him?

5. <u>**Farmers**</u>: *"He also blesses them, and they multiply greatly; and He does not let their cattle decrease"* (38). Farmers are so dependent on God for water, sun, seed, and growth, all in just the right amounts. Have you received His help in specific ways? Did you thank Him?

Golden Oldie (Psalm 108)

If the words to this psalm sound familiar, they are. This one is a combination of two earlier psalms: Psalm 57:7-11 and Psalm 60:5-12. Just as musicians today resurrect old songs and freshen them up for younger ears with a different beat, style, or tune, so the good lyrics of older psalms could be repeated with the same fresh helpfulness as when they were new. The word of God never becomes out-of-date.

imprecatory -asking for a curse to be sent down on someone

God Will Plead Our Case (Psalm 109)

Psalm 109 was one of the ***imprecatory*** psalms in which God was asked to act in revenge for the wrongs done to one of His followers. The passionate feelings of betrayal and injustice felt by David were evident, and he wanted God to do something severe about such ***treachery***. David had been betrayed by someone or some group to whom he had shown love. He was shocked and hurt and appealed to God. In Acts 1:20, this psalm was quoted as applying to what Judas had done to Jesus and the appropriate action to follow that betrayal: *"Let his days be few, and let another take his office"* (8). Many of the psalm's verses were devoted to asking for specific, painful, and long-term action to be taken against traitors. David felt so close to God in their covenant relationship, that he believed his enemies were God's enemies, and that God would want to be just as harsh on them as David would be on God's enemies. His faith was in the right place,

treachery -willful betrayal of a friendship or trust

but we are cautioned in the New Testament to pray for our enemies, not curse them. But we do share this with David: we must turn all our hurts and bitterness over to God and not take vengeance into our own hands.

David's Lord (Psalm 110)

This psalm was quoted in several places in the New Testament to prove some important things about the identity and actions of Jesus. In the opening verses of Psalm 110, David reported what he had heard the LORD (Jehovah, the Father) say to David's Lord (Adonai, the Messiah). You might not have noticed, but in the King James and the New King James Versions of the Bible, there is a distinction made in the word "Lord." When it is written in all capitals (LORD) the original Hebrew word translated was *Jehovah*, the covenant-keeping, Father-God. When it is spelled *Lord*, the original Hebrew word was *Adonai*, which meant "master" or "superior." The distinction is important in this psalm.

But we do share this with David: we must turn all our hurts and bitterness over to God and not take vengeance into our own hands.

In Luke 20:42-44, Jesus defended his claim to the title "Son of God"as well as "Son of David"—in other words, to being fully divine as well as fully human. His critics thought that was impossible. So, He took them to the Scriptures, specifically to Psalm 110: 1: *"The LORD said to my Lord, 'Sit at My right hand, till I make Your enemies Your footstool.'"* Then Jesus made this point: If David called Him "Lord" how could he be merely his son? A father does not call his son a name implying his son is superior to the father—unless the son really is! Jesus was showing that the Scriptures always described Messiah with a double nature—from the human line of David, but so superior to David that He had to be addressed as *Lord*. In essence, that verse recorded God inviting Jesus to share the throne with Himself until they could get all the people on earth and problems there settled forever. So, verse one described Messiah as David's Lord and King, equal to God. Messiah was to be one from the line of David, but still equal to God. That was exactly who Jesus claimed to be.

Another time that Psalm 110 was quoted was in Acts 2:34,35 to prove that the resurrection of Jesus had been in God's plan all along. Peter quoted verse one about the LORD inviting David's Lord to come join Him on the throne in heaven. Peter said this is what Jesus did, and that it never referred to David himself. David did not ascend to heaven—Jesus did, just as the psalm prophesied He would.

In the last reference to Psalm 110, the writer of Hebrews quoted it to prove that Jesus was our rightful high priest forever even though He did not come from the line of Levi, the legal line from which all other priests came. Everything had to be done legally, because God's righteousness never allows Him (or His word) to change or lie. So, there had to be Scripture to back up

Our Jesus has an eternal priesthood; He is always on duty before God on our behalf, just as Scripture prophesied He would be.

tithe -a tenth part

such a claim to the high priesthood. Hebrews 7:1-7 explained that Jesus fulfilled the prophecy of Psalm 110 by becoming a priest after the order or line of Melchizedek.

Now Melchizedek is an interesting person. The only actual record of him can be found in Genesis 14. There Melchizedek, who was king of Salem (which means "peace") and also a priest of the Most High God, met Abram [his name would later be changed to Abraham] with bread and wine. Abraham had just taken part in a successful battle to free his nephew Lot, having been joined by some other kings. According to Genesis 14:19 Melchizedek blessed Abram: *"Blessed be Abram of God Most High, Possessor of heaven and earth; and blessed be God Most High, Who has delivered your enemies into your hand."* Abram responded by giving him "a *tithe* of all." Now, just in that short section of Scripture, the writer of Hebrews found some mighty big truths.

First, the challenge was to show that Jesus could legally (according to Scripture) hold the title of high priest in spite of the fact He did not come from the family line of Levi. Was there another priestly line in the Bible beside Levi's? Yes, the line of Melchizedek who was named in Scripture as a priest without any family lineage being offered. In fact, Melchizedek was a priest before Levi was even born, since Levi would be Abram's great-grandson. So, Jesus was a priest after the order of Melchizedek, the first priest, without a recorded beginning or end to his life or priesthood. Was Melchizedek's priesthood superior to Levi's just because it was earlier? No, it was superior to Levi's because Melchizedek was superior to Abram. The writer of Hebrews used as proof the fact that Abram offered a gift or tithe to Melchizedek, while Melchizedek received it and blessed Abram. To bless someone, you must be greater than they, and so Scripture showed that Melchizedek's priesthood was earlier and greater than the one that would come through Levi, where priests would only serve a certain amount of years, or until death, before being replaced. Our Jesus has an eternal priesthood; He is always on duty before God on our behalf, just as Scripture prophesied He would be. Jesus also would have the titles Melchizedek had had as King of Peace (Salem) and King of Righteousness (which "Melchizedek" actually meant).

He will return to conquer all enemies and judge the world. If we know Him as King of Peace, we will not have to face Him in judgment with the unbelieving world as King of Righteousness.

Besides being David's Lord and Ascended King (1-2) as well as Eternal Priest (3,4), the Messiah described in Psalm 110 was also the coming Warrior-Judge of the world (5-7) who would *"execute kings in the day of His wrath"* and *"judge among the nations."* That part of Messiah's purpose has not yet happened—but as surely as He ascended to Heaven and intercedes as our High Priest, He will return to conquer all enemies and judge the world. If we know Him as King of Peace, we will not have to face Him in judgment with the unbelieving world as King of Righteousness.

**Study and Do
(Psalm 111)**

This is another acrostic psalm of 22 lines and the first of three in a series beginning with "Praise the Lord" or in Hebrew, *"Hallel."* In acrostics where each line must begin with the next letter of the Hebrew alphabet, the thoughts are short and complete and not necessarily related to what follows. Any line could be picked out to offer some good advice or state a wonderful truth about God. Here are a few samples:

"The works of the LORD are great, studied by all who have pleasure in them" (2). If you are reading these notes, you must be a student of the Bible. Do you take pleasure in your study? His works are so great, you should!

"The works of His hands are verity and justice; all His precepts are sure" (7). Have you found that to be true in your life, too?

"A good understanding have all those who do His commandments…" (10). It takes more than studying God's word to make a difference, we must "do" His word, obeying what He teaches.

> *In acrostics where each line must begin with the next letter of the Hebrew alphabet, the thoughts are short and complete and not necessarily related to what follows.*

> verity -truth

**It Shows!
(Psalm 112)**

Have you ever wondered if anyone could see a difference in your life because you love and serve God? This acrostic psalm lists several things that sooner or later will show up in the life of a godly person. The man who *"fears the Lord"* and *"delights greatly in His commandments"* can expect to see these blessings in his lifetime: (2) strong descendants or family members; (3) enough money in his house to meet his needs and more; (4) "light" in dark times; (6) good reputation; and (7) strength in the face of fear because he trusts *"in the LORD."* Others will see in the godly man (1) an eagerness to obey God's commandments; (5) generosity in lending to others; care in directing his own affairs; and (9) an extended ministry to the poor, even those who are far away from him. All these blessings and righteous actions will grieve the wicked, who will definitely be watching the godly in action and *"gnash[ing] their teeth"* (10).

**High, Yet Humble
(Psalm 113)**

This psalm was part of a group called the *Egyptian Hallels* that were used during the Passover service every year. Psalm 113 and 114 were sung before the Passover meal and Psalms 115-118 were sung following the meal. The psalm called its listeners to praise because of the greatness of God (4, 5) and also because God chose to humble Himself to get involved in the lives of His creatures on earth (6-9). That does inspire praise—that the Creator of the universe bends down to bring comfort to the poor, needy, and barren! Praise the Lord!

> *The psalm called its listeners to praise because of the greatness of God (4, 5) and also because God chose to humble Himself to get involved in the lives of His creatures on earth (6-9).*

mythology -a collection of myths (unproven stories) about the origin and history of a people, their gods, ancestors, and heroes.

Creation Responded (Psalm 114)

This psalm mentions Egypt in its opening verse and thus gave the title to this grouping of psalms—the *Egyptian Hallels*. It is important to realize that the faith of Israel and our faith, too, has a basis in historical facts, not **mythology**, as in other world-religions. Repeatedly in Scripture, the "big events" in the history of Israel are described in varying detail. It was and is important not to forget what God has already done for us as well as being informed about what is yet to happen. In this short psalm, creation is described as participating with God in the freeing of Israel from Egypt: the sea fled, the Jordan turned back, the mountains and hills skipped like sheep, and the rock produced water. Before a God of such awesome power and influence, we are called to tremble and worship.

Anything that pulls us away form worshiping and obeying God can be an idol in our lives.

No Need for Idols (Psalm 115)

Idolatry has always been **prohibited** for God's people. The first and second commandments made that clear. Yet, how often the "things" made or invented by human beings, which make our lives more comfortable or exciting, hold our interest and attention far more than they should. Anything that pulls us away from worshiping and obeying God can be an idol in our lives. This psalm illustrated just how foolish that really is. The Gentiles wanted gods they could see; they said of Israel, *"So where is their God?"* The psalmist answered, *"But our God is in heaven; He does whatever He pleases"* (3). In contrast, their idols were man-made and visible, and yet absolutely powerless (4-8). The last half of the psalm urged Israel to *"trust in the Lord"* who is *"their help and their shield"* (9). The true God has a mind and is *"mindful of us"* to bless us (12). God owns everything and has given the earth to men (16). Our response, while we are still alive and able on this earth, should be to praise Him for such loving and generous care. In this life, that is our most important duty.

idolatry -worship of idols

prohibited -forbidden

Answered Prayer (Psalm 116)

Jesus once said about a woman who had expressed love to Him, *"Therefore I say to you, her sins, which are many, are forgiven, for she loved much. But to whom little is forgiven, the same loves little"* (Luke 7:47). Love and appreciation grow in proportion to what has been received, and in this psalm, the speaker had been healed from something that almost caused his death. He was very grateful and expressed his love in the first line: *"I love the Lord, because He has heard my voice and my supplications."* He overflowed with praise and gratitude for what God had done for him when the *"pains of death surrounded me, and the pangs of **Sheol** laid hold of me"* (3). He cheered, *"Gracious is the Lord, and righteous; yes, our God is merciful"* (5). How moving were the lines: *"For You have delivered my soul from death, my eyes from tears, and my feet from falling"* (8)! Have you

Sheol -a place described in the Old Testament as the abode of the dead

ever felt that desperate? Did you pray? Did He answer? Then, with the psalmist, you must ask: *"What shall I render to the LORD for all His benefits toward me?"* (12). The answer was a spiritual response since we can never physically repay God for what He has done. The proper response lay in an attitude and action. The psalmist said he would worship—*"I will take up the cup of salvation and call upon the name of the Lord"* (13). The cup of salvation was the name of one of the four cups of wine used at the Passover meal commemorating God's deliverance of Israel from slavery. Worship, in the attitude of humble gratitude, is always the right reaction to God's goodness. But there is more: obedience. The psalm continued, *"I will pay my vows to the LORD Now in the presence of His people."* Obedience also pleases God, and unashamed obedience (*"in the presence of His people"*) is best. The psalm also included this truth realized by the sufferer, *"Precious in the sight of the LORD Is the death of His saints"* (15). The Lord loves each one of His children and notices and concerns Himself with all of their suffering. *"Praise the Lord!"*

Short but Big (Psalm 117)

This psalm is the shortest in the Psalter and falls almost exactly in the middle of the Bible. It has a big purpose: to call the whole world to praise the Lord *"For His merciful kindness is great toward us, and the truth of the LORD endures forever."* That is still a very powerful message!

This Is the Day! (Psalm 118)

This is the final psalm in the grouping of the *Egyptian Hallels,* and along with Psalm 115, 116, and 117, was sung at the end of the Passover meal. (Matthew 26:30 mentioned this.) Reading the words of this psalm with the idea in mind that Jesus sang it with His disciples on the very night He would be betrayed, makes them all the more meaningful. Jesus went to the Garden of Gethsemane to call *"on the Lord in distress"* (5). The response from this psalm may have comforted Him: *"The LORD is on my side; I will not fear. What can man do to me?"* (6). However, man did do his worst, crucifying the Son of God. The psalmist had escaped that supreme sacrifice (17, 18), but Jesus would not. But in laying down His life for us, He truly fulfilled this verse: *"The stone which the builders rejected has become the chief cornerstone. This was the Lord's doing; it is marvelous in our eyes"* (22, 23). We can still sing, *"God is the LORD, and He has given us light"* (27). Later, the psalmist mentioned the offering of a sacrifice, an animal that would be killed and then tied to the four corners or horns of the brazen altar to be burned as an offering (27). Our Lord was nailed to the ends of a cross as an offering in our place—what a Savior! *"Oh, give thanks to the LORD, for He is good! For His mercy endures forever"* (29).

Reading the words of this psalm with the idea in mind that Jesus sang it with His disciples on the very night He would be betrayed, makes them all the more meaningful.

BIBLE QUEST

Questions

Study Procedure: Read the Scripture references before answering questions. Unless otherwise instructed, use only the Bible in answering questions. Some questions may be more difficult than others but try to answer as many as you can. Pray for God's wisdom and understanding as you study and don't be discouraged if some answers are not obvious at first. Do not read the study notes for this lesson until AFTER you have completed your questions.

Day One: Vocabulary Review - Match the word with its definition.

_____1. consistency

_____2. idolatry

_____3. imprecatory

_____4. mythology

_____5. prohibited

_____6. Sheol

_____7. tithe

_____8. treachery

_____9. verity

a) asking for a curse to be sent down on someone

b) a tenth part

c) similarity in repeated actions; staying the same throughout

d) forbidden

e) truth

f) willful betrayal of a friendship or trust

g) worship of idols

h) a place described in the Old Testament as the abode of the dead

i) collection of myths (unproven stories) about the origin and history of a people, their gods, ancestors, and heroes

Review of Psalms 106-118. Match these quotes with the psalm from which they come.

1. *"The stone which the builders rejected has become the chief cornerstone."* _____

2. *"For you have delivered my soul from death, my eyes from tears, and my feet from falling."*

   _____

3. *"What ails you, O sea, that you fled?"* _____

4. *"Blessed is the man who fears the LORD, Who delights greatly in His commandments."*

   _____

5. *"The LORD said to my Lord, 'Sit at My right hand, Till I make Your enemies Your footstool.'"*

   _____

6. *"Oh, that men would give thanks to the LORD for His goodness, and for His wonderful works to the children of men!"* _____

MEMORY: PSALM 119:9, 11, 33

Day Two: Read Psalm 119:1-40.

1. Psalm 119 is an alphabetic acrostic. Look through the headings (every 8 verses) and write down the Hebrew alphabet as each letter is given in the psalm below. If you are artistic, you might try writing the letter symbol, too. A few are done for you.

   a) aleph   l) _____

   b) beth   m) _____

   c) _____   n) _____

   d) _____   o) _____

   e) _____   p) _____

   f) _____   q) _____

   g) _____   r) _____

   h) _____   s) _____

   i) _____   t) _____

   j) yod   u) _____

   k) _____   v) tau

2. Almost every line of this psalm contains a synonym for the word of God. Find as many as you can from the first 40 verses. Example: v. 1 - law; v. 2 - testimonies _____

   _____

   _____

3. *"How can a young man cleanse his way?"* _____

   _____

4. Which verse would make a good prayer before studying the Bible?_____

   _____

5. Which verse would be helpful when trying to cut back on unnecessary television or video watching? _____

   _____

MEMORY: PSALM 119:72, 105

Day Three: Read Psalm 119:41-88.

1. Fill in the blanks with the missing words about "affliction" from this section. Write down the references, too.

   a) *"This is my comfort in my affliction, for Your word* _____*."*

   b) *"Before I was afflicted,* _____*, but now I keep Your word."*

   c) *"It is good for me that I have been afflicted, that* _____*."*

2. Look at the section entitled "yod" printed in Hebrew below. (This corresponds to verses 73-80.)
   Hebrew is written right to left. Look down the right side. What do you notice about the first letter
   of each line? _____

תהלים   119

(י) 73 יָדֶיךָ עָשׂוּנִי וַיְכוֹנְנוּנִי הֲבִינֵנִי וְאֶלְמְדָה מִצְוֹתֶיךָ:

74 יְרֵאֶיךָ יִרְאוּנִי וְיִשְׂמָחוּ כִּי לִדְבָרְךָ יִחָלְתִּי:

75 יָדַעְתִּי יְהוָה כִּי־צֶדֶק מִשְׁפָּטֶיךָ וֶאֱמוּנָה עִנִּיתָנִי:

76 יְהִי־נָא חַסְדְּךָ לְנַחֲמֵנִי כְּאִמְרָתְךָ לְעַבְדֶּךָ:

77 יְבֹאוּנִי רַחֲמֶיךָ וְאֶחְיֶה כִּי־תוֹרָתְךָ שַׁעֲשֻׁעָי:

78 יֵבֹשׁוּ זֵדִים כִּי־שֶׁקֶר עִוְּתוּנִי אֲנִי אָשִׂיחַ בְּפִקּוּדֶיךָ:

79 יָשׁוּבוּ לִי יְרֵאֶיךָ וְיֹדְעֵי עֵדֹתֶיךָ:

80 יְהִי־לִבִּי תָמִים בְּחֻקֶּיךָ לְמַעַן לֹא אֵבוֹשׁ:

3. Choose one letter of the English alphabet and try to write 8 lines, in the style of this psalm, all
   relating to the word of God.

   _____ _____
   _____
   _____
   _____
   _____
   _____
   _____
   _____

Day Four: Read Psalm 119:89-128.

1. Write out the verse that speaks of the permanence of the word of God. _____
   _____

2. What verses describe how the word of God helps a person grow intellectually, in wisdom and
   understanding? _____
   _____
   _____

3. The familiar verse 105, says, *"Your word is a lamp to my feet and a light to my path."* How has the word been a lamp and a light in your life? Be specific. _____

_____

_____

_____

4. Trivia Question: What verses in this section <u>do not</u> mention one of the synonyms listed earlier for the word of God?_____

Day Five: Read Psalm 119:129-176.

1. From this section, list and explain at least three things the word of God can do for us, in us, or through us. Example: v. 130 *"The entrance of Your words gives light."* When we read and study God's word, we begin to "see" things differently. It is like a "light" has been turned on and what we used to be unsure about, we suddenly understand clearly.

a) _____

_____

b) _____

_____

c) _____

_____

2. At what time of day does the psalmist study God's word? _____

_____

3. Fill in the blank and give the verse reference:

a) *"The _____ of Your word is truth . . ."* (_____)

b) *"I see the treacherous and am disgusted because they do not _____*

(_____).

c) *"Direct my steps by Your word, and let no _____*

(_____).

d) *"My zeal has consumed me because my enemies have _____."*

(_____).

e) *"Salvation is far from the wicked, for they do not _____."*

(_____).

4. Now take a few minutes and read the notes for this lesson.

Notes

The Word of God (Psalm 119)

With the exception of just a few verses, each verse of this psalm makes some reference to the word of God.

An Explanation

Psalm 119 is the longest psalm and the longest chapter in the Bible. It has 176 verses divided into 22 stanzas of 8 lines each. The 8-line stanzas all begin with the same Hebrew letter that appears in the heading of each section. The stanzas are arranged in alphabetic order, making this another example of the acrostic form of Hebrew poetry. With the exception of just a few verses, each verse of this psalm makes some reference to the word of God. The synonyms for Scripture used to vary the phrasing (in the New King James Version) are law, testimonies, ways, precepts, statutes, commandments, judgments, ordinances, and word.

"Law": from the Hebrew *tora* which meant "teach" or "direct." The law is meant to be more than information it is meant to be direction for life.

"Testimonies": from a word meaning "faithful witness."

"Precepts": a word drawn from the life of an overseer or military officer. It describes specific instructions of the Lord, the details.

"Statutes" : this synonym reminds us of the permanence of Scripture, since statutes were engraved or carefully inscribed in case they were needed later as a witness to a transaction.

"Commandments": this word emphasizes authority or the right to give orders.

"Judgments": the standard for dealing fairly with men is the word of God.

"Word": God's truth in any form: a promise, a statement, or a command.

Psalm 119 is not like a string of pearls in a necklace running smoothly along the same fiber, but instead like a treasure chest in which anything pulled out has a beauty and worth all its own, though unrelated to the rest.

Psalm 119 is not like a string of pearls in a necklace running smoothly along the same fiber, but instead like a treasure chest in which anything pulled out has a beauty and worth all its own, though unrelated to the rest. Each verse can stand alone, giving a warning, a praise, a promise, or a truth about the word of God.

| The Authority of Scripture | The word of God is unlike any other written material. It has been inspired and protected by God Himself. |

I. Its truths are permanent:

119: 89 *"Forever, O LORD, Your word is settled in heaven."*

119:144 *"The righteousness of Your testimonies is everlasting...."*

119: 152 *"Concerning Your testimonies, I have known of old that You have founded them forever."*

119: 160 *"The entirety of Your word is truth, and every one of Your righteous judgments endures forever."*

Matthew 5:18 *"For assuredly, I say to you, till heaven and earth pass away, one **jot** or one **tittle** will by no means pass from the law till all is fulfilled.*

> **jot** -the smallest part of a Hebrew letter

> **tittle** -a small mark like an accent or vowel marker over a letter in a word

II. Its truths are powerful:

Psalm 119:50 *"This is my comfort in my affliction, for Your word has given me life."*

Psalm 119: 93 *"I will never forget Your precepts, for by them You have given me life.*

Psalm 119:130 *"The entrance of Your words gives light; It gives understanding to the simple."*

1 Thessalonians 2:13 *"For this reason we also thank God without ceasing, because when you received the word of God which you heard from us, you welcomed it not as the word of men, but as it is in truth, the word of God, which also effectively works in you who believe."*

2 Timothy 3:16,17   *"All Scripture is given by inspiration of God, and is profitable for doctrine, for reproof, for correction, for instruction in righteousness, that the man of God may be complete, thoroughly equipped for every good work."*

Hebrews 4:12 *"For the word of God is living and powerful, and sharper than any two-edged sword, piercing even to the division of soul and spirit, and of joints and marrow, and is a **discerner** of the thoughts and intents of the heart."*

> **discerner** -one able to see even small differences

God's creative word was so precise that the earth continues just as steadily as when He created it - God did not have to issue an update or correction!

III. Its truths are precise:

Psalm 119:90b, 91 *"You established the earth, and it abides. They continue this day according to Your ordinances...."*

> **precise** -exact

God's creative word was so ***precise*** that the earth continues just as steadily as when He created it—God did not have to issue an update or correction! The revealed word of God in the Bible is so precise in its meaning that some great truths hang on one word, one letter, or a simple verb tense. For example, in defending the reality of resurrection to the Sadducees, who denied it although they believed the Scriptures were true, Jesus quoted an Old Testament passage to them: *"But concerning the resurrection of the dead, have you not read what was spoken to you by God, saying, 'I am the God of Abraham, the God of Isaac, and the God of Jacob'? God is not the God of the dead, but of the living"* (Matthew 22:31-32). His whole defense of the resurrection hinged on the tense of the verb:--"I <u>am</u>" not "I <u>was</u>!"

So What?   Since the word of God is permanent, powerful, and precise, what should we do with it? We should **put it into practice**. The blessings of the word are promised to those who obey it.

Psalm 119:1, 2 *"Blessed are the undefiled in the way, who walk in the law of the Lord! Blessed are those who keep His testimonies, who seek Him with the whole heart!"*

Psalm 119:9 *"How can a young man cleanse his way? By taking heed according to Your word."*

Psalm 119:100 *"I understand more than the ancients, because I keep Your precepts."*

Since the word of God is permanent, powerful, and precise, what should we do with it? We should put it into practice. The blessings of the word are promised to those who obey it.

We Don't Have Forever   Psalm 119 praises every aspect of God's word and urges study, memorization, understanding, and obedience. We are so blessed to have the Bible so freely available and methods of study easily found in all forms. But it will not always be so. The prophet Amos foretold of a future time:

> *"Behold, the days are coming," says the Lord GOD, "That I will send a famine on the land, not a famine of bread, nor a thirst for water, but of hearing the words of the LORD. They shall wander from sea to sea, and from north to east; they shall run to and fro, seeking the word of the LORD, but shall not find it.* (Amos 8:11,12)

Would you be able to feed the starving then? Would you know enough—have hidden enough—have obeyed enough to teach those who haven't heard? The word of God needs to be taken seriously and studied diligently.

Questions

Study Procedure: Read the Scripture references before answering questions. Unless otherwise instructed, use only the Bible in answering questions. Some questions may be more difficult than others but try to answer as many as you can. Pray for God's wisdom and understanding as you study and don't be discouraged if some answers are not obvious at first. Do not read the study notes for this lesson until AFTER you have completed your questions.

Day One: Review

MEMORY: PSALM 121:1-8

1. Write a short definition for the following words.

   a) discerner: _____

   b) jot: _____

   c) precise: _____

   d) tittle: _____

2. Give as many synonyms for the word of God that you can remember from Psalm 119.

   _____

   _____

3. Select one or two verses from Psalm 119 that illustrate what the word of God has meant to

   your life this year. _____

   _____

   _____

Day Two: Read Psalms 120-124.

This series of psalms (120-134) is called the "Songs of Ascents." They are sung when people grouped together to make the journey up to Jerusalem for worship for the appointed feasts during the year. Such times of worship met a need to get away from the daily matters that weighed down on God's people.

1. Read Psalm 120. From what did the psalmist need relief? _____

   _____

   _____

2. In Psalm 121, who is worshiped and what does He do for those who trust Him? _____

   _____

3. What location is praised in Psalm 122 and what is the reader asked to do in verses 6-9 in

   response to this information? _____

   _____

   _____

4. Read Psalm 123. With what attitude did the psalmist wait for God to respond to his emotional burdens? _____

_____

_____

5. Read Psalm 124 and then finish this statement with a personal example from your own life: *"If it had not been for the Lord who was on our side, then* _____

_____

_____

MEMORY: PSALMS 126:3; 127:1; 128:1

Day Three: Read Psalms 125-128.

1. Read Psalm 125. What are the results of trusting in God from verses 1-3? _____

_____

2. What does the psalmist ask God to do in verses 4 and 5? _____

_____

3. Read Psalm 126. Judah (southern Israel) had been captured by the Babylonians and had lived in exile from their land for 70 years.

   a) How did they feel when they returned? _____

   _____

   b) What had they learned from the experience? _____

   _____

   _____

4. Read Psalm 127. This psalm gives some truths about the family. Summarize them.

   _____

   _____

   _____

   _____

5. Read Psalm 128. What specific blessings come to the one who *"fears the Lord, who walks in His ways"*? _____

   _____

   _____

Day Four: Read Psalms 129-132.

1. Read Psalm 129. Then select the best summary from the statements below:

   a) Watch out! I've had all I can take! I'm coming after all of you!

   b) I've been knocked down, but, thanks to the Lord, not knocked out, but I hope He'll do something to those who've been doing the knocking!

   c) I am sick and tired of people making me plow crooked furrows! I can't get my work done.

   d) I'm going to tell my Father on you! Oh, my aching back!

2. Read Psalm 130. According to this psalm, we would be in big trouble if the Lord did what?

   _____

3. How much mercy and redemption does God have? _____

   _____

4. Read Psalm 131. The psalmist was humble and content.

   a) To what did he compare himself? _____

   b) Why? _____

   c) How do humility and contentment relate to worship? _____

   _____

5. Read Psalm 132. David had vowed to find an appropriate setting for the ark of the covenant which had remained in a remote area for many years (see 1 Samuel 7:1, 2 and 2 Samuel 6). Just how serious was David about this, according to this psalm?

   _____

   _____

Day Five: Read Psalms 132 (continued) and 133-135.

1. What promises had God made to David and his descendants according to Psalm 132?

   _____

   _____

2. What verses referred to the coming Anointed One or Messiah? _____

   _____

3. Read Psalm 133. The psalmist used two images to describe the beauty of unity among believers.

   a) One was refreshing dew, what was the other? _____

   _____

   b) Read Exodus 25:6; 28:39-41; and 29:6, 7. Why do you think that image was used?

   _____

   _____

4. Read Psalm 134. This was a call to worship for what "shift" of worshipers? Give verse to support your choice: _____

   a) morning　　　　　　b) noon　　　　　　c) night

5. Read Psalm 135. Fill in the blanks below from the psalm.

   a) *"For the Lord has chosen Jacob for Himself, Israel for His* _____*."*

   b) *"Whatever the Lord* _____ *He* _____*, in heaven and in earth . . ."*

   c) *"For the Lord will judge* _____*, and He will have* _____

      on _____*."*

   d) *"The idols of the nations are* _____*, the work of men's hands.*

   e) *"They have ears but do not* _____ *. . . Those who make them are*

      _____*; so is everyone who* _____*."*

6. Now take a few minutes to read your study notes for this lesson.

Notes

A Call to Worship (Psalms 120-135)

Traveling Music

ascents -the acts or processes of going up

Psalms 120-134 are "traveling songs" called "Songs of *Ascents*" and were used when traveling up to Jerusalem for worship. Since, Jerusalem was 2600 feet above sea-level, approaching it from any direction required going "up." In those days, travel was done in groups for safety as well as for fellowship. When Jesus was twelve, He participated with his family in such group travel to and from Jerusalem for Passover (Luke 2:41-45). He would have participated in the singing of these very psalms.

To worship, we must shut out the world. This often requires actually getting away from a situation and going to a quieter place.

deceitful -known for cheating or misleading

Why Do We Worship? (Psalm 120)

Why do we worship? First, because God told us to do so. The first mention in the Bible of the word "worship" was in Genesis 22:5 when Abraham went to obey God and offer Isaac. He told his servants, *"Stay here with the donkey; the lad and I will go yonder and worship, and we will come back to you."* Besides fulfilling our duty to obey God, worship meets a need we have to separate ourselves from earthly responsibilities or problems and get in the presence of God to recover. To worship, we must shut out the world. This often requires actually getting away from a situation and going to a quieter place. In Psalm 120, that's what the psalmist longed to do—to leave the people around him who spoke lies with *deceitful* tongues. He wanted to be near God, but he felt far away: *"I dwell in Meshech...among the tents of Kedar...I am for peace...they are for war"* (5-7). Meshech and Kedar were listed as men in the genealogies of the Bible. Here they represent Arab tribes that hated Israel. The situation is the same way in that region of the world today.

Worship in Jerusalem, for the writer of Psalm 120, promised relief from the constant troubles he faced. We cannot always leave where we are and go away to worship. Sometimes we must mentally shut out interruptions and stop to worship God with praise and thanksgiving right where we are—even among those who want to fight with us.

Whom Do We Worship? (Psalm 121)

The focus of our worship is God Himself, and our motivation to worship is gratitude:

v. 2 "My help comes from the Lord, Who made heaven and earth." God has done so much for us, and Psalm 121 used beautiful language to express gratitude for God's help:

v. 3 *"He will not allow your foot to be moved...."* God helps you stand up and stand strong against all opposition.

v.4 *"He who keeps Israel shall neither slumber nor sleep . . . "* God never goes on vacation or off-duty or even to bed. His help is constant.

v.5 *"The Lord is your keeper...your shade at your right hand...."* God protects and shields us.

We cannot always leave where we are and go away to worship. Sometimes we must mentally shut out interruptions and stop to worship God with praise and thanksgiving right where we are—even among those who want to fight with us.

Find time to take a moment for private worship yourself, making your own list of what God has done and continues to do for you.

Where Do We Worship? (Psalm 122)

For Israel there was one central place for worship, and that was in the city of Jerusalem, at *"the house of the Lord"* (1). First the tabernacle and later the temple housed the ark of the covenant or "Testimony" of Israel (4). We are instructed to *"pray for the peace of Jerusalem"* (6). It is a city still torn apart from time to time with religious and political **rivalries**, and yet God has some unique promises to be fulfilled in that place. Although it will always be a special place, for us today, as Christians, worship is not limited to Jerusalem. Even Jesus made that clear in His discussion with the Samaritan woman in John 4 about the correct place to worship. He said, *"Woman, believe Me, the hour is coming when you will neither on this mountain nor in Jerusalem, worship the Father...But the hour is coming, and now is, when the true worshipers will worship the Father in spirit and truth; for the Father is seeking such to worship Him. God is Spirit, and those who worship Him must worship in spirit and truth"* (John 4:21-24). Worship can take place in especially set-apart places, but it is not limited to a certain location. It is the attitude of the worshiper that is most important to God.

rivalries -the acts of competing

Worship came from the Hebrew word "shaw-khaw" which meant "to depress." In our way of speaking, it would translate to bending our bodies in homage to God to express humility before Him.

How Do We Prepare to Worship? (Psalm 123)

Worship came from the Hebrew word *"shaw-khaw"* which meant "to depress." In our way of speaking it would translate to bending our bodies in homage to God to express humility before Him. That was the position described in Psalm 123. It was revealed at the end of the psalm that the worshiper was very upset at those who had acted as if they were superior to him, but in front of God, when coming to worship, that same person was content to be inferior to God, sitting as a servant or maid, looking obediently for the next instructions. He humbled himself before the Lord. That is the first thing we must do in preparation for worship. We must remember His greatness and not spend energy trying to promote ourselves.

immovable -cannot be moved

We Couldn't Have Made It without God! (Psalm 124)

This psalm urged audience participation in its beginning lines: *"Let Israel now say--"* (1). Then it enthusiastically listed what might have happened had the Lord not been *"on our side"* (2-5). Like a bird let out of a trap, the people were grateful (7). Charles Spurgeon explained, "Our soul is like a bird for many reasons, but in this case the likeness is weakness and the ease with which it is enticed into a snare." So, for the many times God has set us free, thanksgiving should fill our worship times!

exile -banishment; forced removal from your country

Song of Security (Psalm 125)

In Psalm 124 the worshipers looked back at what they had escaped; in Psalm 125, they looked forward to where they were going. They were traveling up to Jerusalem and they sang about its geography! Just as Mount Zion was solid and immovable, standing guard with the other mountains around Jerusalem, so God surrounds His people so that they, too, are secure and **immovable**. God will not even allow another power (*"scepter"* in v. 3) to *"rest"* in His land and tempt His people. The psalmist prayed that God would keep things that way: the good people staying blessed and the ungodly people getting led away (4, 5).

Only those who have been away from home for long periods of time can appreciate the feeling of approaching a familiar place. For the psalmist, it was like a dream come true—unspeakable joy interrupted only by songs, laughter, thanksgiving, and praise.

Coming Home (Psalm 126)

For these travelers, singing about a return after a long *exile*, there really was no place like home. For seventy years Judah (southern Israel), exiled to Babylon, had lived out her "sentence" for her former years of disobedience. This psalm commemorates the exciting return to their homeland. Only those who have been away from home for long periods of time can appreciate the feeling of approaching a familiar place. For the psalmist, it was like a dream come true-unspeakable joy interrupted only by songs, laughter, thanksgiving, and praise. The people had left in sorrow but returned in joy; they had sown seed while weeping but rejoiced while harvesting the full-grown sheaves! That imagery still offers hope for those who are enduring or have just come through a sad period of time. For the Christian, sadness is only temporary. *"Those who sow in tears shall reap in joy"* (5).

Vain without God (Psalm 127)

Three times in the opening lines of Psalm 127 the word *"vain"* was used in reference to man's efforts. The word *"vain"* meant empty or useless. This was a psalm that spoke of life at home. In the home is still the place where Christian values are most tested. Let us examine the advice given.

v.1a *"Unless the Lord builds the house, they labor in vain who build it."* In a marriage, in the relationships of siblings to each other, or in child-parent relationships, unless the Lord is the foundation and highest authority in the home, the human effort spent at trying to keep it going will ultimately fail.

> *In a marriage, in the relationships of siblings to each other, or in child-parent relationships, unless the Lord is the foundation and highest authority in the home, the human effort spent at trying to keep it going will ultimately fail.*

v.1b *"Unless the Lord guards the city, the watchman stays awake in vain."* In the context of the home again, as well as in the larger context of a city, mere humans cannot protect each other from every harmful activity or violent action all the time. The Lord must be trusted as well, or security and peace will not be consistently present.

v.2 *"It is vain for you to rise up early and sit up late, to eat the bread of sorrows; for so He gives His beloved sleep."* Workaholics and **chronic** worriers do not help strengthen a family. Their actions break it down. It takes faith to trust the Lord enough to "let go" and eat, sleep, and even play along with a balanced work schedule. There is a failure to trust God where persons believe they have to work constantly and never rest.

> **chronic** -constant; continuing

The last part of this psalm reminds us that children are God's gift to parents-His reward to them. Children are precious and should be treated so. In this day of abortion and abuse, our society is crumbling at all levels because many have failed to believe that God was correct in placing an inestimable value on each human life—from **conception** to the grave to eternity. Warren Wiersbe wrote in a devotional on this psalm, "Whenever God wanted to do something great, he brought a baby into the world."

> **conception** -the beginning of life, when the sperm successfully fertilizes the egg or ovum

Starting Right (Psalm 128)

This psalm continues with more truth for a strong, godly home. The very first verse is the key: *"Blessed is every one who fears the Lord, who walks in His ways."* What is the result of such living?

1. You will be satisfied with the work you do. (2)
2. Your wife will be successful in her god-given place, in the *"very heart of your house."* (3)

3. Your children will grow up normally and in a healthy way while under your care, *"all around your table."* (3)

4. After the child-raising years, life will continue to be satisfying, especially when grandchildren come along. Children raised to maturity under the godly authority of loving parents will go out into their community as salt and light, helping and improving people and projects for the good of all. There is a very important correlation between the godly home and a moral community. (4-6)

Tough Treatment (Psalm 129)

What happens when you do fear the Lord and walk in His ways, according to Psalm 128, but outside the home you meet with opposition? Psalm 129 assured us that God is able to take care of things out in the world, too. This persecuted man may have been the first to coin the phrase "treated like dirt"! He did complain, *"The plowers plowed on my back; they made the furrows long"* (3). But, what did God do? He did not just unfasten the cords that caused the pain-He cut *"in pieces the cords of the wicked."* The last half of the psalm described the psalmist's suggestions to God for dealing with such evildoers. He wanted them to disappear like withering grass and never to feel the blessing of God. Jesus would more likely have us pray for their salvation.

furrows -a long, narrow, shallow trench made in the ground by a plow

There Is Forgiveness (Psalm 130)

As the pilgrims neared Jerusalem and sang this psalm in the series of the Songs of Ascents, they were looking forward to getting to the temple and offering their sacrifices for their sins. We know the relief of confessing sin and being fully forgiven. With the psalmist we agree: *"If You, Lord, should mark iniquity"* (keep score of sins forever), ... *"who could stand?"* None of us could! Some wonderful news followed that statement: *"But there is forgiveness with You, that You may be feared."* Charles Spurgeon wrote, "None fear the Lord like those who have experienced His forgiving love. Gratitude for pardon produces far more fear and reverence of God than the dread of punishment...." The psalm began with a cry *"out of the depths"* but ended with the assuring statement that *"with the Lord there is mercy, and with Him is <u>abundant</u> redemption. And He shall redeem Israel from <u>all</u> his iniquities"* [emphasis added].

We know the relief of confessing sin and being fully forgiven. With the psalmist we agree: "If You, Lord, should mark iniquity" (keep score of sins forever), . . . "who could stand?" None of us could!

Weaned (Psalm 131)

If you have ever been around little babies, you know that they are content for only very short times in any one place or position. Even in their mother's arms they stir and nuzzle to be fed, comforted, entertained, or changed. Part of the growth process is getting to the point where the ability to wait longer without special attention increases more and more. That is the image David used in this psalm credited to him about humbly waiting before God *"like a weaned child with his mother."*

weaned -to detach from that to which he was accustomed; removed from mother's milk to another form of nourishment

David had grown up enough to be satisfied without special favors, attention, or miracles, and enjoyed just being near God in worship or fellowship. Have you made progress in this area?

Promises to Keep (Psalm 132)

This was a messianic psalm which reviewed God's covenant promises to David that would be continued through those born in his family line. The promises would have their highest fulfillment at the revealing of the Anointed One. "Anointed One" is the same term as Messiah (Hebrew) and Christ (Greek). The family line of David had been dotted with members who were not godly in the way David had been. Those members failed to enjoy the blessings of those staying faithful. But the psalmist began this psalm by reminding God of what a good choice had been made in blessing David, because David certainly loved God. He vowed to find a suitable place for the ark to rest in Jerusalem, and accomplished that (1-9). *"For Your servant David's sake,"* the psalmist pleaded, *"Do not turn away the face of Your Anointed."* In other words, even if we as a people have come short of consistent obedience, for the sake of Your word to David, let Messiah come. God responded that He had certainly chosen Zion (Jerusalem) for His *"resting place"* and that in that city He would ultimately make *"the horn of David grow"* and *"prepare a lamp for My Anointed,"* defeating all enemies and crowning Messiah. The word *"horn"* in v. 17 was frequently used in the Bible as a symbol of power. God promised to let the power with which He had anointed David as king grow to its greatest height in the Anointed One who would one day come. The gospels recorded that power in Christ's first coming to earth, and Jerusalem will be the setting for the revelation of that power when He returns.

The gospels recorded that power in Christ's first coming to earth, and Jerusalem will be the setting for the revelation of that power when He returns.

Beautiful Unity (Psalm 133)

A special blend of fragrance and oil (Exodus 25:6) was used to anoint prophets, priests, and kings for the duties to which God had called them. There was usually a public ceremony at which time the oil would be poured on their heads and allowed to freely run down over their clothing to the ground. It symbolized God's power on them, and, as the fragrance dispersed, the witnesses would be pleasantly encouraged to remember that God was again meeting their needs for leadership and help. In Psalm 133, David wrote that to see brothers living together in unity was just as beautiful an experience as the anointing of a leader, and as refreshing as the morning dew on a mountain top. Unity is soothing, peaceful, and powerful. United people can stand up against outside attack, while divided they fall easily. If there are fussing and fighting in your home, school, business, or church, God is not pleased. He longs for the beauty of godly unity. But there will never be unity without humility. It often only takes one to start changing a negative situation to a positive one. Are you willing to be that one?

United people can stand up against outside attack, while divided they fall easily. If there are fussing and fighting in your home, school, business, or church, God is not pleased. He longs for the beauty of godly unity.

Destination Reached (Psalm 134)

This short song was the last of the Songs of Ascents and marked the arrival of the travelers at the house of the Lord. This psalmist chose to motivate those on nightwatch at the temple as they worshiped the Lord: *"Lift up your hands in the sanctuary, and bless the Lord, the Lord who made heaven and earth Bless you from Zion!"*

Hallelujah! (Psalm 135)

Our lesson ends with a psalm which repeats one of the most familiar psalm phrases, *"Praise the Lord!"* The Hebrew for that was *"hallelujah"* or praise *(hallel)* to Jehovah *(jah)*. This psalm was an appropriate one on which to end, because it reviews for us the basics of worship:

Whom do we worship? The Lord (1).

Why do we worship Him? Because He is good and it is quite pleasant to praise Him (3).

Where do we worship Him? In the special places like the *"house of God"* (2) but also in the "regular" places by choosing to shut out the world for a few moments and concentrate on God and His great goodness toward us.

How long do we worship Him? Forever. *"Your name, O Lord, endures forever"* (13).

Is there any other god to worship? No, all others are just powerless idols (15-18).

Worshiping God requires an emptying of self. Confess your sins, and receive His cleansing.

Just Checking

Is it time for you to go "up to Jerusalem"? To get away from those that don't believe as you do or serve God as you do? Is it time to come apart and look at your family life or friendships and re-order them in God's way? Is it time to worship whole-heartedly--enjoying the daily journey as well as the destination? How do we start? First, commit yourself. Mark a time on your daily calendar as well as weekly calendar. Even consider special events like retreats throughout the year. Next, prepare yourself. Worshiping God requires an emptying of self. Confess your sins, and receive His cleansing. Then, include others. Hebrews 10:25 warned us not to *"forsake the assembling of ourselves together, as is the manner of some, but exhorting one another, and so much the more as you see the Day approaching."* Worshiping in a group is so encouraging! Consider bringing an offering. Our time, talent, and treasure all belong to God-offer them back for His use and direction. Then, expect to be affected. Someone wrote that we become like what we worship. Expect that time in the presence of God will bring positive changes in your life. Finally, enjoy yourself. Sing, speak, look, feel, smile, give thanks and praise as you count your blessings!

Is it time for you to go "up to Jerusalem"? To get away from those that don't believe as you do or serve God as you do?

Questions

Study Procedure: Read the Scripture references before answering questions. Unless otherwise instructed, use only the Bible in answering questions. Some questions may be more difficult than others but try to answer as many as you can. Pray for God's wisdom and understanding as you study and don't be discouraged if some answers are not obvious at first. Do not read the study notes for this lesson until AFTER you have completed your questions.

Day One: Review

1. Vocabulary Review. Fill in the vocabulary word that matches the definitions below:

ACROSS

1. known for cheating or misleading
4. to detach from that to which he was accustomed; removed from mother's milk to another form of nourishment
7. cannot be moved
9. a long, narrow, shallow trench made in the ground by a plow

DOWN

2. the beginning of life
3. the acts of competing
5. banishment; forced removal from your country
6. constant; continuing
8. the acts or processes of going up

Review of Psalms 120-135.

1. Summarize what you learned about worship from the psalms you studied and the notes you read.

_____

_____

_____

_____

2. What two psalms had something to say about a godly home and family? _____

3. Which psalm mentioned the *Anointed One*? _____

Day Two: Read Psalms 136-138.   *MEMORY: PSALMS 136:1; 138:7-8*

1. Read Psalm 136. Write down the line that is repeated like a chorus: _____

   _____

2. Match the following sections with the period of history being described.

   _____ Creation   _____ The Exodus out of Egypt   _____ The Entrance into the Promised Land

   a) 136:21, 22   b) 136:10-20   c) 136:4-9

3. Read Psalm 137 and Jeremiah 25:1-14 and Lamentations 5. Why were the people of Israel in

   Babylon? _____

   _____

   _____

4. What do you think it takes to be able to *"sing the Lord's song in a foreign land"*?

   _____

   _____

   _____

   _____

5. Read Psalm 138. This is the first of eight psalms in this lesson attributed to David. The setting
   of this psalm is a place distant from Jerusalem, yet David still worships God whole-heartedly.
   Which verses indicate that he was trusting God for help with his problems? _____

   MEMORY: PSALMS 139:1-2, 14, 23-24; 141:3

Day Three: Read Psalms 139-142.

1. Read Psalm 139. In your own words, summarize the theme for each section:

   a) vs. 1-6 _____

   _____

   b) vs. 7-12 _____

   _____

   c) vs. 14-18 _____

   _____

   d) vs. 19-22 _____

   _____

   e) vs. 23-24 _____

2. Read Psalm 140. The psalm began, *"Deliver me, O Lord, from evil men."* Give a few examples of just how evil they were. _____

_____

_____

3. Read Psalm 141. Since David was not in Jerusalem to participate in the usual morning and evening sacrifices and worship, what did he ask God to accept instead? _____

_____

4. Write down the verse in Psalm 141 which asked for God's help in controlling the following:

   a) words _____

   b) desires _____

   c) behavior, in general _____

5. Read Psalm 142. The setting of this psalm was a cave in which David was hiding from his enemies. Describe a time when you felt alone and perhaps afraid. What verse of this psalm could you have prayed at that time? Did you pray? What happened? _____

_____

_____

_____

_____

MEMORY: PSALMS 145:8-9, 18

Day Four: Read Psalms 143-145.

1. Read Psalm 143. Draw a line to the phrase that completes the requests taken from verses 7-11.

   a) Answer me   in the land of righteousness.

   b) Cause me   for Your name's sake!

   c) Deliver me from   my enemies; In You I take shelter.

   d) Teach me   to do Your will, For You are my God.

   e) Lead me   speedily, O Lord; my spirit fails!

   f) Revive me   to know the way in which I should walk.

2. Read Psalm 144. List the words or phrases which reveal that David had warfare on his mind at this time in his life. _____

_____

_____

3. Read Psalm 145. List all the synonyms for the verb *praise* that you find in this psalm. _____

_____

4. Psalm 145 reads like an encyclopedia of God's wonderful abilities and activities. List some that you personally appreciate in your present stage of life. _____

_____

_____

Day Five: Read Psalms 146-150.

1. What is the first line of each of these psalms (146-150)? _____

2. The Hebrew word for that phrase is *hallelujah* and these five psalms are called the *"Hallels."*

   a) What verses in Psalm 146 praise God for His personal involvement in the needs of people?

   _____

   b) Who else in the New Testament had this same power to show compassion? _____

   _____

3. Fill in the blanks from Psalm 147.

   a) He heals the _____ and _____.

   b) He counts the number of the _____ and He _____ by name.

   c) His understanding is _____.

   d) The Lord lifts up the _____; He casts the _____ to the ground.

   e) He gives to the _____ its food.

   f) He has blessed your _____ within you.

   g) He causes His _____ to blow and the _____ flow.

4. Read Psalm 148. For what reasons is creation called to praise God? _____

   _____

5. Read Psalm 149 and Ephesians 6:14-17. According to these verses, what are important weapons in spiritual warfare? _____

   _____

6. Read Psalm 150. Answer the following questions about worship with verses from this psalm.

   a) Where do we worship? _____   d) Who should worship Him? _____

   b) Why do we worship Him? _____

   c) How do we worship Him? _____

7. Now take a few minutes and read the notes for this lesson.

Notes

The Hallels (Psalms 136-150)

The Great Hallel (Psalm 136)

This psalm was called "The Great Hallel." It would have been sung by two choirs, the second answering the first with the repeating line: *"For His mercy endures forever."* The word "mercy" was the Hebrew *hesed*, or "covenant love," and would be literally, "His covenant love never ends." The first line, *"Oh, give thanks to the Lord"* implied that the worshiper should carefully consider what God's covenant love had accomplished, and then "speak it out" in thanksgiving. Verses 3-9 described God's work in creation with an emphasis on the fact that He did all those wonderful things in the universe because of His love for people! Verses 10-30 recounted the specific rescues God had made on behalf of Israel during the exodus era. Notice the mention of the kings Sihon and Og. These were mentioned many times in Scripture as examples of God's great help in defense of Israel. At the time Israel faced them, they had not yet had to act as an army—they had been in slavery for four hundred years, untrained in warfare. King Og was the last member of the Rephaim or giants (Deut. 3:11) whose bed, or as some scholars think, whose coffin, was six feet wide and thirteen and a half feet long! Israel really appreciated God's intervention in that struggle! Verses 21 and 22 called for praise to God for His mercy during the settlement in the Promised Land in Canaan, and the final verses summarized, in general terms, God's loving and practical help: *"[God] remembered us in our lowly state, …rescued us from our enemies…[and] gives food to all flesh."* For generations of covenant love, Israel was called to praise God.

"Oh, give thanks to the Lord" implied that the worshiper should carefully consider what God's covenant love had accomplished, and then "speak it out" in thanksgiving.

Singing in a Strange Land (Psalm 137)

To understand this psalm, you need to know the history of that period. The prophet Jeremiah warned Judah (southern Israel) about what was going to happen because they had failed to repent and turn their nation back to God. As their northern sister Israel had done, they would face judgment: *"Therefore thus says the LORD of hosts: 'Because you have not heard My words, behold, I will send and take all the families of the north,' says the LORD, 'and Nebuchadnezzar the king of Babylon, My servant, and will bring them against this land, against its inhabitants, and against these nations all around, and will utterly destroy them, and make them an astonishment, a hissing, and perpetual desolations. Moreover I will take from them the voice of mirth and the voice of gladness, the voice of the bridegroom and the voice of the bride, the sound of the millstones and the light of the lamp. And this whole land shall be a desolation and an astonishment, and these nations shall serve the king of Babylon seventy years'"* (Jeremiah 25:8-11).

According to Psalm 137, once taken into captivity, God's people hung up their harps, feeling they had lost all reason to sing (1-4). They would not sing in response to their captor's request for a song of Zion, and yet, the people that needed to hear God's songs the most, were the people who opposed them. However, they lost their song because they had not dealt with their sin. They wept over being held captive but not over the rebellion against God that caused them to be there. They were blind to their own sins and to the fact that the real problem lay in their relationship to God, not in the removal from their land. How they longed to return to Jerusalem, and vowed never to forget her (5, 6)! Then they called for God to do to Babylon what that nation had done to them, even to the horrible action of dashing babies against rocks to kill them. They wanted out of their painful situation, but they did not want to face the sins that caused the judgment. That sounds familiar. We, too, often moan over what we think is the too-strict discipline of parents, teachers, coaches, or bosses and completely ignore the part our actions had in causing those in authority to "react" to limit the damage. Next time you find yourself in trouble, ask honestly, "What was my part in this?" If the Holy Spirit brings to your mind some specific sin, confess it to God and to the ones you have hurt or disappointed. We should ask for forgiveness of God instead of for vengeance upon those used by God to discipline us.

> *However, they lost their song because they had not dealt with their sin. They wept over being held captive but not over the rebellion against God that caused them to be there.*

David Is Back! (Psalm 138)

The next eight psalms (138-145) were credited to David. In Psalm 138, David was away from his beloved Jerusalem, but that did not stop his worship or praise of God. *"I will praise You with my whole heart;...I will worship toward Your holy temple, and praise Your name for Your lovingkindness and Your truth; in the day when I cried out, You answered me..."* (1-3). Do you still pray when you are away from your home church, your family, or Christian friends?

Next, David made some interesting comments on the power and value of the word of God: *"...You have magnified Your word above all Your name,"* and *"All the kings of the earth shall praise You, O LORD, when they hear the words of Your mouth"* (2c and 4). The word of God, evidently studied and remembered by David, had kept his faith strong in the God who had given it. When distance and loneliness rob us of our "feelings" of closeness to God, the word promises that the relationship is still to be trusted. David knew that and stated, *"Though I walk in the midst of trouble, You will revive me; ...The Lord will **perfect** that which concerns me"* (7, 8). What a statement and hope on which to hold! Separation cannot rob the Christian of his security in God.

> **perfect** -to end, finish, fulfill, or accomplish

Inside and Out (Psalm 139)

This wonderful psalm about how well God knows us and cares about us was written in four stanzas with six verses each. They can be summarized by their main points:

Omniscience (1-4) There is nothing about us that God does not know! *"For there is not a word on my tongue, but behold, O LORD, You know it altogether"* (4). What wonderful truth— He knows everything about us and still loves us! Our lives are significant.

omniscience - knowledge of everything

Omnipresence (7-12) The presence of God cannot be escaped, *"Indeed, the darkness shall not hide from You, but the night shines as the day; the darkness and the light are both alike to You"* (12). Nothing can happen to us that will put us too far away for God to help. Our lives are secure.

omnipresence -ability to be present everywhere at once

Omnipotence (13-18) Even before birth (13-15), even before conception (16), God knew what we would be like and wrote down *"the days fashioned"* for us in His book. The truth that God counts life precious and significant, even in the womb, and that no person is a "mistake" since He knew all about them and their days *"when as yet there were none of them"* (16) should be a "wake-up" call to our nation which has allowed abortion-on-demand for almost three decades. Even before David wrote this psalm, the Old Testament law was clear on the value of life in the womb. A passage in Exodus 21:22-25 stated that if a fight occurred and it resulted in a baby being born dead, then the assailant had to pay with his life. With His laws, God protected the unborn, but we have failed to follow that example.

omnipotence - unlimited and unequaled power

Our part (19-24) In response to such great truths about how much God knows, how unlimited He is in His influence, and how powerful He is in His purposes, David voiced a response. In verses 19-22 he asked for the permanent removal of all who fail to love such a wonderful Lord. He counted God's enemies as his own enemies. But the final verses are the most helpful to us: *"Search me, O God, and know my heart; try me, and know my anxieties; and see if there is any wicked way in me, and lead me in the way everlasting"* (23, 24). God already knows everything, but this prayer is that He would show us those things that we need to see in order to repent and change to please Him. That is the proper response to this psalm's truths about the nature of God. He is so wonderful, and when we really realize it, we should just want to please Him with every minute of our lives.

The truth that God counts life precious and significant, even in the womb, and that no person is a "mistake" since He knew all about them and their days "when as yet there were none of them" (16) should be a "wake-up" call to our nation which has allowed abortion-on-demand for almost three decades.

Help! (Psalm 140)

Everyone who attempts to serve God will face opposition stirred up by Satan. David was no exception. The weapons used in David's time are the same ones used

His attitude of gratitude should be adopted by us when facing our problems because it shows that we trust God to see us through.

today: sharp tongues (1-3) and deliberate traps (4, 5). In verses 6-11, David prayed to God to make them stop, *"Do not grant…the desires of the wicked; Do not further his wicked scheme…."* As usual, David ended with a statement of faith: *"I know that the Lord will maintain the cause of the afflicted, and justice for the poor. Surely the righteous shall give thanks to Your name;…* (12,13). His attitude of gratitude should be adopted by us when facing our problems because it shows that we trust God to see us through.

Away but Worshiping (Psalm 141)

David was away from God's house, but he knew he could worship the Lord even without a priest or an altar. His prayer would be like the incense on the golden altar and the lifting of his hands in praise like the burnt offering on the brazen altar. [See Exodus 30:1-10 and 29:38-41]. His prayer in verse 3 revealed a practical knowledge of our human problem of sinning in what we say, *"Set a guard, …over my mouth; keep watch over the door of my lips."* Then he also prayed about the common temptation to "fit in" with those we are around: *"Do not incline my heart to any evil thing, to practice wicked works with men who work iniquity; and do not let me eat their delicacies"* (4). C.S. Lewis in his book <u>Screwtape Letters</u> commented on this problem of letting ourselves enjoy the same things ungodly people do: "There is a subtle play of looks and tones and laughs by which a *mortal* can imply that he is of the same party as those to whom he is speaking….He will assume, at first only by his manner, but presently by his words, all sorts of *cynical* and *skeptical* attitudes which are not really his. But…they may become his. All mortals tend to turn into the thing they are pretending to be." In order to keep from drifting away from what he knew to be right while surrounded by people who did not love God as he did, David welcomed others to help him stay right with God: *"Let the righteous strike me; it shall be kindness…let my head not refuse it"* (5). Verses 6 and 7 are a bit unclear but seem to mean that David believed that the unrighteous judges would one day see that his words to them were true, and that they should have listened to him, just as he had been willing to listen to righteous correction. He ended with a statement of faith and a prayer for help, and like David, we should keep our eyes on God and take all our directions from Him.

delicacies -carefully selected or choice foods

mortal -a human being

cynical -believing that all people have selfish motives

skeptical -questioning; doubtful

In the Cave (Psalm 142)

The "contemplation" mentioned in the small print before this psalm came from the Hebrew word *maschil* and was used to describe a psalm that gave advice or instruction. This was another of the psalms written while David was head-quartered in a cave while being hunted by Saul. [See 1 Sam.22:1-2;24:1ff.] In verse 1, the *"I cry aloud"* meant literally "I shriek!" David was very emotional in this call for help to God, feeling overwhelmed, alone, and trapped: *"Refuge has failed me; no one cares for my soul"* (4). He was very "low" (6); and he wanted out of his *"prison"* (7). But, as usual, he did not end with a selfish thought; he said he wanted out of his trouble so *"that I may praise Your name"* (7). We need to see things in that way, too. God's help should always be a **stimulus** to tell others about Him.

From the Battlefield (Psalm 143)

From the battlefield of his troubles, David cried out like a wounded soldier. He knew that there was nothing in him personally to cause God to answer him (2), so only on the basis of God's faithful and righteous character, not his own, he cried for help (1). Crushed by the enemy (3,4), David remembered better days and longed for God to return to help him (5,6). The rest of the lines of this psalm were short and intense, typical of the way someone would talk when hurting or afraid: *"Answer me…, Cause me…, Deliver me…, Teach me…, Lead me…, [and] Revive me….For I am Your servant"* (7-12). David humbly recognized, and so should we, that he was God's servant; God was not his. Our attitude should always be humble: we can ask in prayer, but we must not demand His response.

David humbly recognized, and so should we, that he was God's servant; God was not his. Our attitude should always be humble: we can ask in prayer, but we must not demand His response.

Singing Soldier (Psalm 144)

David praised God *"Who trains my hands for war, and my fingers for battle"* (1). A nation must defend itself from outside attack that destroys the peace within. The first action of defense, however, should be to pray about it to God. Humbling himself (3,4), David asked God to show His greatness to all his enemies (5-8). Then, the soldier started singing! In verses 9-11, David suddenly relaxed. Having asked God for help, he had the faith to sing about the future. David looked ahead to his children growing up in safety and beauty. The food supplies would be so abundant that the barns would be full and the animals would be healthy enough to reproduce in great numbers, and there would be peace and happiness for his people (12-14). What is the cause of such happiness? David stated it in the final verse, *"Happy are the people whose God is the Lord."* G. Campbell Morgan gave this application: "The patriotism of the Christian is such love of country that it seeks at all times and under all circumstances to bring the policies and activities of that country into agreement with the will and way of God." Such a country would be truly a happy place!

An Alphabet of Praise (Psalm 145)

This was the final psalm of David included in the Psalter and the last using the acrostic method of composition. However, there was one letter missing in this one, as you can see even in English because there are 21 verses instead of the 22 needed for the entire Hebrew alphabet. The missing letter was *nun*. Some scholars think it was a copying error long ago while others believe it was left out on purpose to illustrate that our praises and prayers are always a bit imperfect. We will not get to speak our greatest praise till heaven! David gave great effort to covering many of God's wonderful characteristics in the twenty-one verses remaining. He praised God's greatness, majesty, awesome acts, grace, mercy, and glory.

The Best Help (Psalm 146)

Each of these last five psalms began with *"Praise the Lord!"* which in Hebrew was *"Hallel!"* Psalm 146 discouraged trust in mere human power, *"Do not put your trust in princes"* (3), while urging hope and trust in *"the God of Jacob"*(5). He reminded the reader of God's place as creator and keeper of everything and everyone (5-7). He even listed the personal care of God for individuals which Jesus so beautifully exhibited when He came to bring salvation (8-9). This certainly is motivation enough to *"praise the Lord"*!

God is so wonderful. He cares for the individual as well as the universe: "He heals the brokenhearted," calls each star by name, and makes grass grow to feed the wild beasts.

Praise Is Beautiful (Psalm 147)

Why should we praise God? *"...For it is good to sing praises to our God; for it is pleasant, and praise is beautiful."* God is so wonderful. He cares for the individual as well as the universe: *"He heals the brokenhearted,"* calls each star by name, and makes grass grow to feed the wild beasts (3-9). The King of Creation is also the Caretaker of His creatures. To such greatness, we must respond. But what can we do to please God? *"The Lord takes pleasure in those who fear Him, In those who hope in His mercy"*(11). God wants us to love, reverence, and obey Him. That will bring blessing to us and pleasure to Him.

No One Excused (Psalm 148)

The writer of this psalm was determined to have a full choir! This psalm read like a roll call of creation. These choir members were recruited for a universal chorus of praise: heavens, heights, angels, hosts, sun, moon, stars, waters, sea creatures, fire, hail, wind, hills, trees, beasts, cattle, insects, birds, kings, judges, and old as well as young men and women. The whole purpose of such a gathering was to *"praise the name of the LORD, for His name alone is exalted."*

Praise as a Weapon (Psalm 149)

In verses 1-4 God's people were called again to *"sing to the Lord a new song"*—to bring fresh expression to their love for Him. With dancing and musical accompaniment they were to sing praises to Him, and the result would be that God would *"beautify the humble with salvation."* The second half introduced a new thought to the Psalms, but one that had been seen before in Israel's history. This truth was that praise can be a powerful spiritual weapon. Several times in Scripture, praising God was all that Israel was asked to do. [See 2 Chronicles 20:1-30.] God responded to their praise by defeating their enemies for them. Another spiritual weapon was named along with praise: *"Let the high praises of God be in their mouth, and a two-edged sword in their hand, to execute vengeance on the nations, and punishments on the peoples"* (6,7). The two-edged sword frequently referred to the word of God. Knowledge and application of the word of God are still essential for spiritual victories (Ephesians 6:17 and Hebrews 4:12).

Knowledge and application of the word of God are still essential for spiritual victories.

The Last Psalm (Psalm 150)

How appropriate that the final psalm of the Hebrew hymnal was a strong but simple call to everyone to praise God. Where should we praise Him?—wherever we are (1). Why should we praise Him?—because of what He does and who He is (2). How should we praise Him?—with voices and instruments (3, 4). Who should praise Him?—everything that breathes (6). We have just finished 150 examples of and reasons for praising God. But here is one more summary of its meaning: "Praise is like a bride's wedding ring. Her husband rejoices to see her wear it; she herself delights in it; and it testifies to all of the appropriateness of the couple's relationship." So praise pleases God, blesses us, and explains to the world that we are in an eternal covenant with a wonderful Lord. Increase your praise!

BIBLE QUEST

Questions

Study Procedure: Read the Scripture references before answering questions. Unless otherwise instructed, use only the Bible in answering questions. Some questions may be more difficult than others but try to answer as many as you can. Pray for God's wisdom and understanding as you study and don't be discouraged if some answers are not obvious at first. Do not read the study notes for this lesson until AFTER you have completed your questions.

Day One: Vocabulary Review - Match the word with its definition.

_____1.	cynical		a) to end, finish, fulfill or accomplish
_____2.	delicacies		b) knowledge of everything
_____3.	mortal		c) ability to be present everywhere at once
_____4.	omnipresence		d) unlimited and unequalled power
_____5.	omnipotence		e) something that excites to action
_____6.	omniscience		f) questioning; doubtful
_____7.	perfect		g) believing that all people have selfish motives
_____8.	skeptical		h) a human being
_____9.	stimulus		i) carefully selected or choice foods

General Review:

1. What are the three main themes of the book of Psalms? (Hint: Each starts with "c.")

    _____

2. Hebrew poetry, like that which is found in the Psalms, uses a device called parallelism which is

    a) rhyming words at the end of each phrase

    b) keeping each line from touching the next one

    c) pairing similar or opposite ideas to describe one main thought

3. Psalms were originally written to be used in personal or group worship of God as

    a) songs   b) sermons   c) study guides

Day Two: Match the following description below with the appropriate psalm.

_____1.	the longest psalm	a) Psalm 1
_____2.	the shortest psalm	b) Psalm 19
_____3.	a psalm by Moses	c) Psalm 51
_____4.	a psalm prophetic of the Crucifixion	d) Psalm 22
_____5.	a psalm written after David's sin with Bathsheba	e) Psalm 91
_____6.	one of the psalms from the group called the *"Hallels"*	f) Psalm 117
_____7.	a psalm which praises God for His creative and His written word	g) Psalm 119
_____8.	a psalm that describes what brings blessing/happiness	h) Psalm 150

MEMORY: PSALM 146:2; 147:5, 11

Day Three: Try to answer the following questions from your memory of Old Testament history and study of the Psalms.

1. Who was the first king of Israel? _____

2. What did he do that angered God and caused God to select another to be king? _____
    _____

3. Who was the prophet that anointed David to be king? _____

4. Why was David so sure that he could defeat the giant Goliath when no one else had dared to
    try? _____
    _____

5. Why did David have to live in the wilderness for so many years after he had been anointed king?
    _____
    _____

6. Who was David's best friend? _____

7. Describe how David and his friend sealed their covenant of friendship._____
    _____
    _____

8. What prophet confronted David about his sin with Bathsheba? _____

9. Which son of David rebelled against him, causing David to go into exile? _____

10. What happened to that son? _____
    _____

11. What relative of Jonathan did David find to bless? _____

12. What are some of the English translations of the Hebrew word *hesed* describing covenant love?
    _____
    _____

Day Four: Finish these quotations and match them with the correct reference. (Note: NKJV was used)

1. *The sacrifices of God are a b_____ s_____, a broken and contrite
    h_____-- these, O God, You will not despise. Psalm _____.*

2. *One thing I have desired of the Lord, that will I seek: that I may d_____ in the h_____ of the
    L_____ all the days of my life. Psalm _____.*

3. *But, You, O Lord, are a s_____ for me, my g_____ and the One who lifts up my h_____.*

   Psalm _____

4. *I will sing of the m_____ of the Lord forever; with my m_____ will I make known Your*

   f_____ to all generations. Psalm _____

5. *Let everything that has b_____ p_____ the Lord. Praise the LORD! Psalm _____*

6. *D_____ yourself also in the LORD, and He shall give you the d_____ of your h_____.*

   Psalm _____

7. *The LORD said to my LORD, "S_____ at My right h_____, till I make Your e_____ Your*

   footstool." Psalm _____

8. *Oh, how I love Your l_____! It is my m_____ all the d_____. Psalm _____*

9. *The LORD is your k_____; the LORD is your s_____, at your r_____ h _____.*

   Psalm _____

10. *Give unto the LORD the g_____ due to His n_____; W_____ the LORD in the*

   b_____ of h_____. Psalm _____

       3:3   27:4   29:2   37:4   51:17   89:1   110:1   119:97   121:5   150:6

MEMORY: PSALM 150:1-6

Day Five:

1. Take a few moments to think about your study of Psalms. Write down below at least three things you have learned from this study. _____

_____

_____

_____

_____

2. If you had to do a short devotional from the Psalms, which psalm would you use as the text and what points would you emphasize. _____

_____

_____

_____

_____

_____

_____

3. Word Search: Try to find the following words which were so common in the book of Psalms.

mercy	praise
obedience	glory
lovingkindness	prayer
peace	transgression
sanctuary	law
enemies	creation
testimony	godly
covenant	

L	O	V	I	N	G	K	I	N	D	N	E	S	S	U
W	P	T	S	O	B	E	D	I	E	N	C	E	A	P
O	K	A	E	I	A	P	C	O	V	E	N	A	N	T
J	Y	Q	I	S	R	D	R	O	T	K	O	O	C	C
J	O	G	M	S	T	P	W	A	L	C	I	F	T	G
K	C	O	E	E	E	I	Q	G	I	K	T	W	U	S
Z	F	D	N	R	B	A	M	L	G	S	A	M	A	Y
C	E	Z	E	G	S	D	Y	O	E	R	E	L	R	S
P	T	U	C	S	M	N	D	R	N	E	R	J	Y	D
T	W	Y	A	N	K	L	H	Y	U	Y	C	O	C	R
R	I	F	E	A	Y	B	T	I	F	A	S	Y	R	L
S	L	K	P	R	F	G	G	T	B	R	I	H	E	E
A	Q	P	S	T	M	C	S	Y	L	P	A	L	M	S

4. Now take a few minutes and read the notes for this lesson for an introduction to Proverbs.

Notes

Proverbs Are Practical

Let's Review

The study of the Book of Job showed us that there is more going on in our lives than meets the eye. A spiritual battle is raging in which Satan, God's enemy, is trying to get us to abandon our faith. Job went through long and terrible suffering—physically, mentally, emotionally, and spiritually—without the knowledge we have that Satan was involved. Yet, even without that information, Job believed God to be sovereign and knew Him to be worthy of worship and obedience even if there were no visible earthly benefits. God revealed Himself as Creator-God—and Job humbled himself and worshiped.

Then we went into the Bible's textbook on praise and worship—the book of Psalms. It was full of examples of prayer and songs of praise. When we are in covenant with God, we are always blessed—even when enemies are trying their best to cut us off. Through the life of David we learned that God is personally involved in the lives of His children.

After we (1) have entered God's covenant through faith as Job did by believing his Redeemer would come [note: we are saved the same way, except we believe our Redeemer has come] and (2) have begun to maintain a regular communication with Him through prayer and praise as David did, then (3) we are ready to put our faith into action in our daily lives. As Job taught us about trust and Psalms taught us about prayer and praise, Proverbs will give practical advice for letting God's light shine through us to a dark world as we

As Job taught us about trust and Psalms taught us about prayer and praise, Proverbs will give practical advice for letting God's light shine through us to a dark world as we go about our everyday activities.

go about our everyday activities. Derek Kidner, writing for Tyndale's Old Testament series said of Proverbs that " it is a book which seldom takes you to church. Like its own figure of Wisdom, it calls across to you in the street about some everyday matter, or points things out at home. Its function in Scripture is to put godliness into working clothes; to name business and society as spheres in which we are to acquit ourselves with credit to our Lord, and in which we are to look for His training" (Proverbs, p. 35).

Someone described a proverb as a short statement based on long experience. Another called proverbs "holy probabilities." Based on the observations of the wisest man in the world, and under the Holy Spirit's direction, the proverbs captured big truths in small spaces.

What Are Proverbs?

Someone described a proverb as a short statement based on long experience. Another called proverbs "holy probabilities." Based on the observations of the wisest man in the world, and under the Holy Spirit's direction, the proverbs captured big truths in small spaces. The word "proverb" in Hebrew means 'to be like,' and so many of the proverbs compare or contrast ideas or actions.

How Do They Look?

Proverbs most commonly are **couplets** in three styles:

couplets -two successive lines of poetry that relate in meaning, sound, or rhythm. From a French word meaning "pair."

Contrasting: A key word in a contrasting proverb is BUT.

> 13:1 *A wise son heeds his father's instruction, BUT a scoffer does not listen to rebuke.*

> 13:24 *He who spares his rod hates his son, BUT he who loves him disciplines him diligently.*

Completing: The key word is AND or SO. The second statement completes the first.

> 16:3 Commit your works to the Lord, AND your thoughts will be established.

Comparing: The key words are BETTER……THAN; AS…..SO; LIKE….SO.

> 11:22 *AS a ring of gold in a swine's snout, SO is a lovely woman who lacks discretion.*

> 15:16 *BETTER is a little with the fear of the Lord THAN great treasure with trouble.*

Who Wrote Them?

King Solomon is credited with the proverbs in chapters 1-29. He uttered some 3,000 proverbs during his reign, of which about 900 are preserved here (1 Kings 4:32). A man named Agur was named as the author of chapter 30 and King Lemuel of chapter 31.

<table>
<tr><td>

Facts about Solomon from 1 Kings

</td><td>

a. Solomon was the son of David and Bathsheba. He had been promised the throne, but brother Adonijah tried to take it first.

b. Solomon was made legal king by David before David died.

</td></tr>
</table>

When Solomon asked for wisdom to lead God's people, God was pleased and gave him that plus wealth and power, too.

c. In 1 Kings 3, after worshiping God, Solomon was visited by God in a dream and was asked what he wanted God to do for him. When Solomon asked for wisdom to lead God's people, God was pleased and gave him that plus wealth and power, too.

intermarry -to marry, a member of another group

d. Solomon did not always obey what he knew. *"But King Solomon loved many foreign women, as well as the daughter of Pharaoh: women of the Moabites, Ammonites, Edomites, Sidonians, and Hittites; from the nations of whom the LORD had said to the children of Israel, 'You shall not* **intermarry** *with them, nor they with you. Surely they will turn away your hearts after their gods.' Solomon clung to these in love. And he had seven hundred wives, princesses, and three hundred* **concubines***; and his wives turned away his heart. For it was so, when Solomon was old, that his wives turned his heart after other gods; and his heart was not loyal to the LORD his God, as was the heart of his father David"* (1 Kings 11:1-4).

concubines -women who live with a man without being married to him; these women usually have inferior legal and social status to lawful wives

However, in his writing of Ecclesiastes, Solomon, at the end of his life after he had tried everything else, wrote: *"Let us hear the conclusion of the whole matter: Fear God and keep His commandments, for this is man's all. For God will bring every work into judgment, including every secret thing, whether good or evil."* (Eccl. 12:13-14)

equity -the state, ideal, or quality of being just, impartial, and fair

<table>
<tr><td>

What Is The Purpose Of Proverbs?

</td><td>

The purpose is given in the opening verses: *"To know wisdom and instruction, to perceive the words of understanding, to receive the instruction of wisdom, justice, judgment, and* **equity***..."* (1:2,3).

</td></tr>
</table>

... the most important part of wisdom is knowing, loving, and obeying God, which is "the fear of the Lord." This fear is positive. Instead of making a person run from God in terror, it draws him to God in great appreciation of His power and glory.

The main theme, then, is the importance of gaining wisdom, but it is repeatedly emphasized that the *"fear of the Lord"* (reverence and obedience coming out of a personal relationship with God), is the beginning of wisdom. In that phrase, "beginning" means the most important, the chief or greater part. So, the most important part of wisdom is knowing, loving, and obeying God, which is *"the fear of the Lord."* This fear is positive. Instead of making a person run from God in terror, it draws him to God in great appreciation of His power and glory. The fear of the Lord motivates and stimulates a person to take notice when God speaks and obey what He commands. Wisdom results from such response.

No one can be truly wise who does not fear God. Information used without godliness will not bring the greatest results.

No one can be truly wise who does not fear God. Information or knowledge used without godliness will not bring the greatest results. For example, Adam and Eve in Genesis 3 wanted knowledge but refused to "fear" the Lord and remain obedient to His command about not eating of the fruit of the Tree of Knowledge. Their choice resulted in a death-sentence for all mankind. That was not very wise!

Concluding Comments

A person could find out about the problems caused because of sin in this world by just living as best he could all by himself, but the results of such a life would be disappointment and bitterness: *"There is a way that seems right to man, but its end is the way of death"* (Proverbs 14:12). The other way (and the better way) to find out about sin and the results of its power is to let God tell him about it through His Word—especially the Proverbs, and then to obey His advice for avoiding it and its resulting problems. *"Happy is the man who finds wisdom, and the man who gains understanding; for her proceeds are better than the profits of silver, and her gain than fine gold. She is more precious than rubies, and all the things you may desire cannot compare with her. Length of days is in her right hand....Her ways are ways of pleasantness, and all her paths are peace. She is a tree of life to those who take hold of her, and happy are all who retain her"* (Proverbs 3:13-18).

Questions

Study Procedure: Read the Scripture references before answering questions. Unless otherwise instructed, use only the Bible in answering questions. Some questions may be more difficult than others but try to answer as many as you can. Pray for God's wisdom and understanding as you study and don't be discouraged if some answers are not obvious at first. Do not read the study notes for this lesson until AFTER you have completed your questions.

Day One: Vocabulary Review - Match the word with its definition.

_____1. equity

a) women who live with a man without being married to him; these women usually have inferior legal and social status to lawful wives

_____2. intermarry

b) two successive lines of poetry that relate in meaning, sound, or rhythm. From a French word meaning "pair."

_____3. concubines

c) to marry a member of another group

_____4. couplets

d) the state, ideal, or quality of being just, impartial, and fair

5. List the three types of proverbs and the key words for each type.

a) _____

b) _____

c) _____

6. Give some information about Solomon from your notes. _____

_____

_____

_____

_____

MEMORY: PROVERBS 1:7-8

Day Two: Read Proverbs 1.

1. The purpose of the book of Proverbs is given in 1:1-6. Read it carefully and then write down what you personally expect to gain from its study. _____

_____

_____

2. According to 1:7, what is the foundation for knowledge, wisdom, and instruction?

_____

3. Match the following references with what they tell about the *"fear of the Lord."*

_____a.   it can be found if you really receive God's Word and seek His wisdom   2:1-5

_____b.   it prolongs days   8:13

_____c.   it leads to life   10:27

_____d.   it is to hate evil   14:26

_____e.   it is the fountain of life   14:27

_____f.   in it is strong confidence   16:6

_____g.   by it one departs from evil   19:23

4. In 1:8-9 and 1:10-19, who is being addressed, what advice is given, and what is the advantage gained by obeying it?

   a) 1:8-9 Address: _____

     Advice: _____

     Advantage: _____

   b) 1:10-19 Address: _____

     Advice: _____

     Advantage: _____

MEMORY: PROVERBS 2:6

Day Three: Proverbs 1 continued and read Proverbs 2.

1. In Proverbs 1:20-33, the wisdom of God is personified (given human characteristics) as a woman calling out loud in all the public places. Answer the following questions about "her."

   a) To whom does she call? (22) _____

   b) What does she advise? (23) _____

     _____

   c) What was the response from the people? (24-30)_____

     _____

   d) Then, what was her response to them? (24-30)_____

     _____

   e) What will happen to those who obey and those who don't? (30-33) _____

     _____

2. Read Proverbs 2:1-9. What does God do for the person who seriously studies and obeys His commands? _____

   _____

3. One of the sins about which many proverbs comment, is sexual sin. From the last half of Proverbs 2, give some description of the immoral woman who tempts men to follow her. _____

_____

Day Four: Read Proverbs 3 and 4.   *MEMORY: PROVERBS 3:1-2, 5-8, 11-13, 27*

1. Fill in the blanks with the missing words from Proverbs 3 and write the number of the verse(s) from

    which they come.

    a) *Trust in the Lord with all your _____ and lean not on your own _____.*

       In all your ways _____ Him and He shall_____your paths. (_____)

    b) *Honor the Lord with your _____, and with the firstfruits of all your increase; (_____)*

    c) *So your barns will be filled with _____, and your vats will_____with new*

       wine. (_____)

    d) *Do not withhold _____ from those to whom it is due, when it is in the _____*

       of your hand to do so. (_____)

    e) *Do not _____ with a man without cause if he has done you no _____. (_____)*

    f) *Surely He scorns the_____, but gives _____ to the humble. (_____)*

2. Read 3:11-12 which speaks of God's discipline. Then read Hebrews 12:3-11 and answer the

    following questions.

    a) What does the chastening or discipline of God reveal about our relationship to Him?

       _____

       _____

    b) What is the difference between the way our parents discipline(d) us and the way God does?

       _____

       _____

    c) What is the result of God's chastening? _____

       _____

3. According to Proverbs 4:1-9, what is the "principal thing" that children should get? _____

4. After reading Proverbs 4:10-19, tell what path you should not enter and why? _____

    _____

    _____

MEMORY: PROVERBS 4:23

Day Five: Proverbs 4 continued and read Proverbs 5.

1. Why do you think Proverbs 4:20-22 is called "God's medicine bottle"?

   a. Because once you have used up God's Word, you cannot get a "refill."

   b. Because when "taken" regularly, God's Word brings life and health to the body and spirit.

   c. Because you can overdose on it and get sick.

   d. All of the above are silly answers, so here's mine_____

   _____

2. Read Proverbs 5. What is the main theme of it? _____

3. Since the Bible teaches that adultery and fornication are wrong, how then has God provided for

   the fulfillment of the sexual desires of His children? (Give verses.) _____

   _____

4. Match the correct definitions to the following words that appear in Proverbs 5.

   _____1. discretion (2)   a) a container for catching and storing rainwater

   _____2. immoral (3, 20)   b) thoughtful and careful action

   _____3. wormwood (4)   c) without any regard for right or wrong

   _____4. cistern (15)   d) a woman who leads a person away from what is sexually right
                                        and proper

   _____5. enraptured (19)   e) something harsh or bitter

   _____6. seductress (20)   f) delighted, thrilled

5. Now take a few minutes and read the notes for this lesson.

Notes

In the Beginning, God (Proverbs 1-5)

Proverbs repeatedly emphasizes that the foundation for the greatest education begins with a fear or reverence for the Lord.

Vest-Button Education

In the time of Solomon, as now, parents were eager to see that their children received the right education. Proverbs repeatedly emphasizes that the foundation for the greatest education begins with a fear or reverence for the Lord. Recognition of and faithful response to the Lord God, Creator of Heaven and Earth, should be the first goal of a child's education. If that is not settled, everything else the child learns will be "off-base," causing confusion. Someone called this principle "vest-button" education. You have probably had the experience of buttoning a vest or sweater all the way up only to look down and see you missed the first button which threw the whole thing off. Or, maybe you have taken a standardized test with a separate answer sheet and skipped a line, only to have every answer following come out wrong.

That's how it is with trying to gain knowledge or wisdom without beginning first with a relationship with God. If that is missed, nothing else will come out right.

Beginning with the Basics
(Proverbs 1:8-19)

A child who really wants to grow and mature must realize some basic truths about the way God works in us. First, God has put us in families and wants us to obey our parents. Obedience in the home is our basic training for further usefulness by God. Second, children must realize that their choice of friends can affect their lives in a very big way. The advice given in 1:10-19 is to say "no" to the temptation to do bad things with those you know. Such activity often leads to death—which, of course, would put an end to a young person's education permanently!

God has put us in families and wants us to obey our parents. Obedience in the home is our basic training for further usefulness by God.

The Wisdom Woman
(Proverbs 1:20-33)

Solomon used a writing technique called **personification** to describe the wisdom God wants us to have. As if she were a woman, Wisdom is depicted as calling out in all the public places to all sorts of people. If any will listen, she will help them understand the will of God. However, many do not listen, with the sad result that when their ignorance gets them into deep trouble, their cries for help will be ignored. All around us today are opportunities to study God's Word. Bibles are plentiful in our country; churches abound. Radio, television, and printed media offer Bible teaching whenever we want it. Are you answering Wisdom's call, or are you one of the foolish **scorners**? Paul warned the Galatians in the New Testament: *"Do not be deceived. God is not mocked; for whatever a man sows, that he will also reap. For he who sows to his flesh will of the flesh reap corruption, but he who sows to the Spirit will of the Spirit reap everlasting life"* (Galatians 6:7,8).

personification -a figure of speech in which nonliving objects or ideas are described as having human characteristics

scorners -persons who reject or despise other people or things

Wisdom's Value
(Proverbs 2)

In this chapter Solomon makes an emotional appeal to his son to get serious about seeking God's wisdom. It takes work to get wisdom, the earthly kind or the heavenly kind. But, the heavenly kind also takes prayer: "Cry out...lift up your voice..." (3). Such praying brings results: *"Then you will understand the fear of the Lord and find the knowledge of God for the Lord gives wisdom; from His mouth come knowledge and understanding"* (5,6). Think about it this way: God knows everything—He never makes a mistake. You do not know everything and you frequently make mistakes. God loves you and wants to help you. Therefore, you would be foolish indeed not to pray for His help in getting His wisdom—which is perfect—for your life. When you do, you will enjoy this promise: *"He is a shield to those who walk uprightly; He guards the paths of justice and preserves the way of His saints"* (7,8). He will show you the difference between right and wrong—you won't have to struggle and fail to find out. He will deliver you from the man who tries to trick you into trouble as well as the immoral woman who tries to talk you into trouble. God's wisdom is worth the work and the praying!

Your faith in God should not be a once-a-week or even a once-a-day experience: "In all your ways acknowledge Him"—that means pray about everything as you go through your day.

Keep at It!
(Proverbs 3:1-6)

The world is full of people who start something but quit before they have finished. This chapter urges you to continue in your study of God's Word: *"...Do not forget my law, but let your heart keep my commands"* (1). How do you do that? How do you keep studying? *"Bind them around your neck, write them on the tablet of your heart"* (3). You might not like the Bible "necklace" idea, but how about this? Keep your Bible and study aids in obvious and convenient places. A small Bible in your pocket or purse and one by the phone or beside your bed would remind you to use every opportunity to read, study, think, memorize, and prayerfully obey God's Word. Your faith in God should not be a once-a-week or even a once-a-day experience: *"In all your ways acknowledge Him"*—that means pray about everything as you go through your day. Ask for His help and direction. Think about what you know about His will from what you have already studied in the Bible or from what you have learned from your parents or teachers. What's the result? *"... He shall direct your paths"* (6).

God's Paths
(Proverbs 3:7-35)

What are some of the directions your path will take if God is in charge?

1. The path of humility: *"Do not be wise in your own eyes"* (7). *"Surely He scorns the scornful, but gives grace to the humble"* (34). The underlying cause of all sin is pride. Let God deal with that in your life and you will miss many, many problems and failures.

2. The path of generosity: *"Honor the Lord with your possessions"* (9). Whatever you have, remember it was all God's first. Let Him use your "stuff" as He wants. He will make sure you will still have all you need. *"Do not withhold good from those to whom it is due, when it is in the power of your hand to do so"* (27). Share your possessions with others who need it. Don't be stingy.

God disciplines us for our good, not His convenience. God loves us too much to let us continue in sinful actions or attitudes.

3. The path of discipline: *"For whom the Lord loves He corrects..."* (12) God's discipline is different from most parents'. How often parents punish a child because the child has inconvenienced or disturbed them! In contrast, God disciplines us for our good, not His convenience. God loves us too much to let us continue in sinful actions or attitudes. He will discipline us to make us better. We should not run from it.

4. The path of peace: *"Do not strive with a man without cause, if he has done you no harm"* (30). Just as in the New Testament, *"blessed are the peacemakers"* (Matthew 5:9).

The Principal Thing (Proverbs 4:1-19)

People who know God personally are the only ones to really speak convincingly about the benefits of studying Scripture. Solomon was grateful for what David had taught him, and in this chapter he makes it known that he wants to pass on that wisdom to others. He calls it the *"principal thing"* (7). The wisdom of God is our foundation, but along with it, we must get understanding. Wisdom is the ability to use knowledge for **productive** purposes, while understanding is related to timing and sensitivity. A person may know what to do and how to do it, but lack the understanding or discernment to know when and where. Understanding or sensitivity is developed in us by the Holy Spirit. Like wisdom, it comes with prayer and effort.

> **productive** -yielding favorable or useful results; constructive

God's Medicine Bottle (Proverbs 4:20-27)

Often, when a person is sick and asks his doctor for help, some type of medicine is prescribed. Such medicine, if taken according to the doctor's instructions, will bring about the necessary changes in the body to accomplish healing. In a similar way, the Scriptures are prescribed to us, and when "taken" regularly will produce *"life to those who find them and health to all their flesh"* (22). Sometimes medicine comes with warnings such as "take with food" or "while using, do not operate heavy machinery." Solomon showed how God's Scripture-medicine, could be most effectively used:

The wisdom of God is our foundation, but along with it, we must get understanding. Wisdom is the ability to use knowledge for productive purposes, while understanding is related to timing and sensitivity.

1. For people with "heart" problems: *"Keep your heart with all diligence for out of it spring the issues of life"* (23). The "heart" in Bible terms is made up of the mind and emotions. What a person reads, hears, thinks, or worries about enters the "heart." If a person wants to be in the best spiritual health, the "heart" should be protected.

2. For use as a "mouthwash": *"Put away from you a deceitful mouth"* (24). This verse could mean that a person should only speak what is right or true, or it could mean that a person should stop listening to people who do not honor God with their words. If the right Scriptural "dosage" is taken every day and yet the words still pour out in a stinky flow, something is keeping the God's "medicine" from being effective. Keep your inner thoughts pure by thinking only about what God would approve, only then will your words be sweet. Regular Bible study makes an effective "mouthwash"!

3. For improvement of vision: One of the results of spending time finding out what God approves and disapproves is that a person begins to "see" things more clearly in his own life. When God's will is known, a person can let his eyes *"look straight ahead"* and he can *"ponder the path" of his feet"*(25-27). It is not necessary to be familiar with all kinds of evil in order to recognize and avoid them. A person only needs to concentrate on God's will, determining to stay in that path, to be blessed. H.A. Ironside commented on this passage in his devotional work on Proverbs: "The true [ship] pilot may not know every rock or reef, but his wisdom consists in taking the safe channel: so the Christian need not make himself aware of all the evils of the day." Bible study definitely improves spiritual vision.

adolescence -the period of physical and psychological development from the onset of puberty to maturity

Being Sexually Wise (Proverbs 5)

With the physical changes of **adolescence** comes the emotional roller-coaster of sexual interest. God is well-aware of the problems and pleasures of such changes and wisely gives guidelines for their control. The temptation to indulge every urge does not stop with adolescence; adults, too, fight similar battles. God intended sexual expression to help people bond into the "one flesh" of marriage. However, it is usually several years after the awakening of sexual desire that a person is mature enough to consider marriage. How is a person supposed to control himself until then?

Just as acceptance of Christ's offer for salvation is a decision, so is obedience to His will after becoming a Christian. Using the words of Joshua, "Choose this day whom you will serve."

1. Make up your mind. Just as acceptance of Christ's offer for salvation is a decision, so is obedience to His will after becoming a Christian. Using the words of Joshua, *"Choose this day whom you will serve."* Once that's settled, pay attention (1) to what you know to be God's plan. As an athlete must stay "in bounds" to be able to win, so a Christian must stay within the boundaries of God's plan to realize the full joy of sexual expression when he gets married.

gratification - satisfaction; pleasure

2. Recognize the signals of someone "in lust" instead of "in love." The immoral woman described in 5:3-11 has some definite methods of operation. First, she wants immediate **gratification** and so does not reveal what will happen afterward: bitterness, death, and hell. (4,5). Next, her attentions are not loyal or long-lasting; *"her ways are unstable"* (6). Also, if a married person has a sexual relationship with someone other than his or her spouse, divorce might well result. How many complain of supporting a new spouse's relatives or having to split up hard-earned assets? These proverbs reveal all that with the warning to avoid sexual sin *"Lest you give your honor to others, and your years to the cruel one; lest **aliens** be filled with your wealth, and your labors go to the house of a foreigner; and you mourn at last, when your flesh and your body are consumed"* because of sexually transmitted diseases (9-11)

aliens -belonging to a group of another; unfamiliar ones

3. Married people should satisfy their sexual needs with their own spouses. That is what *"drink water from your own cistern"* means (15).

God's Will Still Speaks to Today's Problems

Scanning back through these notes you can see that Proverbs is still a very modern book. Every problem Solomon mentioned is still a problem today. Sexual temptation, concern for the best education, humility, discipline, and the mouth are topics for which God has the best guidelines. So, keep studying. God's wisdom is still the *"principal thing"* (4:7).

BIBLE QUEST

Questions

Study Procedure: Read the Scripture references before answering questions. Unless otherwise instructed, use only the Bible in answering questions. Some questions may be more difficult than others but try to answer as many as you can. Pray for God's wisdom and understanding as you study and don't be discouraged if some answers are not obvious at first. Do not read the study notes for this lesson until AFTER you have completed your questions.

Day One: Vocabulary Review - Match the word with its definition.

_____1. adolescence

_____2. aliens

_____3. gratification

_____4. personification

_____5. productive

_____6. scorners

a) belonging to a group of another; unfamiliar ones

b) satisfaction; pleasure

c) the period of physical and psychological development from the onset of puberty to maturity

d) yielding favorable or useful results; constructive

e) persons who reject or despise other people or things

f) a figure of speech in which nonliving objects or ideas are described as having human characteristics

7. Define "vest-button" education. _____

_____

_____

_____

8. Write below something you found helpful in the last lesson. _____

_____

_____

_____

Day Two: Read Proverbs 6.

MEMORY: PROVERBS 6:16-19

1. Read Proverbs 6:1-5. From your own or your parents' or friends' experience, what are the dangers of agreeing to pay someone else's debt (to become "surety") if that person cannot?

_____

_____

2. What can an ant teach us (6:6-11)? _____

_____

3. What does God hate? _____

_____

_____

4. Read 6:20-29 on the dangers of adultery. To what is the damage caused by adultery compared?

_____

Day Three: Read Proverbs 7.

MEMORY: PROVERBS 7:1-3

1. From 7:1-5, what can keep a person from giving in to sexual temptation? _____

_____

2. How does the immoral woman of 7:6-21 get a man's attention? _____

_____

_____

3. What happens to the man who goes with her? _____

_____

Day Four: Read Proverbs 8 and 9.

MEMORY: PROVERBS 9:10

1. Read 8:1-21. What does Wisdom offer that is different from the woman in Proverbs 7?

_____

_____

_____

2. Read 8:22-31. How long has Wisdom been associated with God?

   a. Since man was created

   b. Since the Great Flood

   c. Since before the Creation of the Heaven and Earth

3. Read 8:32-33. Complete these statements about God's wisdom. *"Whoever finds me finds* _____, *and obtains* _____ *from the Lord; but he who* _____ *against me wrongs his own soul; all those who* _____ *me love* _____."

4. Read 9:1-18. Find as many differences as you can between Wisdom and the foolish woman.

   Wisdom: _____

   Foolish woman: _____

MEMORY: PROVERBS 10:1, 12, 27; 11:2

Day Five: Read Proverbs 10 and 11.

1. Read 10:1-5. What will leave you poor and what will make you rich? _____

_____

2. Read 10:6-25. From these verses, what are some characteristics of a wise person?

_____

_____

3. Read 10:27-32. Fill in the blanks. *"The mouth of the righteous brings forth* _____ . . .

The lips of the righteous know what is _____ *."*

4. Read Proverbs 11 and answer the following questions about the upright or righteous person.

a) _____ guides the upright.

b) Righteousness delivers a person from _____ .

c) The righteousness of the blameless will _____ his way correctly.

d) The righteous is delivered from _____ .

e) When it goes well with the righteous, the city _____ .

f) He who sows righteousness will have a sure _____ .

g) The desire of the righteous is only for _____ .

h) The fruit of the righteous is a _____ .

5. Write below one or more of the verses from Proverbs 10 and 11 that were meaningful to you.

_____

_____

6. Now take a few minutes and read the notes for this lesson.

Notes

God's Lists (Proverbs 6-11)

Check It Out

We would be wise to examine God's lists, comparing our own actions and goals with what pleases or displeases Him.

While studying the habits of effective leaders, it was noticed that such persons were list-makers. They took time to identify what was important, to make a list in writing of what they discovered, and then to set aside specific amounts of time to work toward accomplishing those particular things. It should not surprise us that God has made some lists to help us. In Proverbs 6 there are seven things God hates, all listed together. Yet, scattered elsewhere in surrounding verses and chapters, we are told plainly of other things God wants us to do. We would be wise to examine God's lists, comparing our own actions and goals with what pleases or displeases Him.

Be Careful with Money (Proverbs 6:1-5)

This section warns about becoming **surety** for another's debt. That meant promising to pay off a debt in case another became unable to do so. Banks and loan companies still require someone to co-sign with a person seeking a loan if they think the borrower might fail to pay it back as agreed. However, God wants us to be very careful with our money. Since we cannot control what another person might do, it is usually foolish to risk our finances to guarantee theirs. Sometimes we make financial decisions too quickly based on the emotion of a relationship, pride at being thought financially able, or fear of rejection by the person asking. The proverbs here warn that hasty financial decisions might leave a person unhappily caught like a bird by a hunter.

> **surety** -a person who has contracted to be responsible for the debts of another

Don't Be a Sluggard (Proverbs 6:6-11)

There are many proverbs that warn against the problems caused by the lazy person or **sluggard**. Even the lowly ant knows that hard work at the right time brings future benefits, while laziness and **procrastination** make "poverty come on you like a prowler" (11). Below find some of the characteristics of a sluggard. Do you have any of these bad habits?

> **sluggard** -a lazy person

1. He is "hinged" to his bed. (26:14)
2. He makes outrageous excuses for not working. (26:13; 22:13)
3. He will not begin things. (6:9, 10)
4. He will not finish things. (12:27; 19:24; 26:15)
5. He frustrates those who employ him. (10:26)

> **procrastination** -putting off something that should be done now until another time

Watch that Body Language (Proverbs 6:12-15)

In Solomon's time, 3000 years ago, just as today, a person's character could be evaluated by the body language he used as well as the words he spoke. Winking the eye to cover a lie, pointing the finger to express ridicule, or shuffling the feet to mock or imitate another were the tools of a person stirring up trouble. Are you guilty of **vulgar** or aggravating body language?

> **vulgar** -crude, obscene, indecent

The 7 Things God Hates

The lesson on body language continues here. God hates a proud look on a person's face. Only the humble can expect His blessing. *"But on this one will I look: On him who is poor and of a **contrite** spirit, and who trembles at My word"* (Isaiah 66:2b). Following pride on God's "hate list" are lying lips, murderous hands, scheming hearts, and too-anxious-for-evil feet. False witnesses and troublemakers finish the list because they destroy loving unity in any group. Our bodies are supposed to be *"instruments of righteousness"* not tools of Satan (Romans 6:13). God's "hate list" makes that quite clear.

> **contrite** -grieving for sin; sorry for shortcomings

Avoid Sexual Sin
(Proverbs 6:20-35 & 7:1-27)

Did you know that God invented sex? This unique relationship between the male and female was God's idea. He designed sexual expression to be a "super-glue" between a man and his wife. Sexual love within the boundaries of marriage was God's perfect plan. We only get into trouble when we try to go outside of God's guidelines. God's word is given to keep us out of such trouble (6:20-23). This section of Scripture focuses on the problems that come when a person gives in to the temptations for sexual *intimacy* outside of marriage. Here is a summary of this passages' warnings:

> **intimacy** -a close, personal association

> **alluring** -tempting, attractive

1. (6:24,25) Watch out for flattering words and *alluring* eyelids. People who do not care about pleasing God, or those ignorant of His will, may try to tempt you with the way they talk or the way they look at you.

2. (6:26-29) If you play with the sexual fire intended to warm another, you will be burned!

3. (6:30-35) Other kinds of sins are understood and forgiven much more quickly than sexual sins are. Sexual intercourse joins body, soul, and spirit of husband and wife. Breaking that covenant is very serious and the consequences are extremely severe. (See also 1 Corinthians 6:12-20.)

4. (7:1-5) Knowing what God's word has to say about sexual expression and making a commitment to obey it will help you avoid sexual sin.

> *Knowing what God's word has to say about sexual expression and making a commitment to obey it will help you avoid sexual sin.*

5. (7:6-9) Stay in the light! The writer of this passage noticed that a lot of sexual sinning occurred in the dark!

6. (7:10-21) How to spot a sexual tempter/temptress:
   a. Clothing is sexy or sensual (10).
   b. Voice is "loud and rebellious" (11).
   c. Activity is focused outside the home (11b,12).
   d. Shocking boldness is used to get attention (13).
   e. Religion might be used as an excuse for inviting involvement (14,15).
   f. Extra preparations are made to excite the senses (16,17).
   g. Privacy and secrecy are promised (18-20).

7. (7:22-27) The results of giving in to the above tactics will be real injury and perhaps even death.

The Wiser Way
(Proverbs 8)

In sharp contrast to the harlot or foolish woman to be avoided in the last chapters, Wisdom is described here as a most welcomed companion. She represents the will and wisdom of God which we all need to know and obey. Making the idea of wisdom come alive to the reader by describing the idea as if it were a person is called personification and is still a common way of communicating ideas in poetry today. Unlike the harlot, Wisdom does not hide in the dark but calls from a high hill to everyone to listen to her excellent and righteous words which are better than the finest jewels (2, 6-11). Instead of poverty and shame, she promises riches and honor. Anyone who diligently seeks her will find her (17).

Wisdom's History (Proverbs 8:22-36) Similar to passages in Job and Psalms, this section describes vividly the creation of everything by God, and Wisdom declares that *"the Lord possessed me at the beginning of His way, before His works of old....From the beginning before there was ever an earth....I was beside Him as a master craftsman and I was daily His delight."* In the New Testament, the apostle John described the Word of God, Jesus Christ, as God's creative partner in creation (John 1:1-3). Jesus is God's wisdom to and for us (Colossians 2:3). He brought to real life the characteristics of wisdom personified in these chapters of Proverbs.

Wisdom vs. Folly (Proverbs 9) There is a contrast here. Wisdom (1-6) and the foolish woman (13-18) are both ready to entertain guests. Wisdom has a large house, a generous food supply, and many servants; she invites everyone to come into her home and so *"forsake foolishness and live."* Folly lives alone in a small house with only bread and water to offer to the simple who listen to her. They will enter only to find death and hell. The words of Wisdom in verses 10 and 11 summarize the real difference in Wisdom and Folly: *"The fear of the Lord is the beginning of wisdom, and the knowledge of the Holy One is understanding. For by me your days will be multiplied and years of life will be added to you."* What does this have to do with our lives today? Wisdom and folly are still competing for our attention. From the television, radio, and magazine racks we are called away from God's will to the foolish and sinful way of the life God hates. Pride, selfishness, sexual perversion, and bad language are encouraged as good and normal while God's wisdom is criticized as "narrow-minded" and "old-fashioned." These chapters should wake us up to the real results of listening to foolishness instead of God's wisdom.

Pride, selfishness, sexual perversion, and bad language are encouraged as good and normal while God's wisdom is criticized as "narrow-minded" and "old-fashioned."

Contrasting Proverbs (Proverbs 10-11) These chapters contain what are usually thought of as traditional proverbs: short statements contrasting great truths. As introduced earlier, the differences between the wise and the foolish are continued here as well as those between the righteous and the wicked. Several of the proverbs will be briefly highlighted below with some helpful comments.

famish -to starve or cause to starve

10:3 *"The Lord will not allow the righteous soul to* **famish***, but He casts away the desire of the wicked."* The real reason that the wicked fail is that they do not have God's support behind them as the righteous do. A relationship with God makes all the difference between success and failure in the long-term. (See also 10:22, 24, 25,28-30.)

prating -talking foolishly or at great length

10:8 *"The wise in heart will receive commands, but a* **prating** *fool will fall."* No one knows everything. Everyone needs advice and correction from time to time. The wise person is the one who is humble enough to accept advice from others and obey. (See also 10:14,17.)

10:12 *"Hatred stirs up strife but love covers all sins."* There are many proverbs that have to do with words that hurt others. Hate and unforgiveness in our hearts cause us to continually stir up trouble for others by talking about their sins. God wants us to forgive and to love even those who have hurt us. A test of how loving we are would be to see how long we can keep quiet about the sins of others. If we are lovingly quiet, much fighting will stop. (See also 10:18-21 and 11: 12,13.)

abomination -something that is hated or loathed

11:1 *"Dishonest scales are an abomination to the Lord, but a just weight is His delight."* An **abomination** is something God absolutely hates. If a merchant cheats a customer by giving him less than the customer deserves or expects, God notices! Honesty in all things delights God. Lying in word or action will not result in blessing. (See also 11: 3-6, and 16-21.)

11:22 *"As a ring of gold in a swine's snout, so is a lovely woman who lacks discretion."* A gold ring is a lovely thing, but it would be wasted on a pig. In the same way the natural beauty of a woman changes to ugliness when she speaks or acts in an ungodly manner. A person's character is what makes them lovely—outer beauty is a pleasant "extra" in a person with the inner beauty of godliness. It seems wasted on the ungodly.

A person's character is what makes them lovely— outer beauty is a pleasant "extra" in a person with the inner beauty of godliness.

11:24 *"There is one who scatters, yet increases more; and there is one who withholds more than is right, but it leads to poverty."* This principle of generosity was taught by Jesus when He said that a man must lose his life to really find it (Matthew 17:24,25). More verses on the benefits of generosity are found in 11:25-28).

Summing Up

If you listed the things that are important to you, would they be the same as what these chapters taught are important to God? If someone close to you were to describe your character, which of these proverbial themes would you need to improve: honesty, purity, generosity, diligence, financial responsibility, or a thoughtful tongue? Be honest before God and confess your sins and failures. Ask Him to help you to grow in obedience to His will.

Questions

Study Procedure: Read the Scripture references before answering questions. Unless otherwise instructed, use only the Bible in answering questions. Some questions may be more difficult than others but try to answer as many as you can. Pray for God's wisdom and understanding as you study and don't be discouraged if some answers are not obvious at first. Do not read the study notes for this lesson until AFTER you have completed your questions.

Day One: Vocabulary Review.

1. Unscramble the following words to get the correct vocabulary word for the definitions:

   a) nnooaaiitbm _____ something that is hated or loathed

   b) shimaf _____ to starve or cause to starve

   c) rullgain_____ tempting, attractive

   d) nocittre _____ grieving for sin; sorry for shortcomings

   e) gartpin_____ talking foolishly or at great length

   f) timincay _____ a close, personal association

   g) carporsittannio _____ putting off until another time something that should be done now

   h) rusety _____ a person who has contracted to be responsible for the debts of another

   i) draglugs _____ a lazy person

   j) gravul _____ crude, obscene, indecent

2. Make a list from last week's lesson of some of the things God hates and some of the things God blesses. Please make sure and give your references.

God Hates   God Blesses

_____   _____

_____   _____

_____   _____

_____   _____

Day Two: Read Proverbs 12 and 13.

> *MEMORY: PROVERBS 13:24*

1. Doing things God's way—living righteously— pays off in the long run. Doing things your own way — foolishly— does not. Write out below some of the proverbs from chapter 12 that illustrate this principle. _____

_____

_____

2. Match the best summary to each of the proverbs below.

A good wife makes her husband proud; an ungodly one embarrasses him.

(16) *A fool's wrath is known at once, but a prudent man covers shame.*

A foolish person will not control his anger; a wise person will.

(10) *A righteous man regards the life of his animal, but the tender mercies of the wicked are cruel.*

A person who works when he is supposed to work will have what he needs later; the one who plays instead will be surprised at what the future brings.

(4) *An excellent wife is the crown of her husband, but she who causes shame is like rottenness in his bones.*

Lies won't last; truth will.

(19) *The truthful lip shall be established forever, but a lying tongue is but for a moment.*

Be careful in choosing your close friends; ungodly relationships will get you in trouble.

(11) *He who tills his land will be satisfied with bread, but he who follows frivolity is devoid of understanding.*

One who loves God will be kind even to his animals; the ungodly won't.

(26) *The righteous should choose his friends carefully, for the way of the wicked leads them astray.*

3. Read Proverbs 13. Proverbs 12:25 stated, *"Anxiety in the heart of man causes depression, but a good word makes it glad."* What proverb from Chapter 13 tells of another cause for "heart trouble"? _____

4. Fill in the blanks from Proverbs 13.

a) *He who guards his _____ preserves his life . . . (3)*

b) *By _____ comes nothing but strife . . . (10)*

c) *He who despises the _____ will be destroyed . . . (13)*

d) *_____ and _____ comes to him who disdains correction, but he who regards a rebuke will be honored. (18)*

e) *He who walks with _____ men will be _____, but the companion of fools will be destroyed. (20)*

f) *He who spares the _____ hates his son, but he who loves him _____ him promptly. (24)*

MEMORY: PROVERBS 15:1, 3, 5, 8, 13, 16, 29

Day Three: Proverbs 14 and 15.

A. Match the proverb from chapter 14 to the situation it could illustrate.

1. The board members complained to their pastor that the church facilities were being used so much that the furniture was getting worn out. The pastor replied: (_____)

2. A woman was complaining non-stop to a friend about the weaknesses of her husband, her dissatisfaction with her house, and the bad attitudes of her children. The friend replied: (___)

3. A teenage boy felt that he had every reason to confront the neighborhood acquaintance who teased him about being overweight, but he didn't when he remembered the boy was having trouble fitting in and was probably very lonely. (_____)

4. "I thought it would work," she wailed. "Next time I promise I'll pray first!" (_____)

5. My brother patiently listened to the whole sales pitch, but politely refused to spend his money. (_____)

B. From Proverbs 15, find and write down every phrase that has to do with talking.

   1. Regarding talking: _____
      _____

   2. Write down some of the things you learned from the above verses. _____
      _____
      _____

MEMORY: PROVERBS 16:7, 16, 18, 32

Day Four: Read Proverbs 16. Write down the proverb by its summary below.

   1. A person can't see his own mistakes, but God can. _____
      _____

   2. Ungodly human pride is something God hates. _____
      _____

   3. If you want to get along with all kinds of people, get serious about pleasing God._____
      _____

   4. God hates wickedness in high places. _____
      _____

   5. Gold and silver are beautiful, valuable, and useful, but they could be stolen, lost or destroyed; therefore, wisdom and understanding are more valuable. _____
      _____

   6. When a person starts thinking he is the greatest, get ready to see something happen to put him in his right place._____
      _____

7. Just a spoonful of sugar makes the medicine go down. _____

_____

8. Gossip and criticism ruin friendships. _____

_____

9. Old age coupled with a good relationship with God can be wonderful. _____

_____

10. The strongest person is the one who can control his temper. _____

_____

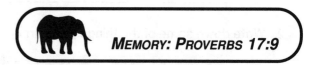

MEMORY: PROVERBS 17:9

Day Five: Read Proverbs 17. Many sins are condemned in this chapter. Write beside each "sin" the proverb(s) that mention it.

1. strife (fighting)_____

2. lying _____

3. mocking the poor, laughing at troubles of others _____

4. gossip _____

5. rebellion _____

6. foolishness _____

7. injustice _____

8. offending (hurting someone's feelings) or fighting (contending) _____

9. taking a bribe _____

10. Now take a few minutes and read the notes for this lesson.

Notes

The Power of the Tongue (Proverbs 12-17)

The Little Dipper

Someone once said that the tongue was like a little dipper, dipping down into the wellspring of the heart and bringing up whatever it found there. Jesus explained it like this: *"Out of the abundance of the heart, the mouth speaks"* (Matthew 12:34). Later you will read in Proverbs 23:7: *"For as he thinks in his heart, so is he…."* The words we speak reveal the true condition of our hearts. Whatever comes out of our mouths was first in our thoughts. In this lesson, we will focus on the power of the spoken word. The goal is to motivate us to examine ourselves—our motives, our desires— and to ask God to clean out what is sinful in us, so that our words will bring life and health to those who hear us instead of destruction and death.

The goal is to motivate us to examine ourselves— our motives, our desires—and to ask God to clean out what is sinful to us, so that our words will bring life and health to those who hear us instead of destruction and death.

It's What's Inside that Counts! (Proverbs 12)

It is impossible to improve our words while hiding sinful attitudes in our minds. This chapter can help us check our inner attitudes for problems.

1. Humility:*"…He who hates correction is stupid" (1b)."…He who heeds counsel is wise"* (15b). If you gripe and grumble when someone corrects you, you have a problem. No one is perfect; everyone needs help from others. If you can remain calm and quiet while being criticized, warned, or corrected, you have a healthy supply of humility, a fruit of the Holy Spirit. (See also Proverbs 14:3 and 16:5.)

2. Goodness: *"A good man obtains favor from the Lord…"(2a)."…The root of the righteous cannot be moved"* (3) *"…He who is of a **perverse** heart will be despised"* (8b). The only way to be good is to let God make you good by accepting His plan for removing sin—accepting the sacrifice of His Son in your place. By faith, our old heart is replaced by a new and good one. Our words and actions should reveal this.

perverse -directed away from what is right or good; stubbornly persisting in a wrong or fault

3. Kindness: *"A righteous man regards the life of his animal…"* (10a). Real kindness on the inside will not remain hidden. It will find its way outside through kind words and actions to others—even to animals! A person who is unkind has a serious "heart" problem.

What Words Can Do (Proverbs 12-17)

When police officers make an arrest, they warn the accused person to be careful about what he says since any comments may be used against him in a court of law. Verse 13 says it this way: *"The wicked is ensnared by the*

235

transgression of his lips, but the righteous will come through trouble." Careless words can "backfire" to hurt even the one speaking them. We, too, need to be careful about what we say and how we say it.

1. Don't try to hurt others with words: *"There is one who speaks like the piercings of the sword, but the tongue of the wise promotes health"* (12:18).

2. Don't lie: *"The truthful lip shall be established forever, but a lying tongue but for a moment"* (12:19). And this: *"Lying lips are an abomination to the Lord, but those who deal truthfully are His delight"* (12:22). Remember lying was #2 on the Proverbs 6 list of what God really hates.

3. Don't talk too much. *"He who guards his mouth preserves his life, but he who opens wide his lips shall have destruction"* (13:3). Most people get into trouble for things they have said, not the things they have not said. James warned: *"...Let every man be swift to hear, slow to speak, and slow to wrath...."* (James 1:19). Do you talk too much?

4. Don't argue. *"By pride comes nothing but strife..."* (13:10). We get into arguments because of our pride. We want to be heard; we want to be understood; but most importantly, we want to be right! If we say it loud enough, fast enough, and mean enough we think we will convince someone. Such talking just keeps a fight going. One person willing to be humble enough to quit arguing can stop a fight. (See also Proverbs 16:27-30, and 32; 17:1, 14.)

5. Don't tell everything you know. *"Every **prudent** man acts with knowledge, but a fool lays open his **folly**"* (13:16). A person with good sense and some godly maturity will think ahead before commenting or taking action, while a foolish person will be unable to control himself and will blabber on and on. Proverbs 17:28a advises: *"Even a fool is counted wise when he holds his peace...."* Someone else said, "You can be quiet and be thought a fool or open your mouth and remove all doubt!" Being honest does not mean giving out all the information you have, but instead it means giving out the necessary and appropriate information for the specific situation in which you find yourself and no more. You do not have to tell everything you know: *"He who covers a transgression seeks love, but he who repeats a matter separates friends"* (17:9). (See also 14:33.)

> **prudent** -wise in practical matters; exercising good judgment

> **folly** -foolishness, a lack of good sense

6. Avoid foolish conversations. *"Go from the presence of a foolish man, when you do not perceive in him the lips of knowledge."* When someone turns the conversation to gossip, complaining, dirty jokes, or other non-Christian topics, try to change the subject or leave. Don't encourage someone in this behavior by giving them an audience. Staying too often around such talk will

cause you to lower your own standards of conversation because you will get used to it. Consider Proverbs 14:9: *"Fools mock at sin, but among the upright there is favor."* You may be criticized when you refuse to participate but remember, *"The evil will bow before the good, and the wicked at the gates of the righteous"*(14:19). (See also Proverbs 17:4.)

7. Don't believe everything you hear. *"The simple believes every word, but the prudent considers well his steps"*(14:15).

Don't believe everything you hear. "The simple believes every word, but the prudent considers well his steps."

8. Don't let long conversations keep you from your work. *"In all labor there is profit, but idle chatter leads only to poverty"*(14:23). Talking too long on the telephone has caused many a project to lie unfinished. Talking with others is good and right, but responsibilities should not be neglected. Ask God to help you with this if this is a particular problem in your life.

9. Lower your voice when someone is angry. *"A soft answer turns away wrath, but a harsh word stirs up anger"*(15:1). When training employees to deal with the complaints of customers, many companies emphasize these points: a) respond in a quieter tone than the customer is using; b) make the pitch of your voice lower than theirs; and c) make the speed of your words slower than theirs. This is based on the truth of this proverb, *"a soft answer stops anger."* Try it. It works with brothers and sisters, teachers and students, as well as with **irate** customers!

irate -angry, enraged

10. Use words that build up, not tear down. *"A wholesome [healing] tongue is a tree of life, but **perverseness** in it breaks the spirit"*(15:4). In an old song, a cowboy told of his enjoyment of the open range "where seldom is heard a discouraging word"— unfortunately, everywhere else there are plenty! It might take a few more seconds to think of something nice and encouraging to say to those around you than it would to criticize or complain, but the extra time is worth it. *"The heart of the righteous studies how to answer, but the mouth of the wicked pours forth evil"*(15:28). There is real healing in thoughtful words spoken in kindness and love. Another proverb states it this way: *"A man has joy by the answer of his mouth, and a word spoken in due season, how good it is"*(15:23).

perverseness -a stubborn persistence in doing what is wrong or evil

11. Talk about what you know for sure. *"The lips of the wise disperse knowledge, but the heart of the fool does not do so."* If you don't know an answer, admit it, but don't rattle on trying to **bluff** your audience.

bluff -to mislead or deceive, to impress or intimidate by display of confidence greater than the facts support

12. Pray often. *"The sacrifice of the wicked is an abomination to the Lord, but the prayer of the upright is His delight."* Words spoken to God in prayer are never wasted.

Our words can hurt or heal, break or bind, lift or lower, or encourage or depress those around us. If your heart and mind are not right, your words will not be right.

13. When giving advice or instructions, be careful. *"Divination is on the lips of the king; his mouth must not transgress in judgment"* (16:10). "Divination" here does not mean using witchcraft or sorcery but speaking important commands to others. It is true that anyone in leadership should be careful in what he says. He should not command out of selfishness or any other sinful motive. *"It is an abomination for kings to commit wickedness, for a throne is established by righteousness"* (16:12). In the same way, those giving advice to leaders must be careful that they are correct in what they say: *"Righteous lips are the delight of kings, and they love him who speaks what is right"* (16:13).

14. "Sweeten" your words with humor or kindness. *"...Sweetness of the lips increases learning"* (16:21b). People can accept what is said to them more easily if it is said pleasantly. Tone of voice, choice of words, and right timing can make all the difference in having your message received and believed. *"Pleasant words are like a honeycomb, sweetness to the soul and health to the bones"* (16:24).

Last Word

There was a lot of advice packed into this lesson, but if there were ever one area in which it were needed, it would certainly be the area of human speech. Our words can hurt or heal, break or bind, lift or lower, or encourage or depress those around us. If your heart and mind are not right, your words will not be right. Start there with prayer. Ask God to show you what is wrong and then allow Him to heal you. Then, review the last section of these notes and make a determined effort to work on the problem areas you find in yourself. Your friends and family will be eternally grateful!

BIBLE QUEST

LESSON 28

Questions

Study Procedure: Read the Scripture references before answering questions. Unless otherwise instructed, use only the Bible in answering questions. Some questions may be more difficult than others but try to answer as many as you can. Pray for God's wisdom and understanding as you study and don't be discouraged if some answers are not obvious at first. Do not read the study notes for this lesson until AFTER you have completed your questions.

Day One: Review

1. Vocabulary Review. Find the vocabulary word that matches the definitions below:

S	O	F	E	V	F	V	P	S	F	T	X	V	J	L
S	S	F	E	O	A	E	A	R	P	K	U	C	G	K
E	G	U	L	M	R	D	T	U	U	C	I	C	B	K
N	K	L	Z	V	Q	P	R	A	B	D	H	E	G	V
E	Y	B	E	A	D	Q	S	U	R	F	E	V	O	A
S	L	R	K	P	F	Q	W	M	F	I	Q	N	D	Q
R	S	F	E	I	U	G	N	R	S	C	M	J	T	Q
E	M	N	Z	X	A	W	N	D	U	L	B	S	V	G
V	U	C	G	I	G	T	A	M	D	O	Z	Q	P	U
R	C	Y	L	E	D	U	F	U	Q	N	I	M	U	C
E	M	Z	O	U	H	T	Z	R	X	F	I	N	I	B
P	W	D	F	P	N	S	N	P	U	H	K	V	D	Q

a) directed away from what is right or good _____

b) wise in practical matters; exercising good judgment _____

c) foolishness; a lack of good sense _____

d) angry; enraged _____

e) a stubborn persistence in doing what is wrong or evil _____

f) to mislead or deceive _____

MEMORY: PROVERBS 18:24

Day Two: Read Proverbs 18 and 19.

1. Read the following proverbs and then match each with the cause of anger or quarreling (contention) described in each.

_____1. 18:1
_____2. 18:2
_____3. 18:3
_____4. 18:6
_____5. 18:7
_____6. 18:12
_____7. 18:13

a) foolish talk (2 match this)

b) wickedness

c) forming an opinion without all the information

d) pride or haughtiness

e) isolation; self-centeredness

f) desire to express own opinion instead of wanting to learn something else

239

2. What proverbs from chapter 18 having something to say about the following:

   a) friends _____

   b) marriage _____

   c) gossip _____

   d) laziness _____

3. From Proverbs 19, what is said about the rich and the poor?

   a) rich: _____

   _____

   b) poor: _____

   _____

   _____

MEMORY: PROVERBS 20:1, 11; 21:2

Day Three: Read Proverbs 20 and 21.

1. Write out the proverbs in chapter 20 that could relate to child-parent relationships and what can be learned from each. _____

   _____

   _____

   _____

   _____

   _____

   _____

   _____

   _____

2. Explain in your own words the meaning of the following proverbs:

   a) 20:1 -- *"Wine is a mocker, strong drink is a brawler ..."* _____

   _____

   b) 20:9 -- *"Who can say, 'I have made my heart clean, I am pure from my sin'"?*

   _____

   c) 20:14 -- *"It is good for nothing," cries the buyer; but when he has gone his way, then he boasts.* _____

3. Use a proverb from chapter 21 to answer the following questions.

   a) Can God control an earthly ruler?_____

   b) What is better to God than sacrifice? _____

   c) What is worse than living in an attic? _____

   _____

   d) If you want help when you need it, what must you do in the meantime? _____

   _____

   e) What is worse than living in the wilderness?_____

   _____

MEMORY: PROVERBS 22:1-2, 6

Day Four: Read Proverbs 22 and 23.

1. After what verse in Proverbs 22 does the style change from the familiar two-part couplet to a

   different style?_____

2. Answer the following questions from Proverbs 22 and give the verse from which your answer
   comes.

   a) What is better than silver and gold?_____

   b) What do the rich and poor have in common? _____

   c) What will make contention (fighting) leave?_____

   d) What removes foolishness from a child's heart? _____

   e) Why should you not make friends with an angry person? _____

   _____

   f) What should you not remove? _____

   g) What will excellence in your work provide? _____

3. Match the following thoughts with the verses from Proverbs 23 to which they apply.

   a) Control yourself when you are offered unaccustomed luxuries, so that you won't look foolish or

   ruin your health. _____

   b) Don't spend your life trying to get more and more money. It won't satisfy you. _____

   c) Honor and obey your parents._____

4. Write down the verses that have to do with consequences of drinking alcohol or having fellowship

   with those who do. What are the consequences? _____

   _____

   _____

Day Five: Read Proverbs 24.

1. The following proverbs have to do with strength or lack of it. What does each one teach?

   a) 24:5 _____

   b) 24:10 _____

   c) 24:11-12 _____

   _____

   d) 24:17-18 _____

2. What was discovered from observing the field of a lazy and foolish man?_____

   _____

   _____

3. Look over Proverbs 18-24 once more and write down . . .

   a) . . . some favorite proverbs _____

   _____

   _____

   _____

   b) . . . some "hard to understand" proverbs (Share these with your teacher or fellow students and

   try to find out their meanings.)_____

   _____

   _____

   _____

4. Now take a few minutes and read the notes for this lesson.

Notes

Stop the Fighting! (Proverbs 18-24)

Finding The Cause (Proverbs 18-20)

Many of the proverbs comment on **strife** in relationships. Other synonyms used to refer to fighting are **contention**, rage, and quarreling. Such things never result in anything good, so why do we allow ourselves to react in anger? There are some proverbs in this lesson that will help us recognize the cause of most strife.

strife -bitter conflict; struggle between rivals

contention -a verbal struggling or dispute

isolation -separation from a group

1. Isolation/self-centeredness *"A man who isolates himself seeks his own desire; he rages against all wise judgment"* (18:1). When we insist on just being interested in our own business, refusing to socialize with or help others, we soon begin to think that we are the center of everything. Then when someone breaks into our **isolation** and asks us to do something or tells us of

some need, we get angry that our privacy is being disturbed. We need balance in our lives. We must be careful about only pleasing ourselves. The selfishness that grows in isolation can be a root cause of anger toward others. Like a spoiled child, we will lash out when asked to share unless we discipline ourselves to participate in the lives and interests of others.

2. Ungodly acquaintances *"When the wicked comes, contempt comes also; and with dishonor comes reproach"*(18:3). Often when we stay near someone who is critical, negative, and unkind, we find ourselves thinking and speaking in a similar way. The resulting words spoken in contempt of others can be the sparks that start a fight. *"Cast out the scoffer and contention will leave; yes, strife and reproach will cease"* (22:10); *"Make no friendship with an angry man, and with a furious man do not go, lest you learn his ways and set a snare for your soul"*(22:24,25).

contempt -open disrespect or willful disobedience

reproach -to blame for something; rebuke

3. Thoughtless comments *"A fool's lips enter into contention..."*(18:6) and *"A fool's mouth is his destruction..."* (18:7). To avoid fighting, ask yourself, "Is what I am about to say really necessary?" If it is not, don't say it. *"It is honorable for a man to stop striving, since any fool can start a quarrel"*(20:3).

4. A feeling of **superiority** *"The poor man uses entreaties, but the rich answers roughly"* (18:23). If we think we are better than someone else because we are richer in some way, we might be tempted through pride to speak roughly to them. Check yourself for this tendency and ask forgiveness for such unkindness.

superiority -a state of being higher in rank, authority, or station

entreaties -earnest request or pleas

5. Being in too big a hurry *"...And he sins who hastens with his feet"* (19:2). When we have to hurry, it is usually because we have planned poorly for something or tried to squeeze in one more phone call or other activity before going to the next appointment. When we are in that situation, if anyone gets in our way or something unexpected happens, we often react in anger. In reality, we are to blame, not others, because if we had been realistic in our handling of time, we would have allowed a "cushion" of a few extra minutes to take care of the frequent interruptions that everyone has to face.

discretion -the quality of being cautious, reserved

6. Unforgiveness *"The discretion of a man makes him slow to anger, and his glory is to overlook a transgression"*(19:11). The very best way to stop fighting is to just "let go" of whatever is upsetting you. Forgive it; let it drop. Then, go on with your life without letting it overwhelm your thoughts and without mentioning it again. That is how God forgives your sins, by the way! Is it possible to stop thinking of something—too stop fretting and grieving? Yes, it is. You cannot help what you feel or what thought pops into your mind but you can choose to "change channels" and direct your thoughts elsewhere. Someone said, "You cannot stop a bird from flying over your head, but you can keep it from building a nest in your hair!" This would stop the nagging for which

You cannot help what you feel or what thought pops into your mind but you can choose to "change channels" and direct your thoughts elsewhere.

so many women are criticized, too, if after stating their wishes, they would let the matter drop. No one likes to be nagged: *"The contentions of a wife are a continual dripping"*(19:13); *"Better to dwell in a corner of a housetop, than in a house shared with a contentious woman"*(21:9). [See also 21:19.]

recompense -to reward or pay

7. A desire for revenge *"Do not say, 'I will **recompense** evil'; wait for the Lord, and He will save you"*(20:22). The Old Testament law demanded *"eye for eye and tooth for tooth…"*(Ex.21:24), but Jesus said, *"…Love your enemies, bless those who curse you, and pray for those who spitefully use you and persecute you…"*(Matt.5:44). A desire to get revenge keeps anger alive and is dangerous for you and others. Tell God about your situation in prayer and let Him have the last word. [See also 24:29.]

Who, Me? (Proverbs 21-24)

"Every way of a man is right in his own eyes, but the Lord weighs the hearts"(21:2). You may have just read through the above list of causes of anger and thought that none applied to you. Think again, or, as a modern proverb says: "He who finds no fault in himself needs a second opinion." Rare is the individual who walks so sincerely in fellowship with God that he does not occasionally lapse into selfishness, the fruit of pride, which leads to uncalled-for anger. Then how are we supposed to get things done if a sense of selfishness is so near the surface?

1. First things first. *"To do righteousness and justice is more acceptable to the Lord than sacrifice"*(21:3). Do you consistently try to do what pleases God wherever you are? Do you ask yourself, "What would Jesus do?" and act accordingly? Answering that question alone could give an eternal focus to your life.

Do you ask yourself, "What would Jesus do?" and act accordingly? Answering that question alone could give an eternal focus to your life.

2. Plan ahead. *"The plans of the diligent lead surely to plenty, but those of everyone who is hasty, surely to poverty."* Remember Ben Franklin's "a stitch in time saves nine"? A few moments spent in planning can give some "space" later on to stop rushing and just enjoy your life. When you are not rushed, it is easier to be more unselfish.

3. Don't get hooked. *"He who loves pleasure will be a poor man; he who loves wine and oil will not be rich"* (21:17). In 1 Corinthians 6, 8, and 10 Paul gave Christians some helpful guidelines for choosing the right things to do. They are these: "Is it helpful?" (1Cor.6:12); "Will it get me under its power?" (1 Cor.6:12); "Will it cause another person to give into temptation when they see me doing this?"(1 Cor.8:12-13); "Will it glorify God?"(1 Cor.10:31). If what you are thinking about can pass those tests it should be all right. In case you did not know, drunkenness and **gluttony** fail every time. The following proverbs offer insight into these age-old problems:

gluttony -excess in eating or drinking

23:20, 21: *"Do not mix with winebibbers, or with gluttonous eaters of meat; for the drunkard and the glutton will come to poverty, and drowsiness will clothe a man with rags."*

23:29-35: *"Who has woe... sorrow... contentions... complaints... wounds without cause... redness of eyes? Those who linger long at the wine...."*

4. Strive to keep a good name. *"A good name is to be chosen rather than great riches, loving favor rather than silver and gold"*(22:1). There are probably certain names which, if spoken to you, would make you happy, sad, or angry just at their mention. From history think of Judas or Hitler. Not many people name their babies those names—their dogs maybe, but not their babies! Why? The evil deeds of those men have become associated with their names. Now hear these: Mother Theresa, Billy Graham, or our own Mrs. Constance who founded Explorer's Bible Study. These are "good" names. Your family and friends share the blessing of your good name. Are you protecting it for those who share it with you and those who may come after you? A good name is maintained through *"humility and fear of the Lord"* (22:4) as well as through good home-discipline (22:6, 15) and generosity to others (22:9). Realizing that what you do affects many people should keep you walking in the ways that please God, living a truly unselfish life.

Realizing that what you do affects many people should keep you walking in the ways that please God, living a truly unselfish life.

5. Money isn't everything! Money is just a tool we have which should be used wisely. Like other tools, it has its purposes and is useful and good if used in the right way. It can be a weapon for our own destruction if wrongly used. While we don't want to be without any, money is never to be our most important goal. If it is, we will soon find ourselves greatly disappointed: *"For riches certainly make themselves wings; they fly away like an eagle toward heaven"*(23:5b,c). Too great a love of money might tempt us to cheat or bully people. Proverbs 16:10 warns, *"Do not remove the ancient landmarks* [change someone's boundary lines to give more to another] *nor enter the fields of the fatherless* [to take advantage of helpless people for personal gain]."Don't even spend time daydreaming about being rich by envying people who have more: *"Do not let your heart envy sinners, but be zealous for the fear of the Lord all the day; for surely there is a hereafter, and your hope will not be cut off."*(23:17, 18; see also 24:1). God will take care of our needs if we seek to love and serve Him above all else.

A Word from Paul (Philippians 2:3-4)

This whole lesson about letting go of self and following God so that fighting, strife, contention, nagging, and quarreling will end is summarized well by Paul's advice to some of his fellow-believers: *"Let nothing be done through selfish ambition or conceit* [strife]*, but in lowliness of mind let each* **esteem** *others better than himself. Let each of you look out no only for his own interests, but also for the interests of others."*

esteem -to think of with respect

BIBLE QUEST

LESSON 29

Questions

Study Procedure: Read the Scripture references before answering questions. Unless otherwise instructed, use only the Bible in answering questions. Some questions may be more difficult than others but try to answer as many as you can. Pray for God's wisdom and understanding as you study and don't be discouraged if some answers are not obvious at first. Do not read the study notes for this lesson until AFTER you have completed your questions.

Day One: Vocabulary Review: Fill in the blanks below with the correct vocabulary word from this list:

contempt   contention   discretion   entreaties   esteem   gluttony

isolation   recompense   reproach   strife   superiority

1. We expected him to show real _____ for the man who had lied about him, but instead he forgave him.

2. You can trust her with your personal problems because she is a person who exercises great

    _____.

3. Some people are hard on people who smoke, but _____ is just as bad.

4. He was so kind and helpful, but he never really received the _____ that was due him.

5. She was on her knees, but he ignored her _____.

6. God wants us to have a loving unity, not _____ and _____.

7. God gradually helped her give up her feelings of _____ in exchange for godly humility.

8. A foolish man will not listen to any _____ so he will not face his sins and change.

9. _____ can make you out-of-touch with the needs and feelings of others, leaving you very self-centered.

10. Serve God, not money, and He will see that you get a fair _____.

11. List from the notes the causes of anger or strife. _____

    _____

    _____

12. Write down anything that you learned from last week's lesson that was helpful in your own life.

    _____

    _____

    _____

    _____

246

MEMORY: PROVERBS 25:21-22

Day Two: Read Proverbs 25 and 26.

1. Locate at least one piece of advice for each of the following situations in Proverbs 25.

   a) being honored or recognized: _____

   _____

   b) settling a problem with your neighbor:_____

   _____

   c) eating sweets: _____

   d) visiting others: _____

   e) being sensitive to the mood of others: _____

   _____

2. From Proverbs 26, match the subject below with the verses that describe it.

   a) the lazy person   26:24-26

   b) the fool   26:20-22

   c) one who hates others   26:3-12

   d) the talebearer   26:13-16

3. Choose <u>at least one</u> of the following proverbs and summarize its main point below.

   a) 26:9 "Like a thorn that goes into the hand of a drunkard is a proverb in the mouth of fools."

   _____

   b) 26:17 "He who passes by and meddles in a quarrel not his own is like one who takes a dog

   by the ears." _____

   _____

   c) 26:27 "Whoever digs a pit will fall into it, and he who rolls a stone will have it roll back on him."

   _____

   _____

Day Three: Read Proverbs 27 and 28.

MEMORY: PROVERBS 27:1

1. Supply the missing words in the proverbs below about friends and friendship from Proverbs 27.

   a) _____are the wounds of a friend, but the kisses of an enemy are deceitful.

   b) Ointment and perfume delight the heart, and the _____ of a man's friend

   gives _____.

   c) Do not forsake your own _____ or your _____, nor go to

       your brother's house in the day of your calamity; better is a _____ nearby than

       a _____ far away.

   d) He who blesses his friend with a _____, rising early in the morning, it will be

       counted a _____ to him

   e) As _____, so a man sharpens the countenance of his friend.

2. What is the main point of Proverbs 27:23-27? _____

_____

_____

3. Read Proverbs 28, paying special attention to the verses that deal with the problems faced by the wicked (those who ignore God's laws and will). Then, choose the best answer in the sentences below. (Hint: The proverbs used appear in order in chapter 28.)

   a. The wicked (fight   fuss   flee) even when no one is after them.

   b. People who forsake the law (praise   curse   kill) the wicked, but such as keep the law

      (side   talk   contend) with them.

   c. Evil men do not understand (logic   love   justice) but those who seek the Lord understand

      all.

   d. A companion of (gardeners   geologists   gluttons) shames his father.

   e. If a person won't obey, he need not (pray play stay).

   f. If a person encourages another to sin, he can expect to (stand back and laugh   fall into his

     own pit   forget it and go on).

   g. When the wicked come to leadership, people (clap   quit   hide).

   h. He who tries to hide his sins will not (get away with it   prosper   live).

   i. The wicked ruler is like a (lion   lamb   lizard) over the poor.

   j. The worst oppressors are those who lack (money   understanding   time).

   k. An evil man will try to get rich quick, but instead he will find (poverty   pain   penalties).

   l. He who is of a (broken   contrite   proud) heart stirs up strife.

   m. If a man ignores the poor, he will have many (curses   chances   critics).

Day Four: Read Proverbs 29 and 30.

MEMORY: *PROVERBS 30:5-6*

1. Write down the proverb(s) from chapter 29 that comment on the subjects below.

   a) taking bribes: _____

   b) flattery: _____

   c) self-control: _____

   d) what the poor and the oppressor have in common: _____

   e) discipline for children: _____

   f) humility: _____

2. Read Proverbs 30. Match the questions below to the correct answers.

Who wrote it?	ants, rocks, badgers, locusts, spiders
What does he say about the Word of God?	give and give
What did Agur ask God not to give him?	poverty and riches
Who are the leech's two daughters?	eagle, serpent, ship, man with a virgin
What never says, "Enough!"	Agur
What are some wonderful things?	lion, greyhound, male goat, king with troops
What are little but wise?	grave, barren womb, dry earth, fire
What are majestic in movement?	it is pure; don't add to it

Day Five: Read Proverbs 31.

1. King Lemuel's mother gave him some wise advice for being a good leader of his people. Beside each topic, summarize what she told him.

   a) about women:_____

   b) about wine: _____

   c) about the defenseless: _____

2. The virtuous wife described in verses 10-31 has been called a "super-woman," and yet she displays qualities and talents that are quite practical—the kind still needed today. Read through the description carefully and see if you can discover a godly "balance" in her life. Some verses may fit in more than one category.

   a) What verses show her spending time on the physical needs of her family and herself?

   _____

b) What verses show a spiritual foundation in her life? _____

_____

c) What verses show a sensitivity to and development of the emotional side of herself and her family such as creativity, responsibility, security, satisfaction, loyalty, and respect?

_____

_____

d) What qualities of hers would you like more of in your own life? _____

_____

_____

3. Now take a few minutes and read the notes for this lesson.

Notes

Time-Tested Truths (Proverbs 25-31)

compiled -collect or compose from several sources

Hezekiah's Help (Proverbs 25)

A new section starts with Proverbs 25 which contains more of Solomon's wisdom **compiled** by some men during King Hezekiah's reign, almost 250 years after Solomon lived. Time-tested truths speak to every age. A few comments follow about some of Solomon's selected wisdom.

omniscience - to be all-knowing

25:2: *"It is the glory of God to conceal a matter, but the glory of kings is to search out a matter."* One of the attributes of God is His **omniscience**. He does not have to experiment and study to uncover truth; He already knows everything. But He has allowed mankind the privilege of uncovering some of that truth, and when it happens, it is glorious! Throughout the centuries, man's gradual understanding of God's wonderfully ordered universe as well as the intricate make up of the human body have helped him harness the resources that God created for building, healing, empowering, transporting, communicating, and any number of other great activities that improve life on planet earth.

25:6,7: *"Do not exalt yourself in the presence of the king...."* Like the observations of Jesus in Luke 14:7-10 about people who rushed for the best seats only to be embarrassed by being asked to move lower, this proverb urges humility, not self-promotion.

25:8-10: *"Do not go hastily to court.... Debate your case with your neighbor, and do not disclose the secret to another...."* Settling differences in private is the main point of these verses. Again, Jesus in the New Testament set up a model for solving differences: *"Moreover if your brother sins against you, go and tell him his fault between you and him alone. If he hears you, you have gained your brother. But if he will not hear, take with you one or two more, that 'by the mouth of two or three witnesses every word may be established.' And if he refuses to hear them, tell it to the church. But if he refuses even to hear the church, let him be to you like a heathen and a tax collector"* (Matthew 18:15-17).

25:11-15: *"A word fitly spoken...."* This group of verses emphasizes the importance of well-chosen and properly-timed words.

25:26: *"A righteous man who falters before the wicked is like a murky spring and a polluted well."* Christians should have the knowledge and the courage to defend their faith and convictions in front of unbelievers. To gain knowledge takes dedication, determination, and discipline, but is within the reach of any willing person. Courage comes as a gift from God as a person seeks to do His will His way. Christians who will not stand up for their Lord are as disgusting as dirty water to those that watch them.

> *Christians should have the knowledge and the courage to defend their faith and convictions in front of believers.*

More about Fools (Proverbs 26:1-12)

Remember from an earlier lesson that a fool is a person who refuses to be taught because he does not fear God and instead believes himself to be the most important person in his own world. He brags, "I did it my way!" and yet that way leads to death. A fool does not have to remain in his foolishness, however. He, too, can be changed in answer to the prayers of those who care about him. No one is out of God's reach if he will only respond to what God offers. Yet, many choose to remain fools. Here follows some proverbs about such stubborn ones.

> *No one is out of God's reach if they will only respond to what God offers.*

26:1 *"As snow in summer and rain in harvest, so honor is not fitting for a fool."* As inappropriate and harmful as snow and rain to a farmer trying to plant or harvest, so is giving any public credit to a fool.

26:4,5: *"Do not answer a fool according to his folly, lest you also be like him. Answer a fool according to his folly, lest he be wise in his own eyes."* These two proverbs seem to contradict one another: *"do not answer..."* and *"answer...."* Dealing with a foolish person puts us in such a **dilemma**. If we do try to respond to their foolishness, we seem to be getting down on their level of foolishness, too. Yet, if we say nothing, as if what they are saying is all right, they will think that they are wise. So, even though it might not solve anything, sometimes (like Paul in 2 Corinthians 11:16-33 and 12:11), we have to make some sort of effort to correct their wrong thinking at the risk of being taken for a foolish person, too. We try, at those times, to share God's wisdom, with the hope that at last they will listen and let God change them.

dilemma -choice between equally undesirable alternatives

26:11: *"As a dog returns to his own vomit, so a fool repeats his folly."* This is a most **graphic** description of how sickening it is for a person to refuse to face God's truth.

graphic -vividly described

Just Joking
(Proverbs 26:19)

26:18 *"Like a madman who throws firebrands, arrows, and death, is the man who deceives his neighbor, and says, 'I was only joking.'"* Humor is a wonderful thing; however, if someone is really acting out of cruelty, but just tries to pass it off as a joke when caught, that is sin. Humor at the cost of someone else's pain or property is not a laughing matter. God knows the difference, and His children should, too. The rest of Proverbs 26 reminds the reader about problems caused by gossip (20-22), hypocrisy (23-26), and lying(28).

Friendship
(Proverbs 27)

There was an earlier proverb that stated, *"To have a friend one must show himself friendly."* Some friendly attitudes are described in the proverbs of this chapter:

Humor is a wonderful thing; however, if someone is really acting out of cruelty, but just tries to pass it off as a joke when caught, that is sin.

27:2: *"Let another praise you, and not your own mouth…."* Bragging wins no friendships.

27:4: *"Wrath is cruel…But who is able to stand before jealousy?"* Friendships have to have some "space" built into them allowing each participant the freedom to succeed at projects, associations, or skills without the control of the other person. *"Love is not jealous"* (1 Cor. 13:4).

27:6 *"Faithful are the wounds of a friend…."* A real friend will tell the truth (with love) as needed. An enemy will flatter, instead, to keep another person from making the corrections that are really necessary for real success.

27:9 *"…The sweetness of a man's friend gives delight by hearty counsel."* A friend can be trusted to give good advice.

27:10 *"Do not forsake your own friend…Better is a neighbor nearby than a brother far away."* Family relationships are important, but friendships can and should require just as great a loyalty.

When we pick quality friends, our own quality will improve. We become like those we are around.

27:14 *"He who blesses a friend with a loud voice, rising early in the morning, it will be counted a curse to him."* It is very important to be sensitive to the needs and differences among our friends. Friendship is not an excuse for giving in to our own selfish moods because the other person is loyal and expected to forgive.

27:17 *"As iron sharpens iron, so a man sharpens the countenance of his friend."* Just as it takes a diamond to cut another diamond, so a person of integrity and excellence is the best one to help another like him to strive for God's best. When we pick quality friends, our own quality will improve. We become like those we are around.

Wickedness Exposed (Proverbs 28-29)

Someone once said that all it takes for wickedness to succeed is for good people to do nothing. The proverbs of this chapter expose wickedness for what it really is and challenge good people to oppose it.

Someone once said that all it takes for wickedness to succeed is for good people to do nothing.

1. It is cowardly: *"The wicked flee when no one pursues, but the righteous are bold as a lion"*(28:1). Often godly people are slow to challenge what they know to be wrong because of a fear of failure. God is on the side of the godly; therefore, only His followers can be truly brave.

2. God's truth can defeat it: *"Those who forsake the law praise [encourage] the wicked, but such as keep the law contend with them"*(28:4).

3. What it gathers by evil means will soon be taken from it: *"One who increases his possessions by usury and extortion gathers it for him who will pity the poor"*(28:8). (See also 28:22.)

usury -lending money for an excessive amount of interest

4. It cannot keep a faithful following: *"...when the wicked arise, men hide themselves"*(28:12). (See also 28:28 and 29:2).

5. It is cruel: *"Like a roaring lion and a charging bear is a wicked ruler over people"*(28:15).

extortion -obtain by force or improper pressure

6. It causes trouble: *"He who is of a proud heart stirs up strife, but he who trusts the Lord will be prospered"*(28:25). (See also 29: 22.)

7. It grieves parents: *"Whoever loves wisdom makes his father rejoice, but a companion of harlots wastes his wealth"*(29:3). (See also 28:7.)

8. It ruins a nation: *"The king establishes the land by justice, but he who receives bribes overthrows it"*(29:4). (See also 29:8 and 29: 18.)

Agur's Turn (Proverbs 30)

The only details of Agur's identity are found here in 30:1. But we can learn about his personality and character from his writings in this chapter. He is humble (*"I neither learned wisdom nor have knowledge of the Holy One."*). He loves God whom he praises as the supreme power of the universe (4). He believes Scripture is holy. Just like the apostles of the New Testament, he reminds his readers that *"Every word of God is pure....Do not add to His words, lest He rebuke you, and you be found a liar"* (5,6). The remaining verses of Agur's chapter give his observations of nature or mankind, which show him to be quite a sharp observer of the wonders of God's creation. His discoveries make us pause and see things in a fresh way.

<u>Two Prayers:</u> *"Remove...lies far from me; give me neither poverty nor riches...lest I be full and deny You...or lest I be poor and steal"* (7-9). Agur knew that man was weak and, when faced with extreme temptations, would

often sin against God. His prayers were good ones. He wanted to be delivered from extremes.

Four Generations: (1) *"There is a generation that curses its father...."* Disrespect and rebellion still plague our current society. (2) *"...that is pure in its own eyes, yet it is not washed from its filthiness."* Spiritual blindness resulting in hypocrisy causes so many to turn away from the help they really need. (3) *"...oh, how lofty are their eyes!"* Pride is the root of every sinful action. (4) *"...whose teeth are like swords...to devour the poor from off the earth"* (11-14). Cruel words come from wicked hearts and lead to evil actions.

Four that Lack Satisfaction: *"The grave, the barren womb,"* the dry earth, and fire (16).

Four Wonderful Ways: *"...an eagle in the air....a serpent on a rock,...a ship in the...sea,...a man with a virgin"* (18,19). Each one makes us smile with appreciation.

Four Things the Earth Cannot Stand: (1) a former servant who gets to be boss; (2) a fool when he's had enough to eat; (3) *"a hateful woman"* who finally gets married; (4) and a *"maidservant who succeeds her mistress."* Each of these situations features a sudden or unexpected promotion which often makes the person in question obnoxious or spiteful (21-23).

crags -steep cliff

Four Little Things that Are Big in Wisdom: Ants are fragile and tiny but work hard at the right time and reap the benefits in the future. They teach us the advantages of industry. Rock badgers are thought to have been vulnerable creatures, with some similarity to rabbits, but unable to burrow or otherwise protect themselves. However, they did have the good sense to choose to live in **crags** of rocks where they could find ready-made protection from their enemies. They teach us about finding security. The third kind of creatures were locusts who could travel together in ranks even though they had no king. Their habits emphasize the importance of cooperation. Finally, the spider, or its alternate translation, lizard, though small in size is useful because it eats smaller creatures. However, it is also clever, because it can gain entrance anywhere it desires, even inside a palace. That creature then encourages **ingenuity** (24-28).

ingenuity -skill or cleverness in planning or inventing

Final Four Majestic Things: These four finish Agur's observations and are certainly still considered majestic in their movements: a lion, a greyhound, a male goat, and a king with his army (29-31).

The Wisdom Of King Lemuel's Mother (Proverbs 31:1-9)

The identity and history of King Lemuel is unknown. There is no other reference to him in Scripture just as there was no other mention of Agur. However, we do know that Lemuel's mother was one wise woman! King Lemuel himself was a very smart man to remember and record his mother's good advice. She told him to prevent the problems that come with leadership by avoiding sexual sin (3), staying away from intoxicating drink (4-7), and paying special attention to the needs of the weak and the poor (8,9). What wonderful guidelines these still are for those in leadership today! We only have to think back over recent television news stories or newspaper headlines to see how many modern-day scandals were caused because a leader sinned in one of these three areas.

The Virtuous Wife (Proverbs 31:10-31)

This section of Scripture is an alphabetic acrostic, complimenting a character trait or activity of the ideal wife for each of the twenty-two letters of the Hebrew alphabet. This woman seems too good to be true, and yet, allowing for differences in culture, personality, and talents, every godly woman can excel spiritually, emotionally, and physically as she does. One young mother said after her husband showed her this passage, "Well, I could do all that, too, if I had several servants!" He responded, "You do have servants: electricity, running water, a refrigerator, a car, a washing machine….!" The point of the passage is not for every female to exhaust herself in trying to duplicate all that this woman was described as doing, but to look at her own life as a whole and evaluate the effects of her activities on the well-being of her family and herself.

This woman seems too good to be true, and yet, allowing for differences in culture, personality, and talents, every godly woman can excel spiritually, emotionally, and physically as she does.

Don't miss these important truths:

1. She had a loving relationship with her husband. He trusted her and she did not betray that trust. She consciously did things with his approval and blessing in mind. In response, he evidently gave her quite a bit of freedom in the use of time and money. He allowed her to make use of her creative talents and energies without criticism. For a wife to be all she should be, she should recognize that her relationship with her husband requires honesty, cooperation, and much loving attention (10-12). Some women have been dishonest with their husbands and so are not given such freedom, while on the other hand, some husbands are too insecure themselves to allow their wives to try new things with their approval and support.

2. This woman was not afraid to try new things, go to extra trouble, or make difficult decisions. She was not lazy. She was concerned about her family and her servants which reveals an unselfish character (13-16).

3.   This woman was physically fit: *"She girds herself with strength and strengthens her arms"* (17).   She also paid attention to her personal appearance: *"She makes tapestry for herself. Her clothing is fine linen and purple"*(22). Those fabrics and colors were not cheap. She focused on quality and recognized that how she looked could reflect favorably or unfavorably on her husband who was *"known in the gates."* That meant he had a leadership role in the community, and from the context, this was at least partly due to his wife's good reputation and noble activities. She brought out the best in him and was careful not to shame his good name with anything she did or failed to do(23,25).

Receiving God's love and loving Him back is the only foundation for life-changing and long-lasting activities of any kind.

4.   She was kind in word and deed. It was said that *"the law of kindness"* was on her tongue (26). A law is something that is observed to be the same in every situation, like the law of gravity. If she spoke with the *"law of kindness,"* she was consistently that way, not just when the mood hit her or things went her way. As earlier proverbs revealed, continually kind words only come from a godly heart. Her actions were kind as well, since she helped the poor and needy (20) and watched carefully over her own household (27). Was this all some sort of "act"?   No, indeed! Her husband and children praised her out loud.   A person might fool a lot of people outside the home, but family members know what is really inside one of their own.

5.   She was a woman who knew and loved God. In the final verses, the secret of her excellence is clearly revealed: *"Charm is deceitful and beauty is passing, but a woman who fears the Lord, she shall be praised"* (30). This is the place every person, male or female, can start. Receiving God's love and loving Him back is the only foundation for life-changing and long-lasting activities of any kind.

Practice the Practical

The study of proverbs has touched on every aspect of our daily existence. It has exposed the good, the bad, and the ugly of human activity and human nature. It has revealed that God's wisdom heard and obeyed will not remove all our problems right now, but it will certainly make whatever we are facing have eternal meaning. Re-read the book of Proverbs regularly. One suggestion is to read one chapter a day, which would allow the whole book to be reviewed monthly. Specifically, the advice is to read Proverbs 1 on the first day of the month, chapter two on the second, and so forth. It must be read prayerfully, asking God to stop the reader on the verse or verses that need to be applied that day.   What improvement the watching world would see in us if we took God's wisdom more seriously! Don't neglect to practice these practical truths; they will yield permanent benefits.

BIBLE QUEST

Questions

Study Procedure: Read the Scripture references before answering questions. Unless otherwise instructed, use only the Bible in answering questions. Some questions may be more difficult than others but try to answer as many as you can. Pray for God's wisdom and understanding as you study and don't be discouraged if some answers are not obvious at first. Do not read the study notes for this lesson until AFTER you have completed your questions.

Day One: Vocabulary Review: Fill in the blanks below with the correct vocabulary word for this list:

crags   usury   graphic   dilemma   compiled   ingenuity   extortion   omniscience

1. The rock badgers wisely chose the _____ of rocks for their home.

2. The young man found himself in a real _____; his friends had planned a fun evening, but he could not locate his parents to get permission to go.

3. The bully of the prison used _____ to gain whatever he wanted.

4. The teacher _____ a list of students that were trustworthy and energetic.

5. God's ability to know everything is called _____.

6. With remarkable _____ the girl took her old clothes and made them look brand new.

7. They left the movie because of the _____ violence.

8. By law, the Jews could not demand _____ when lending money to their own people.

9. Name the three men credited with writing Proverbs.
    - a) S _____
    - b) A _____
    - c) L _____

10. Write below some of the things you learned from your study of Proverbs.

    _____

    _____

    _____

    _____

Day Two: Read Ecclesiastes 1-6.

MEMORY: ECCLESIASTES 4:9-10

1. Solomon is generally accepted as the author of Ecclesiastes even though he is not mentioned by name. Beside the following references, write down what you find that could point to Solomon as the author. (For extra information, read Solomon's history in 1 Kings 7-11.)

   a) 1:1 _____

   b) 1:16 _____

   c) 2:3 _____

   d) 2:7-11 _____

   _____

2. *"Under the sun"* what did Solomon find? (See 1:2 and 12:8.) _____

   _____

3. The purpose of Solomon's search for meaning was given through a question asked in 1:3. Quote what it says in the space provided and then put it in your own words.

   _____

   _____

   _____

   _____

4. Throughout Ecclesiastes the Preacher experimented with all sorts of activities, but for the final answer to his question he had to look *"above"* the sun. What did he find? (See 12:13, 14.)

   _____

Day Three: Read Ecclesiastes 1 and 2 and then write beside each reference below what Solomon was experimenting with in his quest to find real meaning. Then give his conclusion about each experiment.

1. 1:16-18 -- What he tried: _____

   What he learned:_____

   _____

2. 2:1-11-- What he tried: _____

   What he learned:_____

   _____

3. What happens to both the wise and the foolish person? (See 2:12-16) _____

   _____

4. Beside each statement that summarizes what Solomon felt to be unfair or unsatisfying, try and find the passage to which it refers using Ecclesiastes 3-6.

   a) There are equal ends for unequal creatures. _____

   b) The ones needing the most help and comfort, do not receive it. _____

   c) When a person's possessions increase, so does the cost of maintaining them. _____

   d) A hard working man sleeps better than a rich man. _____

   e) At death, all earthly possessions are left behind. _____

   f) Sometimes people with the most money and fame don't even get to enjoy what they have accumulated. _____

5. Read Ecclesiastes 7 and write down below a few of its proverbs that were interesting or helpful to you.

   _____

   _____

   _____

MEMORY: ECCLESIASTES 9:10; 12:1

Day Four: Read Ecclesiastes 8-12 and Song of Solomon 1-4.

1. Fill in the blanks with the missing words from Ecclesiastes 8-12. Remember to put the Scripture reference beside each one.

   a) *"Because the sentence against an evil work is not _____ therefore the heart of the sons of men is fully set in them to do evil." v._____*

   b) *"Whatever your hand finds to do, do it _____; for there is no work or device or knowledge or wisdom in the grave where you are going." v. _____*

   c) *"Wisdom is better than weapons of war; but one _____destroys much good." v. _____*

   d) *"If the ax is dull, and one does not _____, then he must use more _____; but wisdom brings success." v. _____*

   e) *"Cast your bread upon the waters, for you will _____ after many days." v. _____*

   f) *"Remember now your _____ in the days of your youth, . . ." v. _____*

   g) *"For God will bring every work into _____, including every _____ _____, whether good or evil." v. _____*

2. Before you begin reading Song of Solomon, also called the Song of Songs, recognize that it is written almost like a play, with three speaking parts. Read chapter one and then describe or identify these three "parts." (Its plot may not seem as logical as the plays you are used to reading or watching.)

a) the woman:_____

_____

b) the chorus: _____

_____

c) the man: _____

_____

3. This song celebrates the romantic love of a man and a woman who meet, get to know each other, and then marry. On another level, it can speak of Christ's wonderful covenant love for each of us. From Chapter 1:16-2:17, write down a few of the sweet things the man and woman say to or about each other.

_____

_____

_____

4. In chapter 3, what is the identity of the king whom the woman sees and what is the occasion?

_____

5. It is thought by many Bible scholars that Solomon is the shepherd with whom the young woman had fallen in love, and at this point she realizes his true identity. What word in chapter 4 informs the reader that they are now married?_____

Day Five: Read Song of Solomon 5-8.

1. In chapter 5, the Shulamite had a troubled evening.

a) What happened? _____

_____

_____

_____

b) Comment, if you can, on what this situation has to teach married couples today?

_____

_____

_____

2. Read chapter 6. How did the husband describe his wife's teeth and hair? _____

_____

_____

3. Read chapter 7 and 8. Where else had a couple been naked and not ashamed?

_____

4. Why do you think this "love song" was included in the Bible? _____

_____

_____

_____

5. Now take a few minutes and read the notes for this lesson.

Notes

From Vanity of Vanities to the Song of Songs
(Ecclesiastes and Song of Solomon)

Life "Under the Sun"

The name Ecclesiastes has it origin in the Greek word for assembly, *ekklesia*. *Ecclesiastes* means one who addresses an assembly. Here it is translated "the Preacher," but it could have just as easily been translated "the Debater," since Solomon sounds more like a man presenting an argument than one giving a Sunday sermon. Solomon has been credited with writing this book because of the details included in the first and second chapters describing the author as being the son of David, king in Jerusalem, and one who had unequaled wisdom, wealth, and ingenuity. (See 1 Kings 7-11 for details of Solomon's reign as Israel's king.) The book of Ecclesiastes is one that must be read all the way through before coming to any conclusion about its meaning. The main purpose of the book is given in 1:3: *"What profit has a man from all his labor in which he toils under the sun?"* Solomon used all the resources available to him—and they were vast—to find out if man could find meaning and purpose in his earthly life *"under the sun,"* or, to put it another way, by himself, without the spiritual meaning that God could give to his life. One of the key words in this book was *hebel,* from the Hebrew word which literally meant *breath* and was translated *vanity.* At the beginning in 1:2 and at the end in 12:8 Solomon found that nothing *"under the sun"* really satisfied him or brought lasting meaning to his life, all was *"vanity."* However, the book does not leave its readers without hope: *"Let us hear the conclusion of the whole matter: Fear God and keep His commandments, for this is man's all..."* (12:13). A person must look *"above the sun"* to God Himself to find real satisfaction and direction for his life on earth.

A person must look "above the sun" to God Himself to find real satisfaction and direction for his life on earth.

Solomon the Cynic (Ecclesiastes 1-2)

Do you remember Agur's request in Proverbs 30 about being delivered from the extremes of poverty or wealth because he felt that either one would cause him to stray from God's will? Well, Solomon experienced extreme wealth, power, and wisdom and it did draw him across the boundaries God had set for righteous living. Solomon indulged in whatever pleased him, including marriage, and had 300 wives and 700 concubines! Just as God warned, his foreign wives turned him away from God, and he became cynical about life. Nothing pleased him permanently; nothing satisfied him for long. Chapter 2 lists all the things on which he spent his energies, but in the end each left him feeling empty, as when one tries to hold on to the wind.

In his experimenting, he found the work that man had to do was not satisfying for several reasons. First, whether a person were a good worker or bad one, a wise man or a fool, in the end, he would still die. Next, he discovered that any success that was achieved would be quickly forgotten after a person died, and there were not even any guarantees that the work done would be carried on by wise relatives or friends, instead of being destroyed by unworthy fools (2:12-26). This was vanity, too.

Should We Just Quit Trying? (Ecclesiastes 3)

The *"time for everything"* verses of Ecclesiastes 3 probably sound familiar and could be comforting when facing life's difficulties because they point to an order, even a rhythm, in the universe. But in the context of Solomon's search for the meaning of life, they sound as if man can really not change anything, that everything is out of his control. A more godly view was expressed in 3:11 where the Preacher wrote that God puts *"eternity"* in our hearts, and though we can never discover all He does, we can at least enjoy every good thing He gives us. Actually, it is the *"eternal"* that He has placed in our hearts that keeps us from finding any meaning in our earthly existence unless we have a real relationship with God Himself.

> *. . . it is the "eternal" that He has placed in our hearts that keeps us from finding any meaning in our earthly existence unless we have a real relationship with God Himself.*

It's Unfair! (Ecclesiastes 4-10)

The "unfairness" of earthly life bothered Solomon and he commented on several situations that he had noticed:

(1) Death comes to all—the wise and the foolish; to man as well as animals(2:12-16; 4:18-22;).

(2) People suffer so much, it seems better to have never lived (4:1-3).

(3) Accumulating possessions and money does not satisfy (5:10-12; 6:1-2).

(4) A person has to leave behind at his death every earthly thing for which he has worked—you really can't take it with you! (5:15-17).

(5) Often a righteous person dies young while a wicked one lives a long time (7:15).

(6) Fools get honored while the rich are ignored (10:6).

When life is viewed without a knowledge of God's will and methods, then it does not make sense. Paul stated that if there were not a future life in heaven, (a resurrection), which Christians believe there will be based on the promises of Scripture, we would be of all people most to be pitied (1 Cor.15:12-19). Working hard and sacrificing for others would seem foolish without knowing God's overall plan for us and the assurance that He will more than make up for what we have missed when we join Him. Those who do not "fear God" encourage others to "take care of `Number One'!" and "Grab all you can before someone else does!" Jesus taught us to seek God first, and then the rest would be added. And, He taught us not to spend our lives working for things that can be lost, but to work for treasures in heaven that will never disappear (Matthew 6:20,33).

> *When life is viewed without a knowledge of God's will and methods, then it does not make sense.*

Ecclesiastes 11 and 12 Many helpful proverbs can be found in the last half of Ecclesiastes, but these final chapters seem to urge the reader to seek God and follow His plans for life(12:13). God is described as Creator (11:5; 12:1), Judge (11:9), Counselor, to be sought out in our youth, (12:1), and final Comforter in our old age (12:6.7).

An interestingly creative technique was used to describe the aging process in 12:3-5:
- a. Hands--"keepers of the house tremble."
- b. Legs—"strong men bow down."
- c. Teeth—"grinders cease because they are few."
- d. Eyes—"those that look through the windows grow dim."
- e. Ears—"the doors are shut in the streets and the sound of grinding is low."
- f. Emotions--"afraid of height"
- g. Strength— "the grasshopper is a burden."

The body does wear out and life on this earth does end, but the Preacher finally summarizes the results of his experiments with this conclusion: all is vanity unless God is in charge. *"Fear God and keep His commandments, for this is man's all."*

Song of Solomon According to Jewish history, a young man was not allowed to read this book until he was thirty years old. Its vivid love-language was thought to be too stimulating for anyone younger. For the same reason, the Song of Solomon is not used very often as the text for sermons or Sunday school lessons either. Yet, since it is included in the canon of Scripture, it, too, is *given by inspiration of God and is profitable* for our learning (2 Tim. 3:16).

God invented the sexual relationship, and it is wonderfully beautiful when enjoyed within the safe boundaries of the marriage covenant.

The term "Song of Songs" is a superlative similar to "King of Kings" or "Lord of Lords." It is a statement of ultimate excellence. What is the subject of this greatest-of-all-songs? Married love—covenant love between man and wife. Even though our culture keeps absolutely no secrets about sexual activities— our television, movies, music, and magazines are very explicit—there are still many, many normal human beings who remain quite reserved about discussing such things openly, especially in a Bible study group! But God has shown us that romantic and sexual expression, within the boundaries of marriage, for the purpose of pleasure for each spouse, is part of His master-plan for us. Like Adam and Eve, husband and wife can be "naked and unashamed." The Shulamite and her spouse certainly spoke openly about how pleasant they found each other's body (7:1-9). God invented the sexual relationship, and it is wonderfully beautiful when enjoyed within the safe boundaries of the marriage covenant. The couple's special preparations for physical pleasure were described in the references to wonderful fragrances of perfumes and spices (4:12-15) and pleasant surroundings (6:11-12).

The Plot (Sort Of)

Most likely, each Bible commentary you pick up on this book will vary a bit in explaining the plot. This is not like a "normal" play but seems to be ahead of its time in beginning in the present, then flashing back to the past, and then returning to the present. Here is one possible outline of its scenes—there are many others:

1: 1 The title is given—This is Solomon's favorite song.

1:2-4 The Shulamite has been brought to the king's palace for the wedding banquet. She is eager to be alone with him. (Note: Where "Shulam" was, is not known.)

1:5-6 She speaks to her husband, recounting how he first met her. He had expressed love for her in spite of the fact that she had been made by her brothers to work in the family's vineyard and had not been able to protect her skin from the darkening rays of the sun. She referred to her lack of opportunity for the beauty treatments other girls enjoyed when she said, *"My own vineyard I have not kept."*

1:7 She recounts how when she first met him, she knew him only as a shepherd. She recalled wanting to see him again and asking him where he rested with his flocks at noon.

1:8-10 Her beloved responded by telling her to *"follow in the footsteps of the flock."* He evidently was going away and could not take her with him right then but did not want her following any other shepherd. Then he praised her beauty, sweetly and appropriately, since they were then unmarried, by mentioning her cheeks and neck only. He thought she was beautiful even though she had had to work in the vineyard.

1:12-14 The Shulamite switches back to the present and speaks delightedly of their marriage and her dreams and desire for her husband.

1:16-2:7 More sweet talk about their new life together.

2:8-14   This sounds like a flashback to the time the young man offered to marry her but had to go away first.

2:15   Her brothers gave her more work to do. They might not have believed that someone would really want to marry their sister.

2:16-17 She believed her beloved was sincere and called for him to return soon.

3:1-5   She went to find him and did, but did not want to let him go till they could be married.

3: 6-11 Evidently she did have to let him go because this section described his glorious return for her—not as a humble shepherd, but as the king of Israel!

4:1-16 They were married here since he frequently called her his "spouse." This section is filled with a description of his delight with their physical relationship. He obviously is thrilled with her.

5:2-16 In this section, the Shulamite hesitated in responding to her beloved's request for entry into her bedroom. Her excuse was that she had already taken off her robe and gotten in bed. If she were to get up and let him in, her feet would get dirty! Before she could rethink her selfishness, he left. This is an interesting look at married love. There are times when one spouse does not "feel" like responding to the other, but such selfishness always brings problems. The Shulamite went looking for him but was hurt in the process. However, she took the opportunity to publicly praise him and describe his handsome features.

6,7,8   These last chapters showed their relationship on proper ground again and described vividly their love for one another.

God and Israel; Christ and the Church

Many see another meaning in the Song of Solomon. They see not just the covenant love of husband and wife, but the covenant love of God for Israel and Christ for His Bride, the Church (Eph. 5:22-33 and Rev. 19:7,8). He called us, saw beauty where we saw none, and made promises to us. Then, when we responded to Him and accepted His loving plan for us, He told us to wait for Him. In fact, we still wait for the return of Jesus one day. His return will be greater than Solomon's procession when He comes to get His Bride! Some may think that we are unworthy or at least unlikely to be selected as Christ's beloved, but we can know that His promises to us are true. We also work while we wait for Christ to take us to His banqueting table, and as the Shulamite with her older brothers, we might have some unpleasant and unbelieving people surrounding us in the mean time or difficult "foxes" to try to eliminate from our local vineyard. Learn from the Song of Solomon, the work and the waiting are worth it! Our Shepherd is the King of Kings!